COMPLETE
MathSmart®

$$\begin{array}{r} 5 \\ \cancel{6}\cancel{3}\cancel{8} \\ -\ \ 349 \\ \hline 289 \end{array}$$

Contents

Level 3 – Applications

Dear Parent or Guardian,

Thank you for choosing our book to help sharpen your child's math skills. Our primary goal is to provide a learning experience that is both fun and rewarding. This aim has guided the development of the series in a few key ways.

Our *Complete MathSmart* series has been designed to help children achieve mathematical excellence. Each grade has 3 levels. In level 1, your child learns all the basic math concepts necessary for success in his or her grade. Key concepts are accompanied by helpful three-part introductions: "Read This" explains the concept, "Example" demonstrates the concept, and "Try It" lets your child put the concept to use. In level 2, and to a greater extent in level 3, these concepts are worked into relatable problem-solving questions. These offer a greater challenge and point children to the every-day usefulness of math skills.

Fun activities, lively illustrations, and real-world scenarios throughout the book help bring the concepts to life and engage your child. Additionally, the QR codes in the book link to motion graphics that explain key ideas in a fun and active way. After your child has completed the core content, they will find two assessment tests. These will test your child's general ability to apply the concepts learned, and prepare them for standardized testing. Finally, your child can use the answer key in the back of the book to improve by comparing his or her results and methods.

With the help of these features, we hope to provide an enriching learning experience for your child. We would love to hear your feedback, and encourage you to share any stories of how *Complete MathSmart* has helped your child improve his or her math skills and gain confidence in the classroom.

Your Partner in Education,
Popular Book Company (Canada) Limited

LEVEL 1
BASIC SKILLS

1 Whole Numbers

• representing and comparing whole numbers

A place value chart is a chart that helps determine the place values of the digits in large numbers.

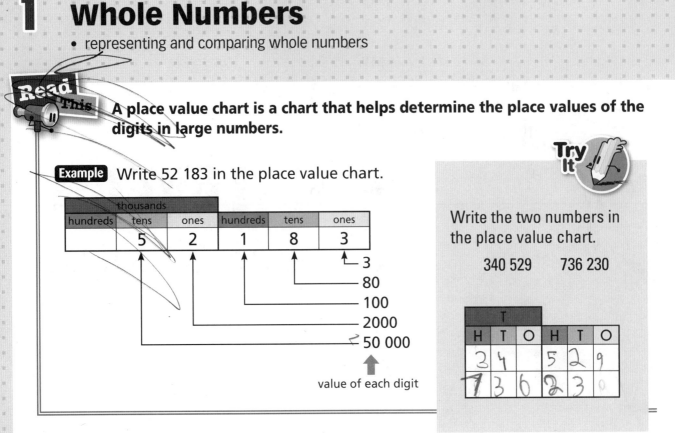

Example Write 52 183 in the place value chart.

thousands					
hundreds	tens	ones	hundreds	tens	ones
	5	2	1	8	3

— 3
— 80
— 100
— 2000
— 50 000

value of each digit

Try It

Write the two numbers in the place value chart.

340 529   736 230

	T				
H	T	O	H	T	O
	3	4	5	2	9
7	3	6	2	3	0

Write the numbers in the place value chart.
Then write them in expanded form and in words.

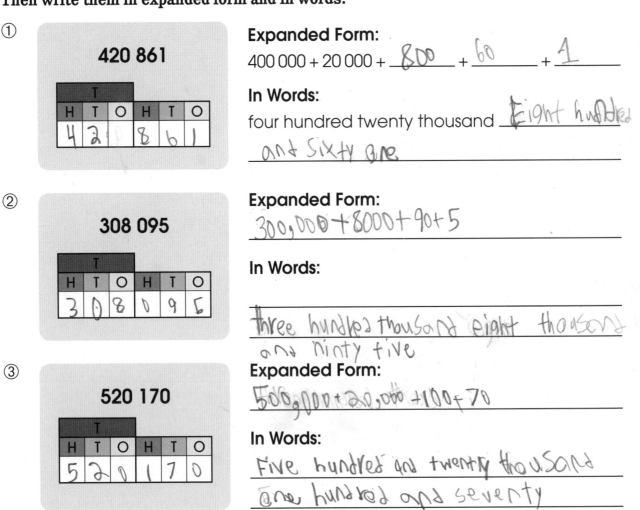

① **420 861**

	T				
H	T	O	H	T	O
4	2		8	6	1

Expanded Form:
400 000 + 20 000 + __800__ + __60__ + __1__

In Words:
four hundred twenty thousand __Eight hundred__
__and Sixty one__

② **308 095**

	T				
H	T	O	H	T	O
3	0	8	0	9	5

Expanded Form:
300,000 + 8000 + 90 + 5

In Words:
three hundred thousand eight thousand and ninty five

③ **520 170**

	T				
H	T	O	H	T	O
5	2	0	1	7	0

Expanded Form:
500,000 + 20,000 + 100 + 70

In Words:
Five hundred and twenty thousand one hundred and seventy

④

92 900

	T				
H	T	O	H	T	O
	9	2	9	0	0

Expanded Form:

90,000 + 2,000 + 900

In Words:

Nintey two thousand and Nine hundres

⑤

256 803

	T				
H	T	O	H	T	O

Expanded Form:

200,000 + 50,000 + 6000 + 800 + 3

In Words:

Two hundred and Fifty Six thousand eight hundres and three

Represent each number as specified.

⑥ **numeral → words**

a. 439 225 Four hundred and thirty nine thousand two hundred and twenty five

b. 568 308 Five hundred and sixtey eight thousand three hundred and eight

c. 702 844 Seven hundred and two thousand eight hundred and fourty four

⑦ **expanded form → numeral**

a. 500 000 + 1000 + 400 + 80 + 7   501,487

b. 20 000 + 8000 + 700 + 10 + 5   28715

c. 300 000 + 10 000 + 400 + 40 + 1   310,441

⑧ **words → expanded form**

a. six hundred fifty-two thousand ninety-three

600,000 + 50,000 + 2000 + 90 + 3

b. two hundred eighty-eight thousand five hundred sixty

200,000 + 80,000 + 8000 + 500 + 60

c. thirty-five thousand seven hundred thirteen

30000, 5,000, 700, 10, 3

Write the value of each digit in bold. Then answer the questions.

⑨ a. 251 732 _50000_

b. 935 675 _5000_

c. 118 **872** _800_

d. 650 **4**09 _400_

e. 701 9**1**1 _10_

f. 843 57**6** _6_

g. **3**70 267 _300,000_

h. 587 5**6**5 _7000_

⑩ Consider the digit 8 in the number 857 280.

a. Which 8 has a greater place value? Name the place value.

handred thousand

b. How many times greater is it?

_79,920_

⑪ Consider the digits 1 and 5 in the number 410 358.

a. Which digit has a greater place value? Name the place value.

ten thousand

b. How many times greater is it?

_9,950_

Check the numbers that match the descriptions.

⑫ The digit 3 has a value of thirty thousand.

A) 853 541   (✓) 534 440   C) 319 487   D) 730 865

⑬ The digit 7 has a value of seven thousand.

A) 471 140   B) ✓ 837 691   C) 74 258   D) 617 485

⑭ The number is greater than five hundred thousand.

A) 472 337   B) 50 891   C) 512 920   D) ✓ 600 327

⑮ The number is less than seventy-five thousand.

✓ A) 58 197   B) 68 205   C) 750 319   D) 604 312

⑯ The number is between one hundred thousand and three hundred forty-five thousand.

A) 28 716   B) ✓ 290 617   C) 305 000   D) 453 000

Locate the numbers on the number lines. Then compare each pair of numbers and put "<" or ">" in the circle.

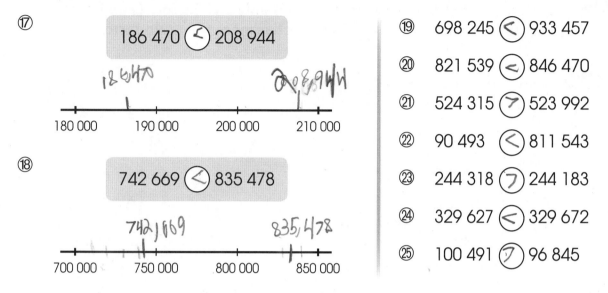

⑰ 186 470 ⟨<⟩ 208 944

186470   208,944

| | | | | |
180 000   190 000   200 000   210 000

⑱ 742 669 ⟨<⟩ 835 478

742,669   835,478

| | | | | |
700 000   750 000   800 000   850 000

⑲ 698 245 ⟨<⟩ 933 457

⑳ 821 539 ⟨<⟩ 846 470

㉑ 524 315 ⟨>⟩ 523 992

㉒ 90 493 ⟨<⟩ 811 543

㉓ 244 318 ⟨>⟩ 244 183

㉔ 329 627 ⟨<⟩ 329 672

㉕ 100 491 ⟨>⟩ 96 845

Put each set of numbers in order.

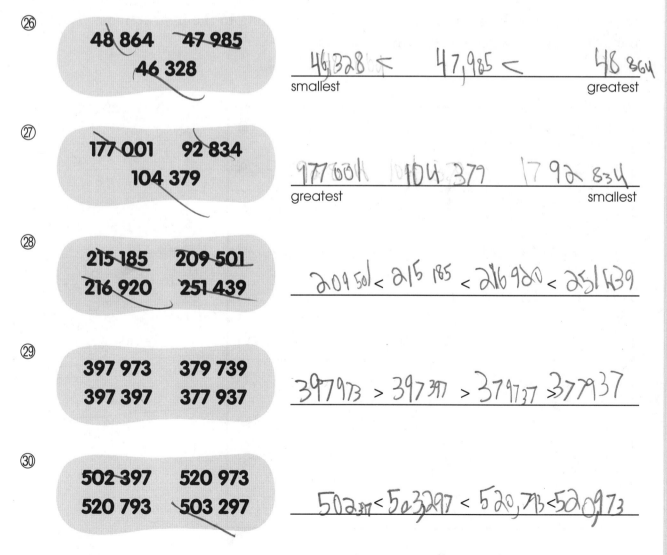

㉖
48 864   47 985
46 328

46,328 < 47,985 < 48 864
smallest   greatest

㉗
177 001   92 834
104 379

177001   104 379   1 92 834
greatest   smallest

㉘
215 185   209 501
216 920   251 439

209 501 < 215 185 < 216 920 < 251 439

㉙
397 973   379 739
397 397   377 937

397 973 > 397 397 > 379 737 > 377 937

㉚
502 397   520 973
520 793   503 297

502 397 < 503 297 < 520 793 < 520 973

2 Prime and Composite Numbers

- identifying prime and composite numbers

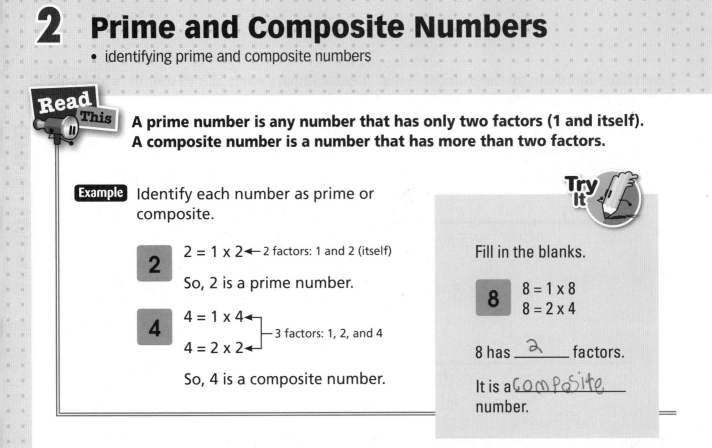

Read This

A prime number is any number that has only two factors (1 and itself).
A composite number is a number that has more than two factors.

Example Identify each number as prime or composite.

2 $2 = 1 \times 2$ ← 2 factors: 1 and 2 (itself)

So, 2 is a prime number.

4 $4 = 1 \times 4$
$4 = 2 \times 2$ ⎦ 3 factors: 1, 2, and 4

So, 4 is a composite number.

Try It

Fill in the blanks.

8 $8 = 1 \times 8$
$8 = 2 \times 4$

8 has ___2___ factors.

It is a _composite_ number.

Cross out the numbers on the hundreds chart according to the instructions. Then list the prime numbers and answer the questions.

①

1	2	3	4	5	6	7	8	9	10
11	12	13	14	15	16	17	18	19	20
21	22	23	24	25	26	27	28	29	30
31	32	33	34	35	36	37	38	39	40
41	42	43	44	45	46	47	48	49	50
51	52	53	54	55	56	57	58	59	60
61	62	63	64	65	66	67	68	69	70
71	72	73	74	75	76	77	78	79	80
81	82	83	84	85	86	87	88	89	90
91	92	93	94	95	96	97	98	99	100

Instructions

Cross out:
- multiples of 2 except 2 ✓
- multiples of 3 except 3 ✓
- multiples of 5 except 5
- multiples of 7 except 7

1 neither a prime nor composite number

Numbers with a cross: **composite**

Numbers with no cross: **prime**

② Fill in the first 25 prime numbers.

The First 25 Prime Numbers

2	3	5	7	11	13	17	19
23	29	31	37	4T	53	47	53	59
61	67	71	73	79	83	89	97

③ Identify the numbers described.

a. an even prime number ___2___

b. the smallest composite number ___H___

c. the largest 1-digit prime number ___7___

d. the smallest 3-digit composite number ___100___

e. the smallest 2-digit composite number ___10___

f. the largest 2-digit prime number ___97___

Circle "T" for true and "F" for false.

④ The product of 2 prime numbers is a prime number. T /(F)

⑤ 1 is neither composite nor prime. (T)/ F

⑥ All prime numbers are odd numbers. T /(F)

⑦ The product of 1 prime number and 1 composite number is a composite number. T /(F)

⑧ All numbers that end in "4" are composite numbers. T /(F)

⑨ All numbers that end in "2" are composite numbers. T /(F)

Write each number as a product of prime numbers.

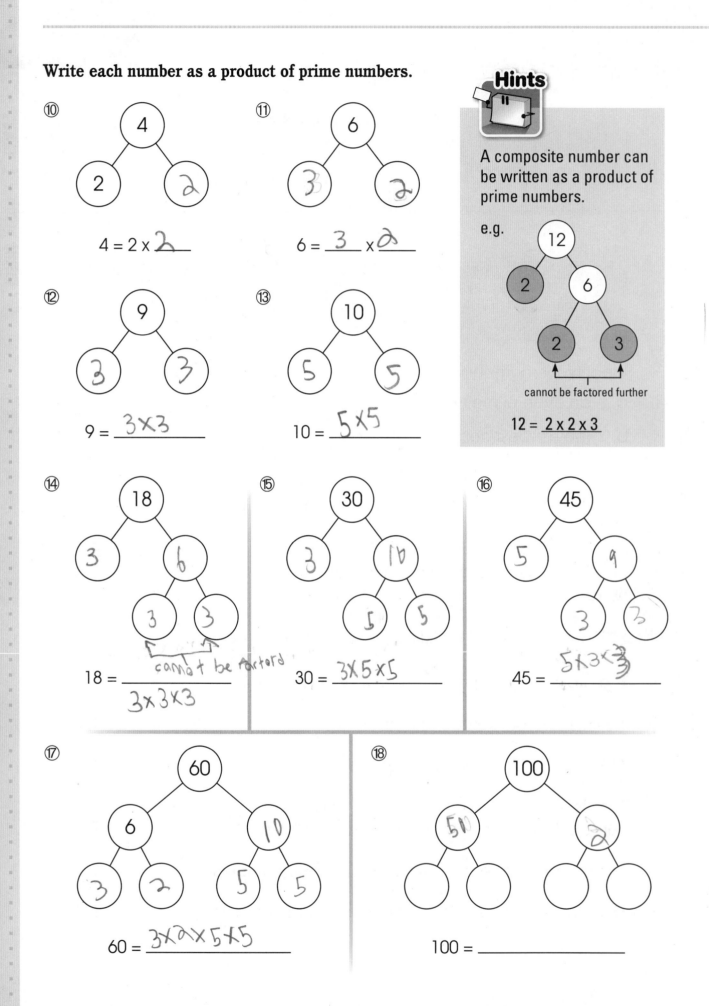

⑩

(tree: 4 → 2, 2)

4 = 2 x 2

⑪

(tree: 6 → 3, 2)

6 = 3 x 2

Hints

A composite number can be written as a product of prime numbers.

e.g.

(tree: 12 → 2, 6; 6 → 2, 3)

cannot be factored further

12 = 2 x 2 x 3

⑫

(tree: 9 → 3, 3)

9 = 3 x 3

⑬

(tree: 10 → 5, 5)

10 = 5 x 5

⑭

(tree: 18 → 3, 6; 6 → 3, 3)

18 = ___ cannot be factored
3 x 3 x 3

⑮

(tree: 30 → 3, 10; 10 → 5, 5)

30 = 3 x 5 x 5

⑯

(tree: 45 → 5, 9; 9 → 3, 3)

45 = 5 x 3 x 3

⑰

(tree: 60 → 6, 10; 6 → 3, 2; 10 → 5, 5)

60 = 3 x 2 x 5 x 5

⑱

(tree: 100 → 50, 2)

100 = _____

Look at the numbers below. If a number is a prime number, write "prime"; if it is a composite number, write it as a product of prime numbers.

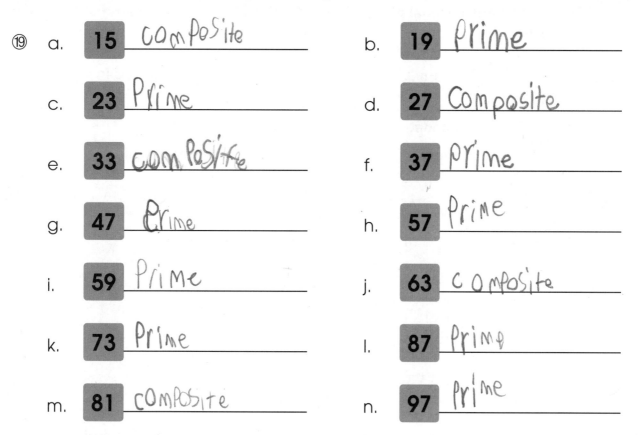

⑲ a. 15 composite

b. 19 Prime

c. 23 Prime

d. 27 Composite

e. 33 composite

f. 37 prime

g. 47 Prime

h. 57 Prime

i. 59 Prime

j. 63 composite

k. 73 Prime

l. 87 Prime

m. 81 composite

n. 97 Prime

Answer the questions.

⑳ James wants to know if 104 is a prime or composite number. Describe how you would find the answer.

i would divide 104 by 2 ang add them up and found out it is composite

㉑ Robin thinks that 121 is a prime number because it is not divisible by 2, 3, 5, or 7. Is Robin correct?

_____

_____

㉒ Bernice says, "169 equals 13 x 13, so it only has 2 factors: 13 and itself. Therefore, 169 is a prime number." Is Bernice correct? Explain.

_____

_____

3 Decimals

• representing and comparing decimals to thousandths

Read This

To write the decimal place of a digit, we add "th" to the name of the place value.

Example Write 24.539 in the place value chart, in expanded form, and in words.

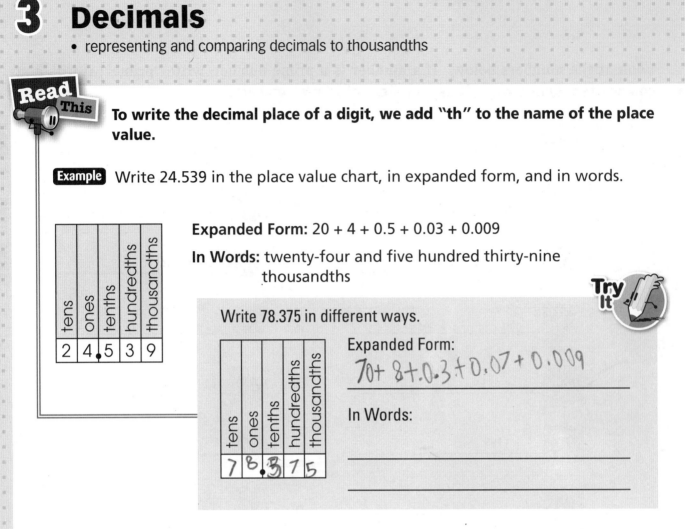

tens	ones	tenths	hundredths	thousandths
2	4	5	3	9

Expanded Form: 20 + 4 + 0.5 + 0.03 + 0.009

In Words: twenty-four and five hundred thirty-nine thousandths

Try It

Write 78.375 in different ways.

tens	ones	tenths	hundredths	thousandths
7	8	3	7	5

Expanded Form:

70 + 8 + 0.3 + 0.07 + 0.009

In Words:

_____

_____

Write each decimal in the place value chart, in expanded form, and in words.

①
   A 216.471
   B 315.082
   C 409.201

	hundreds	tens	ones	tenths	hundredths	thousandths
A	2	1	6	4	7	1
B	3	1	5	0	8	2
C	4	0	9	2	0	1

A

Expanded Form	200 + 10 + 6 + 0.4 + 0.07 + 0.001
In Words	

B

Expanded Form	
In Words	

C

Expanded Form	
In Words	

Mehereen

Write the value of each digit in bold.

② 9.**4**65

0.4

③ 13.90**8**

0.008

④ 38.8**5**4

0.05

⑤ 30.**1**69

0.1

⑥ **9**1.262

90

⑦ 129.0**7**3

0.07

⑧ 354.05**2**

0.002

⑨ 3**6**6.780

60

⑩ 752.**2**08

0.2

Circle the decimals as specified.

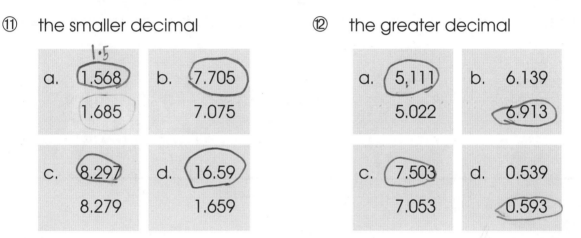

⑪ the smaller decimal

a. (1.568) / 1.685   (1·5)

b. (7.705) / 7.075

c. (8.297) / 8.279

d. (16.59) / 1.659

⑫ the greater decimal

a. (5,111) / 5.022

b. 6.139 / (6.913)

c. (7.503) / 7.053

d. 0.539 / (0.593)

Put each group of decimals in the specified order.

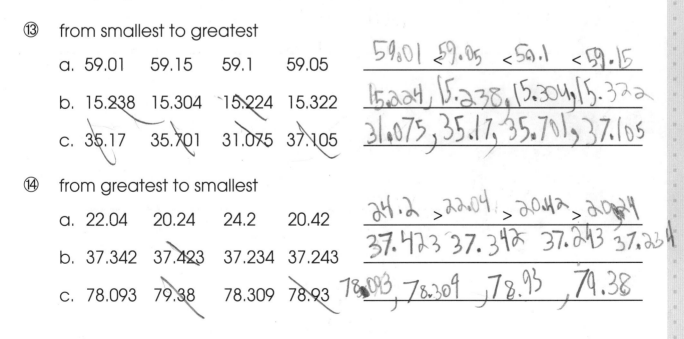

⑬ from smallest to greatest

a. 59.01 59.15 59.1 59.05

59.01 < 59.05 < 59.1 < 59.15

b. 15.238 15.304 15.224 15.322

15.224, 15.238, 15.304, 15.322

c. 35.17 35.701 31.075 37.105

31.075, 35.17, 35.701, 37.105

⑭ from greatest to smallest

a. 22.04 20.24 24.2 20.42

24.2 > 22.04 > 20.42 > 20.24

b. 37.342 37.423 37.234 37.243

37.423 37.342 37.243 37.234

c. 78.093 79.38 78.309 78.93

78.093, 78.309, 78.93, 79.38

Write the value of the decimal each letter represents.

⑮

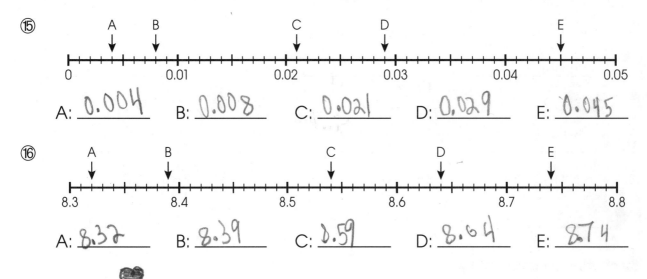

A: 0.004   B: 0.008   C: 0.021   D: 0.029   E: 0.045

⑯

A: 8.32   B: 8.39   C: 8.59   D: 8.64   E: 8.74

Locate the decimals in each set on the number line. Then identify the greatest decimals.

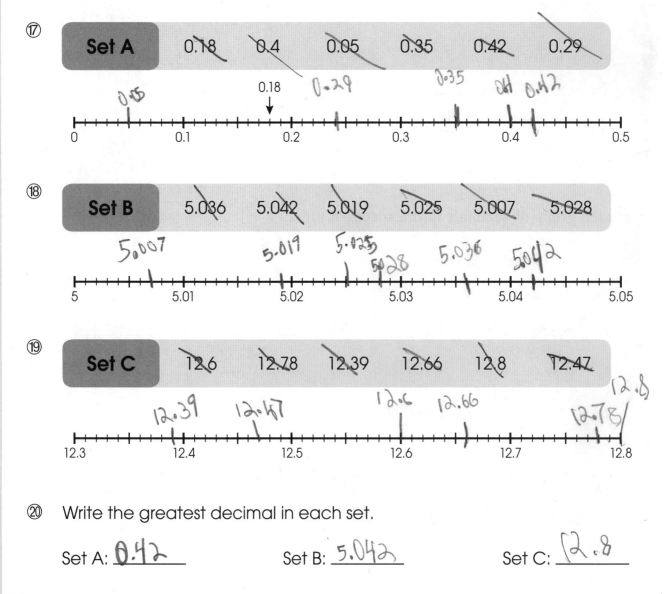

⑰

Set A   0.18   0.4   0.05   0.35   0.42   0.29

⑱

Set B   5.036   5.042   5.019   5.025   5.007   5.028

⑲

Set C   12.6   12.78   12.39   12.66   12.8   12.47

⑳ Write the greatest decimal in each set.

Set A: 0.42   Set B: 5.042   Set C: 12.8

Round the decimals.

Round to the Nearest

		one	tenth	hundredth
㉑	15.509	15.50	15.5	15.51
㉒	41.698	42	42.7	42.710
㉓	18.091	_____	_____	_____
㉔	25.499	_____	_____	_____
㉕	36.501	_____	_____	_____

LEVEL 1 – BASIC SKILLS

Hints

Follow the steps below to round a decimal.

❶ To round a decimal to a specified place value, look at the digit to the right of the place value.

❷ If it is 5 or more, round up; otherwise, round down.

e.g. Round 2.683 to the nearest hundredth.

hundredth place → 2.68<u>3</u> ← 3 < 5; so round down

2.683 $\xrightarrow{\text{rounded}}$ <u>2.68</u>

Put "<", ">", or "=" in the circles.

㉖	3.271	$<$	3.712		㉗	4.3	$=$	4.30
㉘	8.32	$>$	8.032		㉙	6.97	$>$	6.907
㉚	7.980	$=$	7.98		㉛	33.43	$<$	34.33
㉜	5.1	$=$	5.100		㉝	19.21	$>$	19.021
㉞	46.179	$<$	46.197		㉟	14.29	$=$	14.290

Check all the decimals that fit between each pair.

㊱   3.417 < **?** < 3.521

   Ⓐ 3.496   Ⓑ 3.540

   Ⓒ 3.408   Ⓓ 3.505

㊲   10.397 < **?** < 10.973

   Ⓐ 10.307   Ⓑ 10.739

   Ⓒ 10.093   Ⓓ 10.793

㊳   22.000 > **?** > 21.473

   Ⓐ 21.734   Ⓑ 21.000

   Ⓒ 21.400   Ⓓ 21.700

㊴   49.209 > **?** > 48.908

   Ⓐ 49.902   Ⓑ 48.89

   Ⓒ 48.98   Ⓓ 49.029

4 Adding Decimals

• adding decimals to thousandths

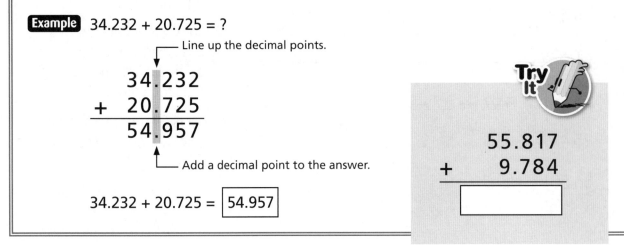

Read This

To add decimals, line up the decimal points in vertical addition and add as usual. Then add a decimal point to the answer.

Example 34.232 + 20.725 = ?

— Line up the decimal points.

```
   34.232
 + 20.725
   54.957
```

— Add a decimal point to the answer.

34.232 + 20.725 = 54.957

Try It

```
   55.817
 +  9.784
```

Add.

①
```
   5.976
 + 3.012
```

②
```
   4.027
 + 2.402
```

③
```
   16.923
 +  8.170
```

④
```
   9.126
 + 0.331
```

⑤
```
   8.204
 + 1.593
```

⑥
```
   21.470
 + 18.931
```

⑦
```
    3.190
 + 10.217
```

⑧
```
    7.999
 + 12.001
```

⑨
```
   14.093
 +  0.178
```

⑩
```
   28.023
 + 31.481
```

⑪
```
    0.604
 + 40.237
```

⑫
```
   31.007
 + 24.908
```

Add.

⑬ 8.15 + 3.457   = _____

⑭ 7.532 + 1.898   = _____

⑮ 4.86 + 0.071   = _____

⑯ 7.233 + 9.3   = _____

⑰ 13.845 + 15.97 = _____

Add "0" as a placeholder when needed.

e.g.   7.81 + 4.253 = ?

$$
\begin{array}{r}
7.810 \leftarrow \text{placeholder} \\
+\quad 4.253 \\
\hline
12.063
\end{array}
$$

⑱ 23.496 + 35.5   = _____   ⑲ 43.6 + 31.616   = _____

⑳ 36.128 + 14.527 = _____   ㉑ 18.319 + 26.05   = _____

㉒ 42 + 53.657   = _____   ㉓ 30.413 + 1.9   = _____

㉔ 186.53 + 16.319 = _____   ㉕ 235.07 + 154.238 = _____

㉖ 15.69 + 273.027 = _____   ㉗ 116.713 + 229.28 = _____

Do your work here.

LEVEL 1 – BASIC SKILLS

Find each sum. Then estimate to determine whether your answer is reasonable.

Hints

Estimate an answer by rounding the decimals to the nearest whole numbers.

e.g. 3.915 + 4.432 = ?

Sum	Estimate
3.915	4
+ 4.432	+ 4
8.347	8

The answer is close to 8, so it is reasonable.

㉘

79.132	**19.196**
Sum	Estimate

$$\begin{array}{r} 79.132 \\ + 19.196 \\ \hline \end{array}$$ + _____

㉙

47.748	**62.517**
Sum	Estimate

㉚

194.057	**88.708**
Sum	Estimate

㉛

70.831	**185.098**
Sum	Estimate

Estimate to determine whether each given answer is reasonable. If so, put a check mark in the circle; if not, put a cross and write the correct answer.

㉜ 29.147 + 30.39 = *59.537* ◯

㉝ 36.541 + 64.205 = *99.746* ◯

㉞ 17.91 + 80.398 = *100.308* ◯

㉟ 73.763 + 25.504 = *99.267* ◯

㊱ 58.009 + 41.514 = *102.523* ◯

㊲ 27.826 + 50.589 = *76.415* ◯

Do your work here.

Add.

㊳
```
      22.416
      38.297
  +    7.305
```

㊴
```
     128.450
      83.064
  +   22.355
```

㊵
```
      66.819
      42.326
  +  271.169
```

㊶ 124.89 + 82.404 + 67.097   = _____

㊷ 177.028 + 86.937 + 241.742 = _____

㊸ 417.829 + 145.81 + 223.77 = _____

㊹ 210.07 + 39.2 + 400.019   = _____

Clara is packing for her trip. Look at the weight of each item. Help Clara find the answers.

㊺ The total weight of her

    a. backpack and travel kit:

    _____

    b. running shoes and suitcase:

    _____

    c. tops and shorts:

    _____

    d. sleeping bag and running shoes:

    _____

5.613 kg

Tops: 4.265 kg
Shorts: 3.66 kg

2.688 kg

0.382 kg

Sleeping Bag

Travel Kit

0.629 kg

1.658 kg

㊻ The weight limit for a carry-on suitcase on a flight is 18 kg. If Clara puts her running shoes, tops, shorts, and sleeping bag in the suitcase, will it exceed the weight limit?

_____

5 Subtracting Decimals

- subtracting decimals to thousandths

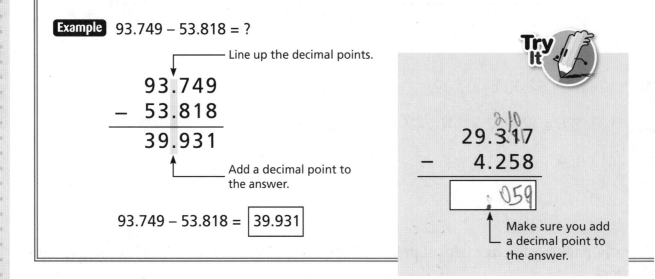

Read This

To subtract decimals, line up the decimal points in vertical subtraction and subtract as usual. Then add a decimal point to the answer.

Example 93.749 − 53.818 = ?

Line up the decimal points.

$$
\begin{array}{r}
93.749 \\
- 53.818 \\
\hline
39.931
\end{array}
$$

Add a decimal point to the answer.

93.749 − 53.818 = $\boxed{39.931}$

Try It

$$
\begin{array}{r}
29.3\overset{2\,10}{1}7 \\
- 4.258 \\
\hline
.059
\end{array}
$$

Make sure you add a decimal point to the answer.

Subtract.

①
$$
\begin{array}{r}
5.2\overset{7}{8}1 \\
- 3.046 \\
\hline
2.235
\end{array}
$$

②
$$
\begin{array}{r}
8.399 \\
- 7.205 \\
\hline
1.194
\end{array}
$$

③
$$
\begin{array}{r}
10.\overset{9\;\;9}{0}00 \\
- 4.135 \\
\hline
15.465
\end{array}
$$

④
$$
\begin{array}{r}
6.0\overset{9}{0}6 \\
- 0.254 \\
\hline
6.752
\end{array}
$$

⑤
$$
\begin{array}{r}
11.4\overset{3\;6}{7}0 \\
- 8.095 \\
\hline
3.375
\end{array}
$$

⑥
$$
\begin{array}{r}
14.\overset{13\;\;2}{0}35 \\
- 9.218 \\
\hline
4.816
\end{array}
$$

⑦
$$
\begin{array}{r}
23.340 \\
- 14.177 \\
\hline
9.163
\end{array}
$$

⑧
$$
\begin{array}{r}
30.500 \\
- 21.209 \\
\hline
9.301
\end{array}
$$

⑨
$$
\begin{array}{r}
26.\overset{5\;10\;16}{1}69 \\
- 15.380 \\
\hline
10.789
\end{array}
$$

⑩
$$
\begin{array}{r}
138.0\overset{9\;17}{8}0 \\
- 120.495 \\
\hline
18.585
\end{array}
$$

⑪
$$
\begin{array}{r}
141.\overset{0\;\;6}{7}36 \\
- 136.080 \\
\hline
5.656
\end{array}
$$

⑫
$$
\begin{array}{r}
201.4\overset{9\;\;8}{9}0 \\
- 187.303 \\
\hline
14.187
\end{array}
$$

I LOVE SAMPATH
soooo much

Subtract.

⑬ 6.92 – 5.344 = 1.584

⑭ 8.166 – 3.095 = 5.071

⑮ 9.254 – 0.316 = 8.938

⑯ 10.8 – 7.406 = 3.406

⑰ 8.71 – 4.613 = 4.103

⑱ 12.38 – 9.048 = 3.348

⑲ 15.179 – 12.341 = 2.838

⑳ 78.9 – 7.436 = 71.536

㉑ 20.55 – 16.098 = 4.161

㉒ 31.473 – 28.95 = 2.523

㉓ 43 – 38.019 = 5.019

㉔ 50.46 – 16.391 = 34.069

㉕ 100 – 39.256 = 70.844

㉖ 168.39 – 79.007 = 89.383

㉗ 216.409 – 187 = 39.409

㉘ 180.73 – 98.218 = 92.512

㉙ 105.21 – 41.109 = 64.101

㉚ 110 – 20.082 = 90.018

㉛ 191.7 – 37.093 = 154.707

Tips

When needed, add "0" as a placeholder to the decimals.

e.g. 15.1 – 7.263 = ?

$$15.\underline{100} \leftarrow \text{placeholders}$$
$$- \quad 7.263$$
$$\overline{\quad 7.837}$$

Do your work here.

(handwritten working shown)

Find each difference. Then estimate to determine whether your answer is reasonable.

③② **16.479 − 10.64 = ?**

Difference	Estimate
4.139	6.83

(handwritten work:)
-109.420
61.069
48.449
54.947
22.833

③③ **25.17 − 19.525 = ?**

Difference	Estimate
4.355	6.665

(handwritten work near center:)
10.5
16.479
4179
510.6
38.574
54.947
1.127
54.947
109.42

③④

	Difference	Estimate
a. 54.947 − 36.174 = ?	22.833	18.773
b. 109.42 − 61.069 = ?	48.449	
c. 133.217 − 125.845 = ?		
d. 256.197 − 185.709 = ?		

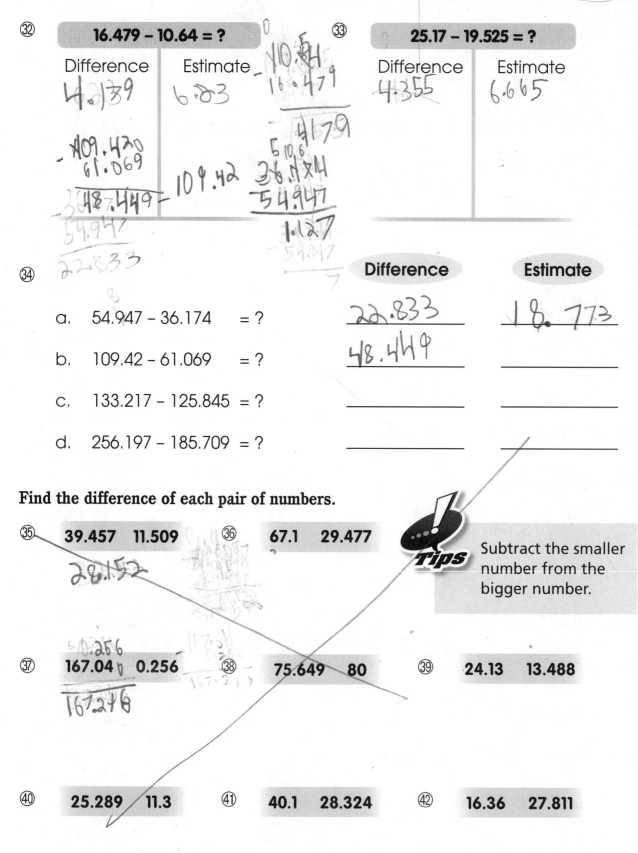

Find the difference of each pair of numbers.

③⑤ **39.457   11.509**   28.152

③⑥ **67.1   29.477**

Tips   Subtract the smaller number from the bigger number.

③⑦ **167.04   0.256**   167.296

③⑧ **75.649   80**

③⑨ **24.13   13.488**

④⓪ **25.289   11.3**

④① **40.1   28.324**

④② **16.36   27.811**

Billy and his friends participated in a 10-km run. The distances that they covered after an hour are recorded in the chart.

㊸ How much does each runner have left to run?

Runner	Distance covered (km) after 1 hour
Billy	6.725
Carol	3.1
Daniel	5.05
Eliza	7.203
Freddy	4.781

a.   Billy   _3.275_

b.   Carol   _6.9_

c.   Daniel   _4.95_

d.   Eliza   _2.797_

e.   Freddy   _5.219_

㊹ How much farther did Eliza run than Billy?   _____

㊺ How much farther did Eliza run than Daniel?   _____

㊻ How much farther did Eliza run than Carol?   _____

㊼ If Carol runs an additional 5.258 km after another hour, how much will she have left to run?   _____

A new bus route is available. The distance of each stop from Terminal A is shown. Answer the questions.

㊽ What is the distance between

a.   Creek Centre and Rouge Park?

   _____

b.   Shore Plaza and King City?

   _____

c.   Terminal B and Rouge Park?

   _____

㊾ Zoe rides the bus from Creek Centre to King City, and then returns to Rouge Park. How many kilometres did she travel in all?

_____

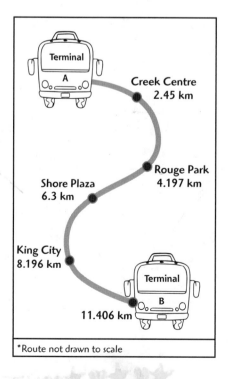

Terminal A

Creek Centre 2.45 km

Rouge Park 4.197 km

Shore Plaza 6.3 km

King City 8.196 km

Terminal B

11.406 km

*Route not drawn to scale

6 Multiplying Decimals

• multiplying decimals by whole numbers

Read This

When multiplying a decimal by a whole number, the number of decimal places in the product is the same as the original decimal.

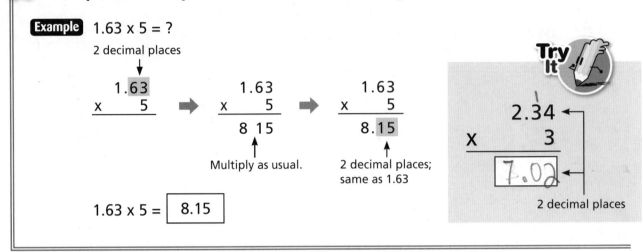

Example 1.63 x 5 = ?

2 decimal places

```
  1.63          1.63          1.63
x    5    ➡   x    5    ➡   x    5
               8 15          8.15
```

Multiply as usual.

2 decimal places; same as 1.63

1.63 x 5 = [8.15]

Try It

```
   2.34
x     3
  7.02
```

2 decimal places

Multiply.

①
```
  2.3
x   4
  9.2
```

②
```
  3.6
x   7
 25.2
```

③
```
  5.4
x   6
 32.4
```

④
```
  8.3
x   9
 74.7
```

⑤
```
 10.31
x    5
 51.55
```

⑥
```
  6.57
x    8
 52.56
```

⑦
```
 12.33
x    6
 63.98
```

⑧
```
 15.08
x    2
 30.16
```

⑨
```
 13.25
x    5
 56.25
```

⑩
```
 14.37
x    6
 86.22
```

⑪
```
  7.19
x    8
 57.52
```

⑫
```
  9.03
x    7
 63.21
```

⑬
```
 12.36
x    5
 61.80
```

⑭
```
  8.43
x    8
 67.64
```

⑮
```
  5.08
x    3
 15.24
```

⑯
```
 17.13
x    4
 68.52
```

Multiply.

⑰ $\overset{2}{5.3} \times 8 = \underline{42.4}$

⑱ $2.11 \times 6 = \underline{12.66}$

⑲ $3.21 \times 4 = \underline{12.84}$

⑳ $5.01 \times 3 = \underline{15.03}$

㉑ $8.5 \times 2 = \underline{17.0}$

㉒ $\overset{2}{7.9} \times 3 = \underline{23.7}$

㉓ $\overset{22}{4.65} \times 4 = \underline{18.60}$

㉔ $\overset{1}{1.2} \times 8 = \underline{9.6}$

㉕ $\overset{22}{3.77} \times 3 = \underline{11.31}$

㉖ $\overset{1}{5.19} \times 2 = \underline{10.38}$

㉗ $\overset{14}{6.28} \times 5 = \underline{30.40}$

㉘ $\overset{4}{7.71} \times 7 = \underline{48.97}$

㉙ $10.\overset{1}{15} \times 2 = \underline{20.30}$

㉚ $\overset{67}{2.68} \times 9 = \underline{24.12}$

> Use estimation to determine whether your answer is reasonable.

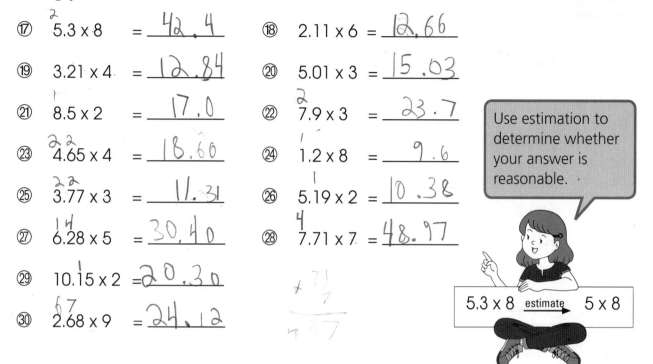

$5.3 \times 8 \xrightarrow{\text{estimate}} 5 \times 8$

Write the number of zeros there are in each multiplier. Then find the products mentally by moving the decimal point.

㉛

	number of zeros	product
a. 2.31×10	1	23.31
b. 4.5×10	1	45.0
c. 3.99×100	2	399
d. 13.6×100	2	136
e. 14.15×100	2	141.5
f. 4.56×1000	3	4560
g. 8.09×1000	3	8090
h. 11.28×1000	3	1128.
i. $5.43 \times 10\ 000$	4	54300
j. $16.48 \times 10\ 000$	4	16480

Hints

When multiplying a decimal by 10, 100, 1000, and 10 000, move the decimal point to the right the same number of places as there are zeros in the multiplier.

e.g. $1.23 \times 10 = 12.3$
1 zero, 1 place

$1.23 \times 100 = 123.$
2 zeros, 2 places

$1.23 \times 1000 = 1230.$
3 zeros, 3 places

$1.23 \times 10000 = 12300.$
4 zeros, 4 places

Note: Remember to add zeros as needed.

Determine how many places the decimal point has to be moved to the left. Then find the answer.

③② 45 x 0.1 = __4.5__

move the decimal point ____ place(s) to the left

③③ 3 x 0.01 = __.03__

move the decimal point ____ place(s) to the left

③④ 315 x 0.001 = __0.315__

move the decimal point ____ place(s) to the left

③⑤ 510 x 0.01 = __5.10__

move the decimal point ____ place(s) to the left

③⑥ 90 x 0.01 = __0.90__

move the decimal point ____ place(s) to the left

③⑦ 2 x 0.001 = __0.002__

move the decimal point ____ place(s) to the left

③⑧ 17 x 0.01 = __0.17__

move the decimal point ____ place(s) to the left

Hints

When multiplying a number by 0.1, 0.01, and 0.001, move the decimal point to the left the same number of places as there are decimal places in the multiplier.

e.g.　30 x 0.1 = 3.0

30 x 0.01 = 0.30

30 x 0. 001 = 0.030

Note: Remember to add zeros as needed.

Multiply each number by the given numbers.

③⑨

4.5

x 2　= __90__

x 3　= __13.5__

x 10　= __50__

④①

8

x 1.5　= __12.0__

x 4.2　= __33.6__

x 0.1　= __0.8__

④③

1.14

x 4　= __4.56__

x 5　= __5.70__

x 100　= __14.00__

④⓪

6.3

x 6　= __37.8__

x 7　= __44.1__

x 100　= ~~42~~

④②

6

x 2.4　= _____

x 5.1　= _____

x 0.01　= _____

④④

4

x 2.7　= _____

x 1.8　= _____

x 0.1　= _____

Look at the prices and product details of the beverages. Find the answers.

㊺ Find the total cost of each quantity of beverages.

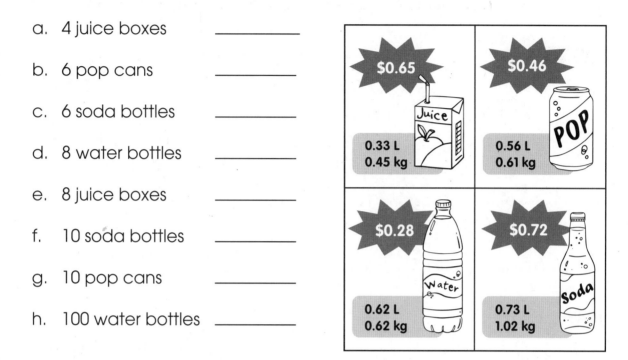

a. 4 juice boxes _____

b. 6 pop cans _____

c. 6 soda bottles _____

d. 8 water bottles _____

e. 8 juice boxes _____

f. 10 soda bottles _____

g. 10 pop cans _____

h. 100 water bottles _____

㊻ Find the total volume of each quantity of beverages.

a. 6 water bottles _____   b. 8 juice boxes _____

c. 10 juice boxes _____   d. 10 water bottles _____

e. 100 juice boxes _____   f. 100 pop cans _____

g. 1000 water bottles _____   h. 10 000 soda bottles _____

㊼ Find the total weight of each quantity of beverages.

a. 5 juice boxes _____   b. 10 juice boxes _____

c. 5 pop cans _____   d. 100 pop cans _____

e. 5 water bottles _____   f. 1000 water bottles _____

g. 5 soda bottles _____   h. 10 000 soda bottles _____

7 Dividing Decimals

• dividing decimals by whole numbers

When dividing a decimal by a whole number, the position of the decimal point in the quotient is the same as that in the original decimal.

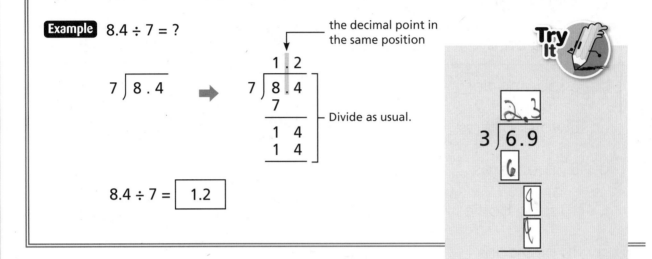

Example 8.4 ÷ 7 = ?

the decimal point in the same position

Divide as usual.

8.4 ÷ 7 = [1.2]

Try It

Divide.

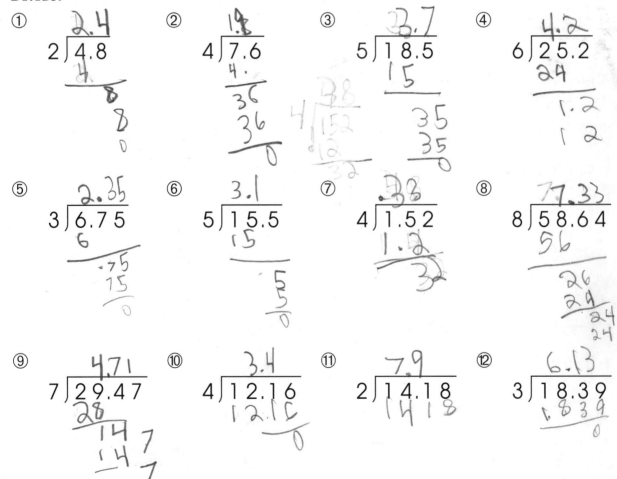

① 2)4.8 → 2.4

② 4)7.6 → 1.8

③ 5)18.5 → 3.7

④ 6)25.2 → 4.2

⑤ 3)6.75 → 2.35

⑥ 5)15.5 → 3.1

⑦ 4)1.52 → .38

⑧ 8)58.64 → 7.33

⑨ 7)29.47 → 4.71

⑩ 4)12.16 → 3.4

⑪ 2)14.18 → 7.9

⑫ 3)18.39 → 6.13

Divide.

⑬ 9.2 ÷ 4 = _2.3_

⑭ 16.5 ÷ 5 = _3.3_

⑮ 11.2 ÷ 7 = _1.6_

⑯ 26.28 ÷ 9 = _2.92_

⑰ 28.44 ÷ 4 = _7.11_

⑱ 14.6 ÷ 4 = _3.65_

⑲ 19.9 ÷ 2 = _9.95_

⑳ 49.2 ÷ 6 = _8.2_

㉑ 31.2 ÷ 8 = _3.9_

㉒ 19.17 ÷ 9 = _2.13_

㉓ 16.44 ÷ 6 = _2.7_

㉔ 14.7 ÷ 6 = _2.45_

Tips

If needed, add "0" as a placeholder in the quotient or the dividend to continue the division.

e.g. 5.2 ÷ 5 = ?

```
        a placeholder
      1.0 4
  5 ) 5.2 0 ◄
      5
      2 0
      2 0
```

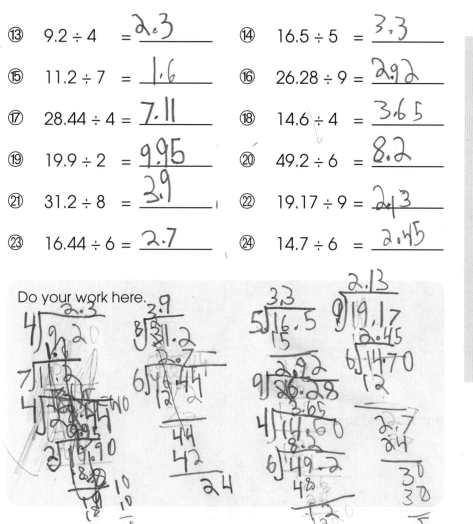

Do your work here.

Draw arrow(s) under the number to show the movement of the decimal point for each division question. Then write the answer.

㉕ 2.9 ÷ 10   = _.29_

㉖ 4.5 ÷ 10   = _4.5_

㉗ 3.50 ÷ 100   = _3.50_

㉘ 24.3 ÷ 100   = _.245_

㉙ 1409 ÷ 1000 = _1.409_

㉚ 6 ÷ 10   = _.6_

㉛ 7.5 ÷ 100   = _.075_

㉜ 13.9 ÷ 1000 = _.139_

Hints

When dividing a number by 10, 100, 1000, and 10 000, move the decimal point to the left the same number of places as there are zeros in the divisor.

e.g. 1234 ÷ 10 = 123.4
        1 zero   1 place

      1234 ÷ 1 00 = 12.34
        2 zeros   2 places

      1234 ÷ 1 000 = 1.234
        3 zeros   3 places

Find each divisor mentally by comparing the dividend and the quotient. Write "1", "10", "100", or "1000" in the box.

㉝ $58.2 \div \boxed{10} = 5.82$

㉞ $251.3 \div \boxed{} = 2.513$

㉟ $246.5 \div \boxed{100} = 2.465$

㊱ $425 \div \boxed{} = 0.425$

㊲ $28.59 \div \boxed{1} = 28.59$

㊳ $239.4 \div \boxed{} = 23.94$

㊴ $4 \div \boxed{1000} = 0.004$

㊵ $87 \div \boxed{} = 8.7$

㊶ $0.13 \div \boxed{100} = 0.0013$

㊷ $50 \div \boxed{} = 0.5$

㊸ $0.7 \div \boxed{100} = 0.007$

㊹ $16 \div \boxed{} = 0.16$

Divide each number by the given divisors.

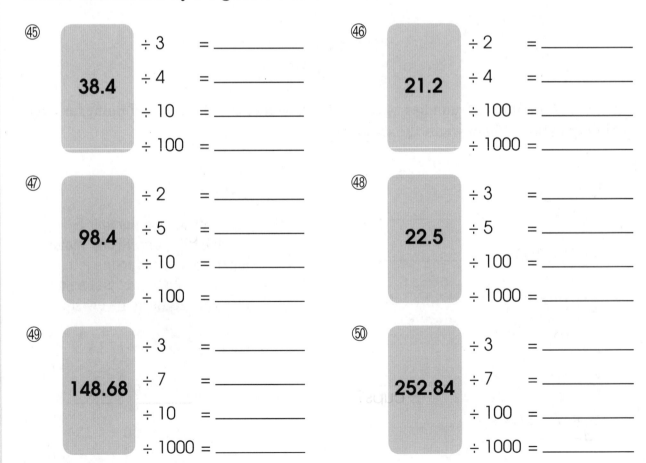

㊺ **38.4**
$\div 3 = \underline{\hspace{3cm}}$
$\div 4 = \underline{\hspace{3cm}}$
$\div 10 = \underline{\hspace{3cm}}$
$\div 100 = \underline{\hspace{3cm}}$

㊻ **21.2**
$\div 2 = \underline{\hspace{3cm}}$
$\div 4 = \underline{\hspace{3cm}}$
$\div 100 = \underline{\hspace{3cm}}$
$\div 1000 = \underline{\hspace{3cm}}$

㊼ **98.4**
$\div 2 = \underline{\hspace{3cm}}$
$\div 5 = \underline{\hspace{3cm}}$
$\div 10 = \underline{\hspace{3cm}}$
$\div 100 = \underline{\hspace{3cm}}$

㊽ **22.5**
$\div 3 = \underline{\hspace{3cm}}$
$\div 5 = \underline{\hspace{3cm}}$
$\div 100 = \underline{\hspace{3cm}}$
$\div 1000 = \underline{\hspace{3cm}}$

㊾ **148.68**
$\div 3 = \underline{\hspace{3cm}}$
$\div 7 = \underline{\hspace{3cm}}$
$\div 10 = \underline{\hspace{3cm}}$
$\div 1000 = \underline{\hspace{3cm}}$

㊿ **252.84**
$\div 3 = \underline{\hspace{3cm}}$
$\div 7 = \underline{\hspace{3cm}}$
$\div 100 = \underline{\hspace{3cm}}$
$\div 1000 = \underline{\hspace{3cm}}$

Sandra is organizing a party. Help her divide the food.

I wonder how to divide things into equal portions.

(51)

1.8 kg

Sandra cuts the cake into equal slices. How heavy is each slice if there are

a. 9 slices? ____________

b. 10 slices? ____________

c. 12 slices? ____________

(52)

POP

1.8 L

Sandra then prepares the drinks by pouring all the pop evenly into cups. How much is in each cup if a bottle can fill

a. 6 cups? ____________

b. 8 cups? ____________

c. 10 cups? ____________

(53)

455.04 g

Sandra then evenly divides and puts all the salad on plates. How much salad is on each plate if there are

a. 8 plates? ____________

b. 9 plates? ____________

c. 10 plates? ____________

(54)

Cereal
popcorn

509.04 g

421.2 g

Sandra puts the cereal and the popcorn equally into cups. How much of each snack will each cup contain if there are

a. 5 cups? ____________ of cereal, ____________ of popcorn

b. 6 cups? ____________

c. 8 cups? ____________

d. 10 cups? ____________

8 Equivalent Fractions

- representing and comparing equivalent fractions

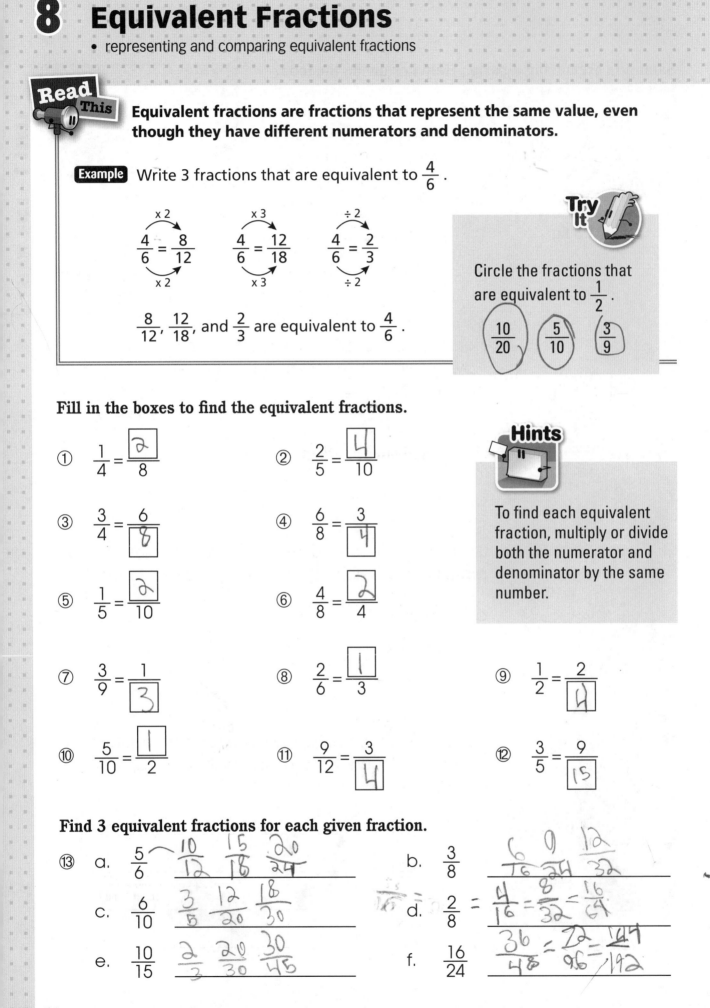

Read This

Equivalent fractions are fractions that represent the same value, even though they have different numerators and denominators.

Example Write 3 fractions that are equivalent to $\frac{4}{6}$.

$$\underset{\times 2}{\overset{\times 2}{\frac{4}{6} = \frac{8}{12}}} \qquad \underset{\times 3}{\overset{\times 3}{\frac{4}{6} = \frac{12}{18}}} \qquad \underset{\div 2}{\overset{\div 2}{\frac{4}{6} = \frac{2}{3}}}$$

$\frac{8}{12}$, $\frac{12}{18}$, and $\frac{2}{3}$ are equivalent to $\frac{4}{6}$.

Try It

Circle the fractions that are equivalent to $\frac{1}{2}$.

$\frac{10}{20}$ $\frac{5}{10}$ $\frac{3}{9}$

Fill in the boxes to find the equivalent fractions.

Hints

To find each equivalent fraction, multiply or divide both the numerator and denominator by the same number.

① $\frac{1}{4} = \frac{2}{8}$

② $\frac{2}{5} = \frac{4}{10}$

③ $\frac{3}{4} = \frac{6}{8}$

④ $\frac{6}{8} = \frac{3}{4}$

⑤ $\frac{1}{5} = \frac{2}{10}$

⑥ $\frac{4}{8} = \frac{2}{4}$

⑦ $\frac{3}{9} = \frac{1}{3}$

⑧ $\frac{2}{6} = \frac{1}{3}$

⑨ $\frac{1}{2} = \frac{2}{4}$

⑩ $\frac{5}{10} = \frac{1}{2}$

⑪ $\frac{9}{12} = \frac{3}{4}$

⑫ $\frac{3}{5} = \frac{9}{15}$

Find 3 equivalent fractions for each given fraction.

⑬ a. $\frac{5}{6}$ $\frac{10}{12}$ $\frac{15}{18}$ $\frac{20}{24}$

b. $\frac{3}{8}$ $\frac{6}{16}$ $\frac{9}{24}$ $\frac{12}{32}$

c. $\frac{6}{10}$ $\frac{3}{5}$ $\frac{12}{20}$ $\frac{18}{30}$

d. $\frac{2}{8} = \frac{4}{16} = \frac{8}{32} = \frac{16}{64}$

e. $\frac{10}{15}$ $\frac{2}{3}$ $\frac{20}{30}$ $\frac{30}{45}$

f. $\frac{16}{24}$ $\frac{36}{48} = \frac{72}{96} = \frac{144}{192}$

Determine whether the pairs of fractions are equivalent. If so, write "=" in the circle. Then write one more equivalent fraction in the shaded box.

⑭ $\frac{5}{20}$ ⊜ $\frac{1}{4}$ $\frac{10}{40}$

⑮ $\frac{3}{7}$ ◯ $\frac{6}{10}$

⑯ $\frac{4}{6}$ ⊜ $\frac{8}{12}$ $\frac{16}{24}$

⑰ $\frac{1}{10}$ ⊗ $\frac{10}{11}$

⑱ $\frac{8}{20}$ ⊗ $\frac{4}{10}$ $\frac{16}{40}$

⑲ $\frac{3}{2}$ ⊜ $\frac{18}{12}$ $\frac{36}{24}$

⑳ $\frac{14}{10}$ ⊜ $\frac{7}{5}$ $\frac{24}{20}$

㉑ $\frac{9}{6}$ ⊗ $\frac{7}{4}$

㉒ $\frac{12}{9}$ ⊜ $\frac{4}{3}$ $\frac{24}{18}$

㉓ $\frac{25}{10}$ ⊜ $\frac{5}{2}$ $\frac{50}{20}$

㉔ $\frac{9}{21}$ ⊗ $\frac{7}{3}$

㉕ $\frac{8}{18}$ ⊜ $\frac{4}{9}$ $\frac{16}{36}$

Cross out the fraction that is not equivalent to the rest of the set.

㉖ $\frac{6}{9}$ $\frac{12}{18}$ $\frac{9}{12}$ $\frac{2}{3}$

㉗ $\frac{1}{3}$ $\frac{4}{12}$ $\frac{3}{4}$ $\frac{2}{6}$

㉘ $\frac{3}{5}$ $\frac{5}{8}$ $\frac{6}{10}$ $\frac{12}{20}$

㉙ $\frac{10}{8}$ $\frac{15}{12}$ $\frac{5}{4}$ $\frac{4}{5}$

Write each fraction in simplest form.

㉚ $\frac{18}{20}$ $\frac{9}{10}$

㉛ $\frac{25}{30} = \frac{5}{6}$

㉜ $\frac{12}{16} = \frac{3}{4}$

㉝ $\frac{10}{15} = \frac{2}{3}$

㉞ $\frac{4}{16}$ $\frac{1}{4}$

㉟ $\frac{12}{24} = \frac{1}{2}$

㊱ $\frac{90}{100}$ $\frac{9}{10}$

㊲ $\frac{15}{33}$ $\frac{3}{11}$

㊳ $\frac{49}{56}$ $\frac{7}{8}$

㊴ $\frac{38}{40} = \frac{19}{20}$

㊵ $\frac{28}{36}$ $\frac{7}{9}$

㊶ $\frac{45}{50}$ $\frac{9}{10}$

Hints

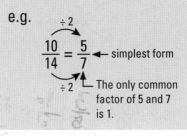

A fraction is in its simplest form when its numerator and denominator have 1 as their only common factor.

e.g.

$\frac{10}{14} = \frac{5}{7}$ ← simplest form

÷ 2

The only common factor of 5 and 7 is 1.

Write each improper fraction as a mixed number in simplest form.

	simplest form	mixed number

㊷ $\dfrac{10}{6}$ = $\dfrac{5}{3}$ = $1\dfrac{2}{3}$ ㊸ $\dfrac{12}{10}$ = $\dfrac{6}{5}$ = $1\dfrac{1}{5}$

㊹ $\dfrac{15}{9}$ = $\dfrac{5}{3}$ = $1\dfrac{2}{3}$ ㊺ $\dfrac{20}{8}$ = $\dfrac{5}{2}$ = $2\dfrac{1}{2}$

㊻ $\dfrac{18}{16}$ = $\dfrac{9}{8}$ = $1\dfrac{1}{8}$ ㊼ $\dfrac{12}{8}$ = $\dfrac{6}{4}$ = $1\dfrac{2}{4}$

㊽ $\dfrac{28}{21}$ = $\dfrac{4}{3}$ = $1\dfrac{1}{3}$ ㊾ $\dfrac{21}{15}$ = $\dfrac{7}{5}$ = $1\dfrac{2}{5}$

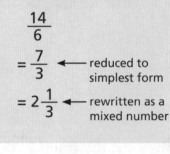

Start by reducing an improper fraction to its simplest form. Then rewrite it as a mixed number.

e.g. Write $\dfrac{14}{6}$ as a mixed number in simplest form.

$\dfrac{14}{6}$

$= \dfrac{7}{3}$ ← reduced to simplest form

$= 2\dfrac{1}{3}$ ← rewritten as a mixed number

㊿ $\dfrac{60}{14}$ = $\dfrac{30}{7}$ ㊿⑤¹ $\dfrac{12}{5}$ = _____   ⑤² $\dfrac{37}{12}$ = _____   ⑤³ $\dfrac{50}{16}$ = _____

⑤⁴ $\dfrac{48}{12}$ = _____   ⑤⁵ $\dfrac{24}{16}$ = _____   ⑤⁶ $\dfrac{18}{15}$ = _____   ⑤⁷ $\dfrac{95}{9}$ = _____

Colour to show the fractions. Then write them as mixed numbers in simplest form.

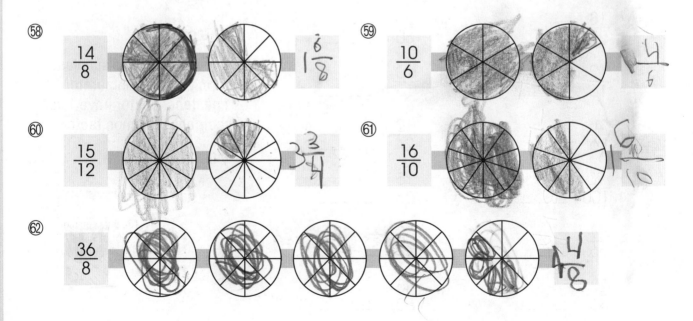

⑤⁸ $\dfrac{14}{8}$ $1\dfrac{6}{8}$

⑤⁹ $\dfrac{10}{6}$ $\dfrac{4}{6}$

⑥⁰ $\dfrac{15}{12}$ $3\dfrac{3}{4}$

⑥¹ $\dfrac{16}{10}$ $\dfrac{6}{10}$

⑥² $\dfrac{36}{8}$ $4\dfrac{4}{8}$

Put a check mark in the circle if the fractions in each pair are equivalent; otherwise, put a cross.

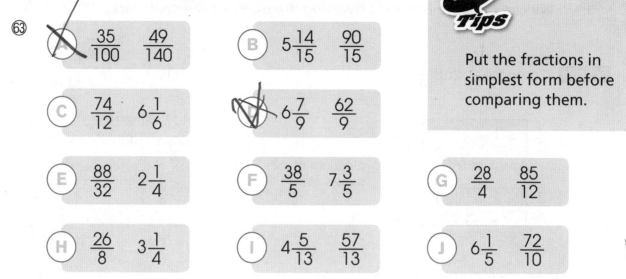

Tips

Put the fractions in simplest form before comparing them.

63

(A) $\dfrac{35}{100}$ $\dfrac{49}{140}$

(B) $5\dfrac{14}{15}$ $\dfrac{90}{15}$

(C) $\dfrac{74}{12}$ $6\dfrac{1}{6}$

(D) $6\dfrac{7}{9}$ $\dfrac{62}{9}$

(E) $\dfrac{88}{32}$ $2\dfrac{1}{4}$

(F) $\dfrac{38}{5}$ $7\dfrac{3}{5}$

(G) $\dfrac{28}{4}$ $\dfrac{85}{12}$

(H) $\dfrac{26}{8}$ $3\dfrac{1}{4}$

(I) $4\dfrac{5}{13}$ $\dfrac{57}{13}$

(J) $6\dfrac{1}{5}$ $\dfrac{72}{10}$

Change each improper fraction to a mixed number in simplest form. Then do the matching to find out what Emma says.

64

$\dfrac{6}{4} =$ _____ **I**

$\dfrac{27}{15} =$ _____ **E**

$\dfrac{17}{6} =$ _____ **M**

$\dfrac{13}{6} =$ _____ **K**

$\dfrac{10}{8} =$ _____ **F**

$\dfrac{29}{18} =$ _____ **C**

$\dfrac{13}{2} =$ _____ **P**

$\dfrac{22}{10} =$ _____ **R**

$\dfrac{25}{18} =$ _____ **S**

$\dfrac{7}{3} =$ _____ **T**

$\dfrac{23}{18} =$ _____ **A**

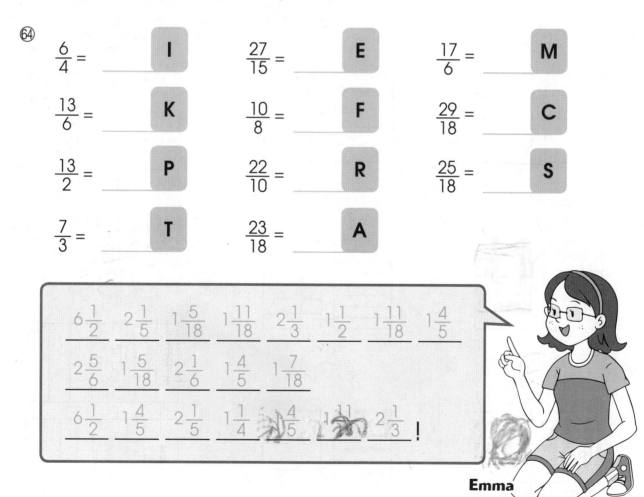

$6\dfrac{1}{2}$ $2\dfrac{1}{5}$ $1\dfrac{5}{18}$ $1\dfrac{11}{18}$ $2\dfrac{1}{3}$ $1\dfrac{1}{2}$ $1\dfrac{11}{18}$ $1\dfrac{4}{5}$
_____ _____ _____ _____ _____ _____ _____ _____

$2\dfrac{5}{6}$ $1\dfrac{5}{18}$ $2\dfrac{1}{6}$ $1\dfrac{4}{5}$ $1\dfrac{7}{18}$
_____ _____ _____ _____ _____

$6\dfrac{1}{2}$ $1\dfrac{4}{5}$ $2\dfrac{1}{5}$ $1\dfrac{1}{4}$ $\dfrac{4}{5}$ $1\dfrac{11}{18}$ $2\dfrac{1}{3}$!
_____ _____ _____ _____ _____ _____ _____

Emma

9 Ordering Fractions

• ordering and comparing fractions

We can compare fractions by using diagrams of the same size.

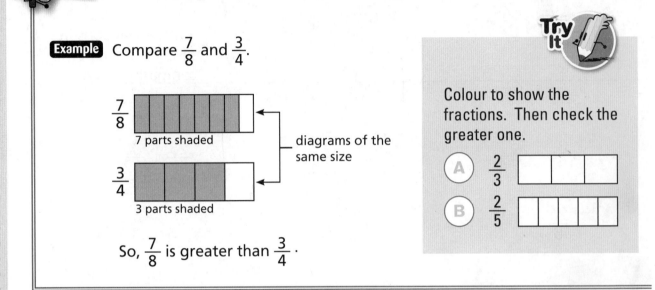

Example Compare $\frac{7}{8}$ and $\frac{3}{4}$.

$\frac{7}{8}$ 7 parts shaded

$\frac{3}{4}$ 3 parts shaded

diagrams of the same size

So, $\frac{7}{8}$ is greater than $\frac{3}{4}$.

Try It

Colour to show the fractions. Then check the greater one.

A $\frac{2}{3}$

B $\frac{2}{5}$

Colour the fractions. Then compare them and write ">" or "<" in the circle.

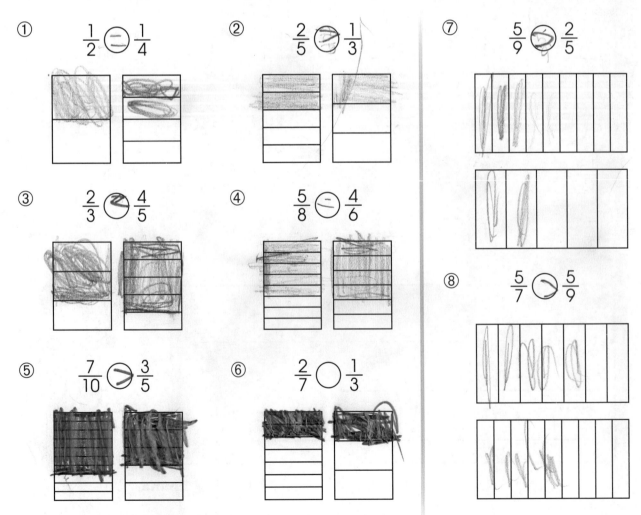

① $\frac{1}{2}$ ◯ $\frac{1}{4}$

② $\frac{2}{5}$ ◯ $\frac{1}{3}$

⑦ $\frac{5}{9}$ ◯ $\frac{2}{5}$

③ $\frac{2}{3}$ ◯ $\frac{4}{5}$

④ $\frac{5}{8}$ ◯ $\frac{4}{6}$

⑧ $\frac{5}{7}$ ◯ $\frac{5}{9}$

⑤ $\frac{7}{10}$ ◯ $\frac{3}{5}$

⑥ $\frac{2}{7}$ ◯ $\frac{1}{3}$

Rewrite each pair of fractions as fractions with the same denominator. Then compare them and write ">" or "<" in the circle.

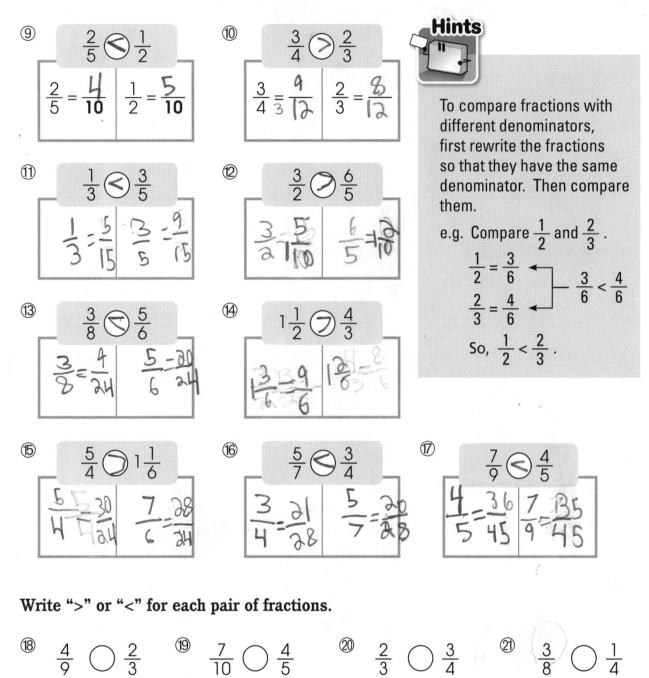

⑨ $\frac{2}{5} \bigcirc< \frac{1}{2}$

$\frac{2}{5} = \frac{4}{10}$ $\frac{1}{2} = \frac{5}{10}$

⑩ $\frac{3}{4} \bigcirc> \frac{2}{3}$

$\frac{3}{4} = \frac{9}{12}$ $\frac{2}{3} = \frac{8}{12}$

Hints

To compare fractions with different denominators, first rewrite the fractions so that they have the same denominator. Then compare them.

e.g. Compare $\frac{1}{2}$ and $\frac{2}{3}$.

$\frac{1}{2} = \frac{3}{6}$

$\frac{2}{3} = \frac{4}{6}$

$\frac{3}{6} < \frac{4}{6}$

So, $\frac{1}{2} < \frac{2}{3}$.

⑪ $\frac{1}{3} \bigcirc< \frac{3}{5}$

$\frac{1}{3} = \frac{5}{15}$ $\frac{3}{5} = \frac{9}{15}$

⑫ $\frac{3}{2} \bigcirc> \frac{6}{5}$

$\frac{3}{2} = \frac{5}{10}$ $\frac{6}{5} = \frac{}{}$

⑬ $\frac{3}{8} \bigcirc< \frac{5}{6}$

$\frac{3}{8} = \frac{4}{24}$ $\frac{5}{6} = \frac{20}{24}$

⑭ $1\frac{1}{2} \bigcirc> \frac{4}{3}$

$1\frac{3}{6} = \frac{9}{6}$ $1\frac{2}{6} = \frac{8}{6}$

⑮ $\frac{5}{4} \bigcirc> 1\frac{1}{6}$

$\frac{5}{4} = \frac{30}{24}$ $\frac{7}{6} = \frac{28}{24}$

⑯ $\frac{5}{7} \bigcirc< \frac{3}{4}$

$\frac{3}{4} = \frac{21}{28}$ $\frac{5}{7} = \frac{20}{28}$

⑰ $\frac{7}{9} \bigcirc< \frac{4}{5}$

$\frac{4}{5} = \frac{36}{45}$ $\frac{7}{9} = \frac{35}{45}$

Write ">" or "<" for each pair of fractions.

⑱ $\frac{4}{9} \bigcirc \frac{2}{3}$

⑲ $\frac{7}{10} \bigcirc \frac{4}{5}$

⑳ $\frac{2}{3} \bigcirc \frac{3}{4}$

㉑ $\frac{3}{8} \bigcirc \frac{1}{4}$

㉒ $\frac{10}{15} \bigcirc \frac{5}{10}$

㉓ $\frac{3}{6} \bigcirc \frac{6}{9}$

㉔ $\frac{7}{21} \bigcirc \frac{7}{14}$

㉕ $\frac{4}{7} \bigcirc \frac{3}{8}$

㉖ $\frac{5}{8} \bigcirc \frac{7}{10}$

㉗ $\frac{8}{16} \bigcirc \frac{4}{12}$

㉘ $\frac{11}{3} \bigcirc \frac{7}{2}$

㉙ $2\frac{3}{5} \bigcirc \frac{18}{7}$

Put each set of fractions in order from smallest to greatest.

③⓪ $\dfrac{5}{8}$ $\dfrac{7}{8}$ $\dfrac{4}{8}$

$\dfrac{4}{8} < \dfrac{5}{8} < \dfrac{7}{8}$

③① $2\dfrac{4}{5}$ $3\dfrac{1}{5}$ $2\dfrac{3}{5}$

$2\dfrac{3}{5} < 2\dfrac{4}{5} < 3\dfrac{1}{5}$

③② $\dfrac{4}{5}$ $\dfrac{6}{15}$ $\dfrac{7}{10}$

$\dfrac{4}{5} > \dfrac{7}{10} > \dfrac{6}{15}$

③③ $\dfrac{7}{12}$ $\dfrac{2}{3}$ $\dfrac{1}{4}$

$\dfrac{1}{4} < \dfrac{7}{12} < \dfrac{2}{3}$

③④ $\dfrac{5}{12}$ $\dfrac{1}{2}$ $\dfrac{5}{6}$ $\dfrac{2}{3}$

$\dfrac{2}{3} > \dfrac{1}{2} > \dfrac{5}{6} > \dfrac{5}{12}$

③⑤ $1\dfrac{11}{15}$ $\dfrac{5}{3}$ $1\dfrac{1}{3}$ $\dfrac{7}{5}$

$< 1\dfrac{11}{15}$

③⑥ $\dfrac{24}{10}$ $2\dfrac{1}{2}$ $\dfrac{13}{5}$ $2\dfrac{7}{10}$

$2\dfrac{7}{10} > \dfrac{13}{5} > 2\dfrac{1}{2} = \dfrac{24}{10}$

③⑦ $1\dfrac{3}{4}$ $\dfrac{18}{20}$ $\dfrac{30}{20}$ $2\dfrac{1}{5}$

Circle the correct fraction in each set.

③⑧ the greater one

a. $\dfrac{5}{6}$ ⃝ $\dfrac{5}{8}$

b. $\dfrac{9}{11}$ ⃝ $\dfrac{9}{13}$

③⑨ the smaller one

a. $\dfrac{9}{10}$ ⃝ $\dfrac{9}{8}$

b. $\dfrac{10}{7}$ $\dfrac{10}{9}$

④⓪ the greatest one

$\dfrac{6}{7}$ $\dfrac{6}{5}$ ⃝ $\dfrac{6}{15}$ $\dfrac{6}{10}$

④① the smallest one

$\dfrac{9}{12}$ $\dfrac{9}{11}$ $\dfrac{9}{10}$ $\dfrac{9}{14}$ ⃝

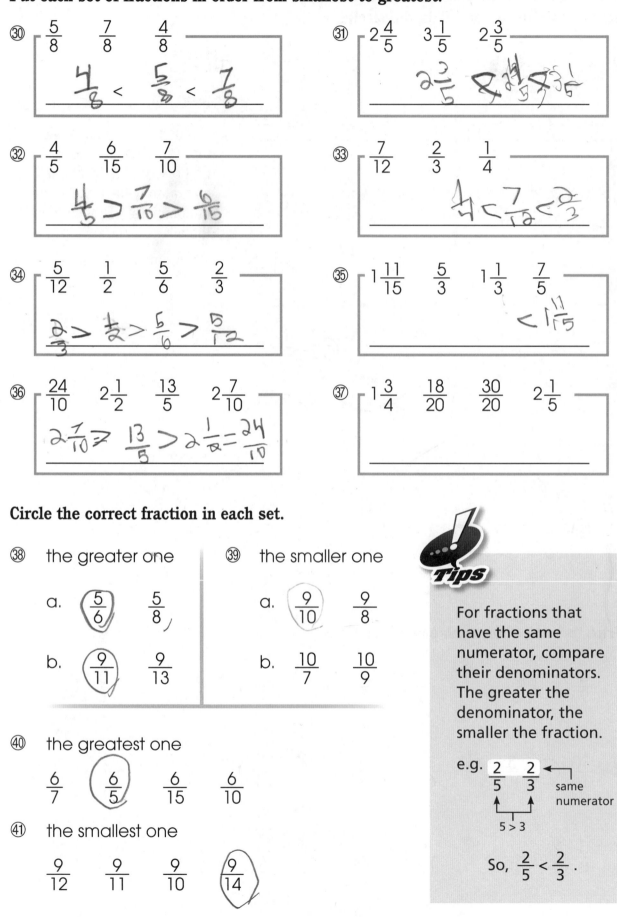

Tips

For fractions that have the same numerator, compare their denominators. The greater the denominator, the smaller the fraction.

e.g. $\dfrac{2}{5}$ $\dfrac{2}{3}$ ← same numerator

5 > 3

So, $\dfrac{2}{5} < \dfrac{2}{3}$.

Rewrite each pair of fractions as fractions with the same numerator. Then compare them and write ">" or "<" in the circle.

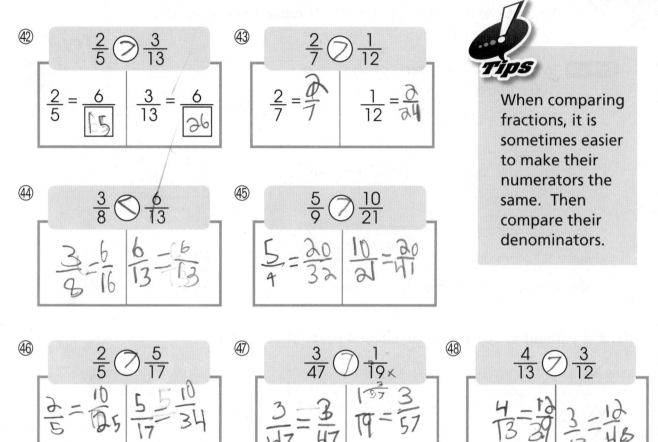

42) $\frac{2}{5}$ ⟳ $\frac{3}{13}$

$\frac{2}{5} = \frac{6}{\boxed{15}}$ $\frac{3}{13} = \frac{6}{\boxed{26}}$

43) $\frac{2}{7}$ ⟳ $\frac{1}{12}$

$\frac{2}{7} = \frac{2}{7}$ $\frac{1}{12} = \frac{2}{24}$

Tips

When comparing fractions, it is sometimes easier to make their numerators the same. Then compare their denominators.

44) $\frac{3}{8}$ ⟳ $\frac{6}{13}$

$\frac{3}{8} = \frac{6}{16}$ $\frac{6}{13} = \frac{6}{13}$

45) $\frac{5}{9}$ ⟳ $\frac{10}{21}$

$\frac{5}{4} = \frac{20}{32}$ $\frac{10}{21} = \frac{20}{41}$

46) $\frac{2}{5}$ ⟳ $\frac{5}{17}$

$\frac{2}{5} = \frac{10}{25}$ $\frac{5}{17} = \frac{10}{34}$

47) $\frac{3}{47}$ ⟳ $\frac{1}{19}$ ×

$\frac{3}{47} = \frac{3}{47}$ $\frac{1}{19} = \frac{3}{57}$

48) $\frac{4}{13}$ ⟳ $\frac{3}{12}$

$\frac{4}{13} = \frac{12}{39}$ $\frac{3}{12} = \frac{12}{48}$

Put each set of fractions in order from smallest to greatest.

49) $\frac{10}{13}$ $\frac{7}{6}$ $\frac{10}{11}$ $\frac{5}{6}$

_____ < _____ < _____ < _____

50) $\frac{6}{19}$ $\frac{2}{7}$ $\frac{8}{19}$ $\frac{3}{11}$

_____

51) $\frac{3}{5}$ $\frac{4}{5}$ $\frac{11}{17}$ $\frac{12}{17}$

_____

52) $\frac{7}{9}$ $\frac{4}{5}$ $\frac{8}{9}$ $\frac{3}{10}$

_____

53) $\frac{17}{6}$ $2\frac{1}{6}$ $\frac{11}{3}$ $\frac{17}{8}$

_____

54) $\frac{17}{4}$ $\frac{9}{2}$ $4\frac{5}{8}$ $\frac{9}{5}$

_____

10 Percents

• representing percents

Read This

Percent (%) means "out of 100". It represents parts of 100 equal parts.

Example Write the shaded parts of the 100-square grid as a percent.

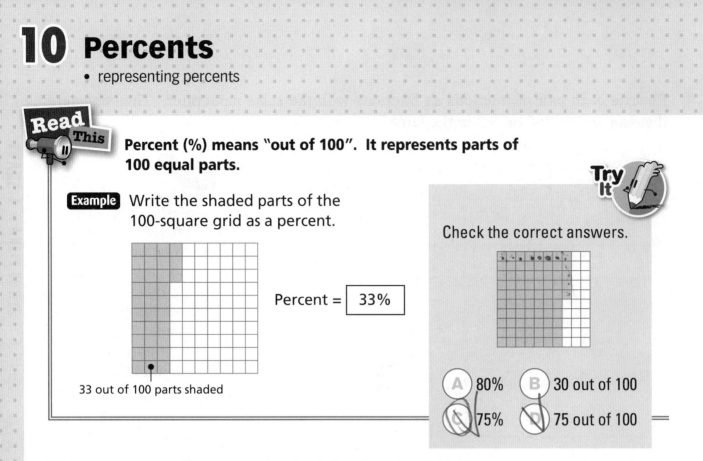

Percent = 33%

33 out of 100 parts shaded

Try It

Check the correct answers.

A) 80%   B) 30 out of 100

C) 75%   D) 75 out of 100

Write a percent to represent the shaded parts of each grid.

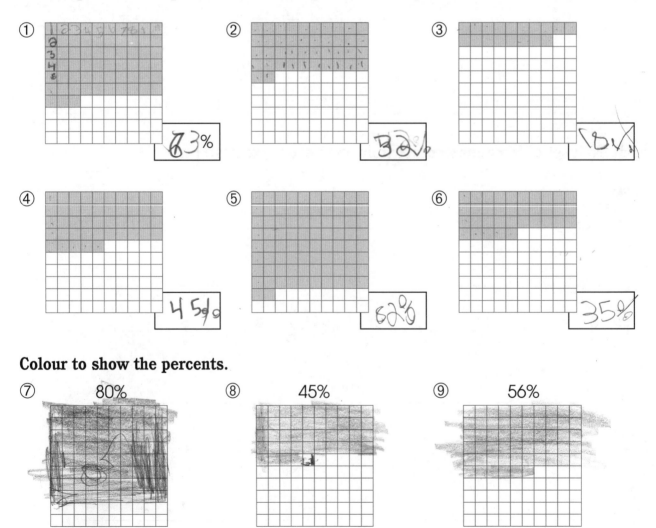

① 83%

② 32%

③ 18%

④ 45%

⑤ 62%

⑥ 35%

Colour to show the percents.

⑦ 80%

⑧ 45%

⑨ 56%

Check the letter if the given percent represents the shaded parts of each grid correctly. If not, put a cross and write the correct percent.

⑩

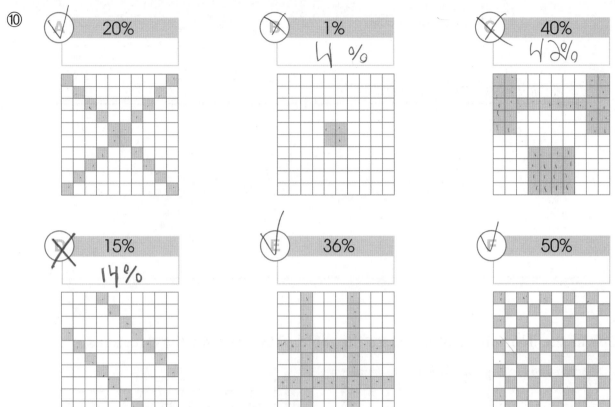

A ✓ 20%

B ✗ 1%
    4 %

C ✗ 40%
    42%

D ✗ 15%
    14%

E ✓ 36%

F ✓ 50%

Write a percent to represent the shaded parts of each diagram.

⑪

A 44%

B 32%

C

D 24%

E 45%

Locate and label the percents on each line.

⑫

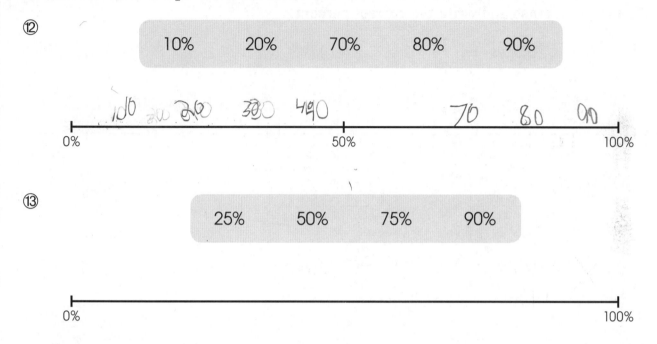

10%   20%   70%   80%   90%

⑬

25%   50%   75%   90%

0%   100%

Look at the floor plan and complete the table. Then answer the questions.

⑭

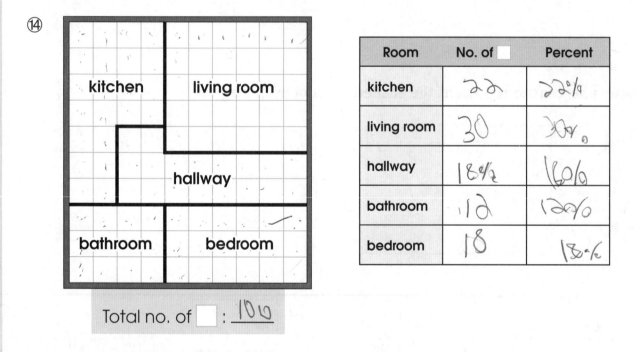

Room	No. of ☐	Percent
kitchen	22	22%
living room	30	30%
hallway	18½	16%
bathroom	12	12%
bedroom	18	18%

Total no. of ☐: 100

⑮ What percent of the area of the house is

a. the bathroom and the hallway combined?   30☐

b. the kitchen and the living room combined?   52☐

⑯ Which two rooms have a total of 42% of
    the whole floor?   Living room and
    bathroom

I COPe PLOPYOPOOP 😛 😬 ⊙ ⊙ ⊙ 😃

Look at the shapes. Then fill in the blanks.

⑰
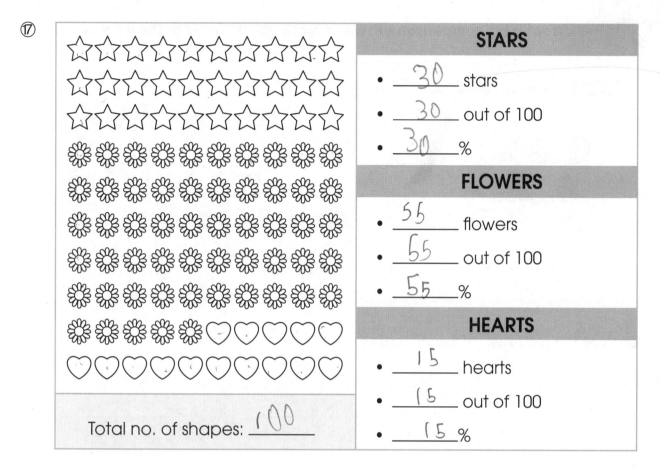

STARS
- __30__ stars
- __30__ out of 100
- __30__ %

FLOWERS
- __55__ flowers
- __55__ out of 100
- __55__ %

HEARTS
- __15__ hearts
- __15__ out of 100
- __15__ %

Total no. of shapes: __100__

Find the totals and write each kind of treat as a percent.

⑱

Total: __100__ treats

Percents

a. cookies __32__ %

b. chocolates __45%__

c. candies __23%__

⑲

Total: __00__ treats

Percents

a. candies __22%__

b. chocolates __50%__

c. cookies __28%__

d. not cookies __72%__

I see YOU POOP ♥ HAHA

11 Ratios

• representing ratios

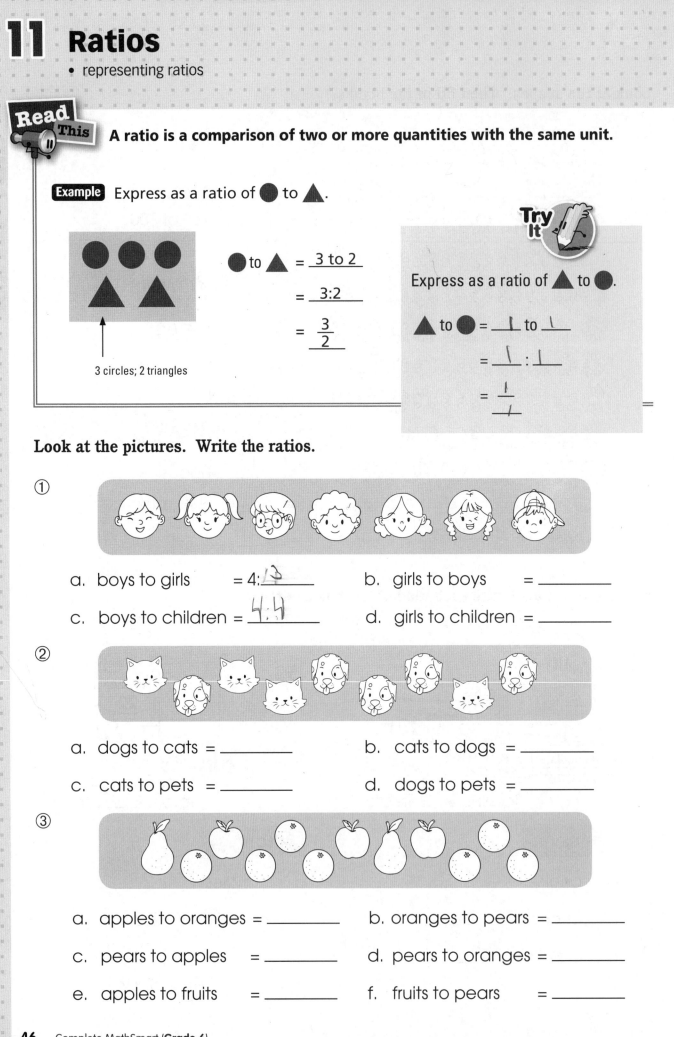

Read This

A ratio is a comparison of two or more quantities with the same unit.

Example Express as a ratio of ● to ▲.

● to ▲ = 3 to 2

= 3:2

= $\frac{3}{2}$

3 circles; 2 triangles

Try It

Express as a ratio of ▲ to ●.

▲ to ● = 1 to 1

= 1 : 1

= $\frac{1}{1}$

Look at the pictures. Write the ratios.

①

a. boys to girls   = 4:3

b. girls to boys   = _____

c. boys to children = 4:4

d. girls to children = _____

②

a. dogs to cats = _____

b. cats to dogs = _____

c. cats to pets = _____

d. dogs to pets = _____

③

a. apples to oranges = _____

b. oranges to pears = _____

c. pears to apples   = _____

d. pears to oranges = _____

e. apples to fruits   = _____

f. fruits to pears   = _____

Write each ratio in two other ways.

④ 2:3 _____ _____

⑤ 15 to 4 _____ _____

⑥ 6 to 13 _____ _____

⑦ $\frac{3}{8}$ _____ _____

⑧ 3:10 _____ _____

⑨ 5:8 _____ _____

⑩ 7 to 9 _____ _____

⑪ $\frac{11}{12}$ _____ _____

Write two equivalent ratios for each ratio.

⑫ 3:4 _____ _____

⑬ 4:2 _____ _____

⑭ 2:6 _____ _____

⑮ 8:10 _____ _____

⑯ 6:9 _____ _____

⑰ 7:4 _____ _____

⑱ 2:1 _____ _____

⑲ 6:15 _____ _____

⑳ 5:3 _____ _____

Hints

To find an equivalent ratio, multiply or divide both terms by the same number.

e.g. **by multiplication**

$$\overset{\text{×2}}{\underset{\text{×2}}{4 : 6 = \mathbf{8} : \mathbf{12}}}$$

by division

$$\overset{\text{÷2}}{\underset{\text{÷2}}{4 : 6 = \mathbf{2} : \mathbf{3}}}$$

4:6, 8:12, and 2:3 are equivalent ratios.

Write each ratio in simplest form.

㉑ 10:15 = _____

㉒ 21:24 = _____

㉓ 12:16 = _____

㉔ 36:45 = _____

㉕ 14:35 = _____

㉖ 98:4 = _____

㉗ 95:10 = _____

㉘ 91:63 = _____

㉙ 6:72 = _____

㉚ 30:45 = _____

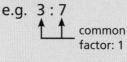

Tips

A ratio is in its simplest form when the only common factor of the terms is 1.

e.g. 3 : 7

common factor: 1

So, 3:7 is a ratio in simplest form.

Match the ratios with the correct groups of flowers.

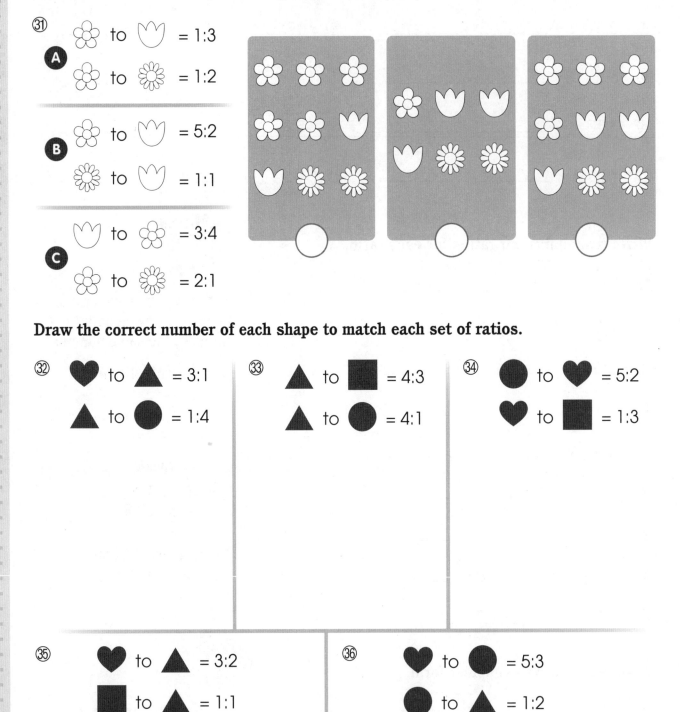

③ A

🌼 to 🌷 = 1:3

🌼 to 🌸 = 1:2

B

🌼 to 🌷 = 5:2

🌸 to 🌷 = 1:1

C

🌷 to 🌼 = 3:4

🌼 to 🌸 = 2:1

Draw the correct number of each shape to match each set of ratios.

③ ♥ to ▲ = 3:1

▲ to ● = 1:4

③ ▲ to ■ = 4:3

▲ to ● = 4:1

③ ● to ♥ = 5:2

♥ to ■ = 1:3

③ ♥ to ▲ = 3:2

■ to ▲ = 1:1

■ to ● = 1:3

③ ♥ to ● = 5:3

● to ▲ = 1:2

● to ■ = 3:4

Colour the pictures to match each set of ratios. Then find the ratio(s).

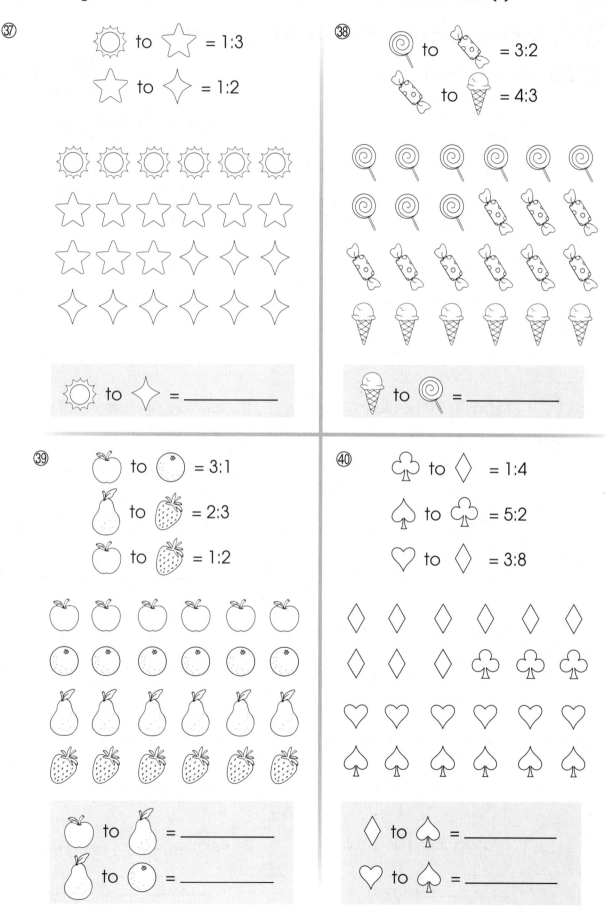

37

○ to ☆ = 1:3

☆ to ◇ = 1:2

○ to ◇ = _____

38

◎ to 🍬 = 3:2

🍬 to 🍦 = 4:3

🍦 to ◎ = _____

39

🍎 to 🍊 = 3:1

🍐 to 🍓 = 2:3

🍎 to 🍓 = 1:2

🍎 to 🍐 = _____

🍐 to 🍊 = _____

40

♣ to ◇ = 1:4

♠ to ♣ = 5:2

♡ to ◇ = 3:8

◇ to ♠ = _____

♡ to ♠ = _____

12 Rates

• representing rates

A rate is a comparison of two quantities with different units.

Example Jim runs 14 km in 2 hours. At what rate does he run?

$14 \div 2 = 7$

His rate is 7 km/h (7 km per hour).

Try It

Nelson runs 10 km in 2 hours. At what rate does he run?

Rate: **5** km/h

Find the rates.

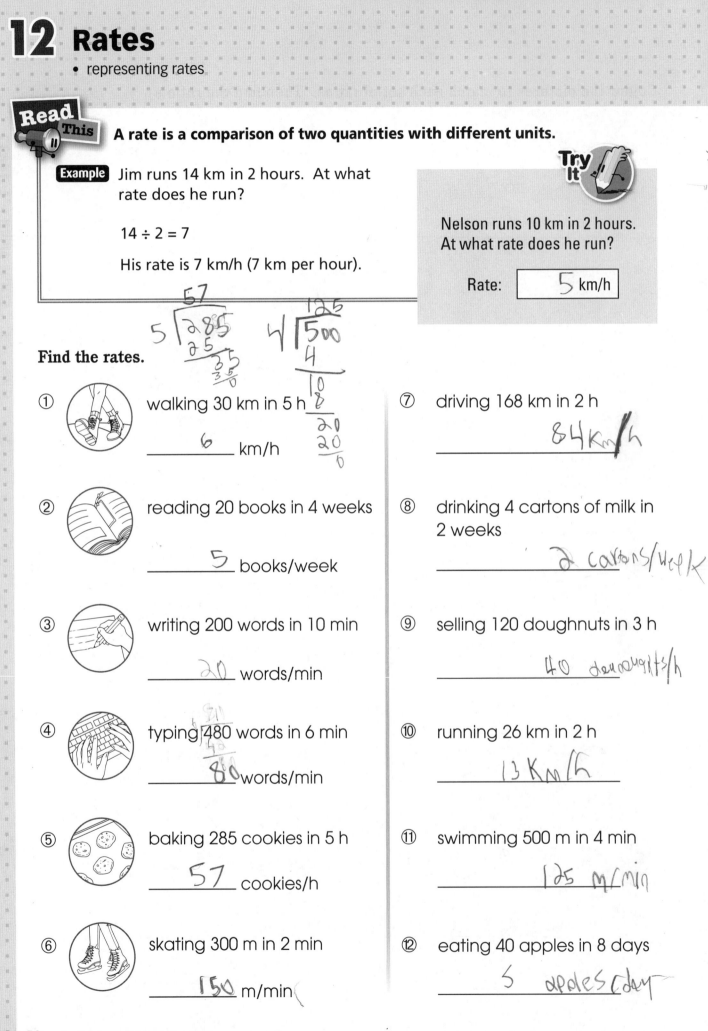

① walking 30 km in 5 h

_____**6**_____ km/h

② reading 20 books in 4 weeks

_____**5**_____ books/week

③ writing 200 words in 10 min

_____**20**_____ words/min

④ typing 480 words in 6 min

_____**80**_____words/min

⑤ baking 285 cookies in 5 h

_____**57**_____ cookies/h

⑥ skating 300 m in 2 min

_____**150**_____ m/min

⑦ driving 168 km in 2 h

_____**84 km/h**_____

⑧ drinking 4 cartons of milk in 2 weeks

_____**2 cartons/week**_____

⑨ selling 120 doughnuts in 3 h

_____**40 doughnuts/h**_____

⑩ running 26 km in 2 h

_____**13 km/h**_____

⑪ swimming 500 m in 4 min

_____**125 m/min**_____

⑫ eating 40 apples in 8 days

_____**5 apples/day**_____

Find the unit prices.

⑬ **5 oranges for $5**

$ __1__ /orange

⑭ **10 cans for $20**

Soup 10

$ __2__ /can

Hints

Unit price is a special rate that represents the cost of one unit. To calculate it, divide the total cost by the number of units.

e.g.   3 kg of pasta for $3.45

$$3.45 \div 3 = 1.15$$

total cost   quantity   unit price

unit price = $1.15/kg

⑮ **2 kg for $6**

Candies 2 kg

$ __3__ /kg

⑯ **4 apples for $4.80**

$ __1.20__ /apple

⑰ **$4.20**

$ __1.4__ /bottle

⑱ **$10**

CHIPS

$ _____ /bag

㉓ 25 boxes of pencils for $75

__1 box of Pencils = $3__

⑲ **$6.25**

$ _____ /cupcake

⑳ **$2.46**

$ _____ /pear

㉔ 4 cans of soda for $6

_____

㉕ 3 T-shirts for $34.50

_____

㉑ Crayons **$22**

$ _____ /box

㉒ **$19.05** Cookies

$ _____ /bag

㉖ 6 tacos for $27.30

_____

㉗ 2 L of milk for $6.42

_____

Look at the flyer. Then answer the questions.

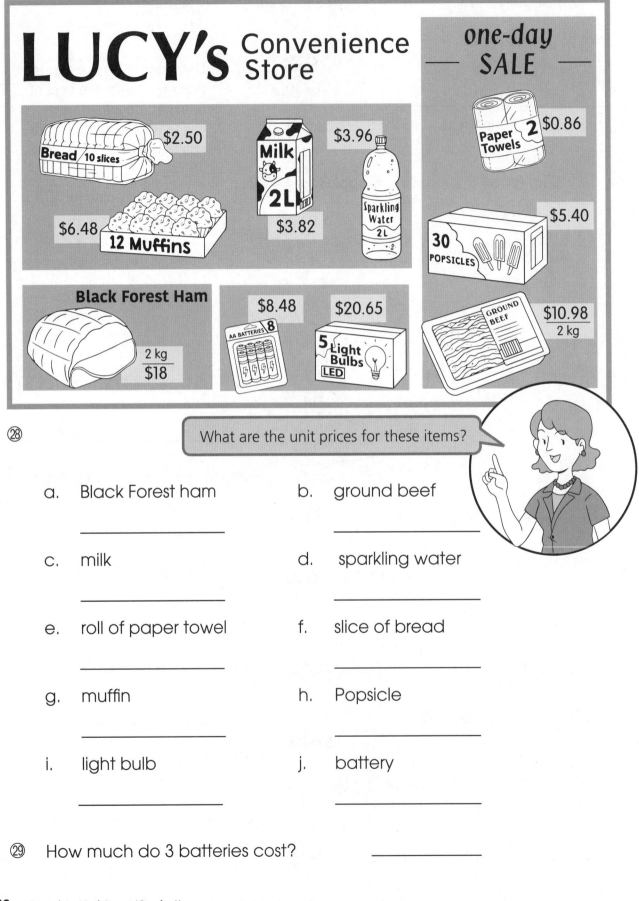

LUCY's Convenience Store

one-day SALE

Bread 10 slices $2.50

$6.48 12 Muffins

Milk 2L $3.96

Sparkling Water 2L $3.82

Paper Towels 2 $0.86

30 POPSICLES $5.40

Black Forest Ham 2 kg $18

AA BATTERIES 8 $8.48

5 Light Bulbs LED $20.65

GROUND BEEF $10.98 2 kg

㉘ What are the unit prices for these items?

a. Black Forest ham

_____

b. ground beef

_____

c. milk

_____

d. sparkling water

_____

e. roll of paper towel

_____

f. slice of bread

_____

g. muffin

_____

h. Popsicle

_____

i. light bulb

_____

j. battery

_____

㉙ How much do 3 batteries cost? _____

Find the unit price for each item. Then find the answers.

30 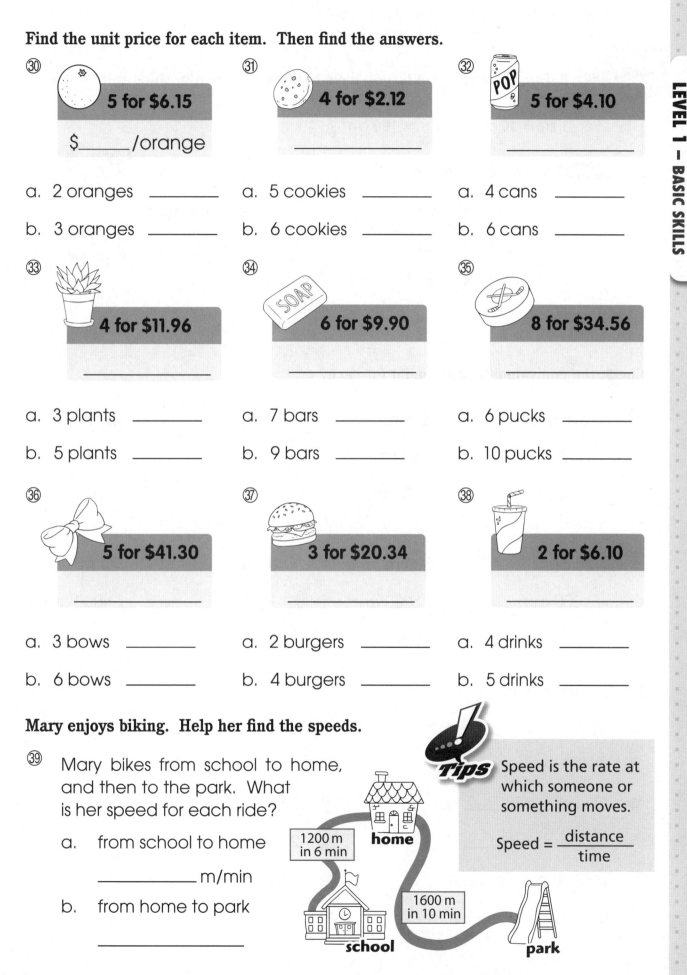 **5 for $6.15**

$_____/orange

a. 2 oranges _____
b. 3 oranges _____

31 **4 for $2.12**

_____

a. 5 cookies _____
b. 6 cookies _____

32 POP **5 for $4.10**

_____

a. 4 cans _____
b. 6 cans _____

33 **4 for $11.96**

_____

a. 3 plants _____
b. 5 plants _____

34 SOAP **6 for $9.90**

_____

a. 7 bars _____
b. 9 bars _____

35 **8 for $34.56**

_____

a. 6 pucks _____
b. 10 pucks _____

36 **5 for $41.30**

_____

a. 3 bows _____
b. 6 bows _____

37 **3 for $20.34**

_____

a. 2 burgers _____
b. 4 burgers _____

38 **2 for $6.10**

_____

a. 4 drinks _____
b. 5 drinks _____

Mary enjoys biking. Help her find the speeds.

39   Mary bikes from school to home, and then to the park. What is her speed for each ride?

a.   from school to home

_____ m/min

b.   from home to park

_____

Tips Speed is the rate at which someone or something moves.

$$\text{Speed} = \frac{\text{distance}}{\text{time}}$$

1200 m in 6 min   **home**

1600 m in 10 min

school

park

13 Unit Conversion

- using and converting units of measurement

Before converting units, you have to know the relationships among the units.

$$1 \text{ cm} = 10 \text{ mm} \qquad 1 \text{ m} = 100 \text{ cm} \qquad 1 \text{ km} = 1000 \text{ m}$$

Example Do the conversions.

$$7 \text{ cm} = \boxed{70} \text{ mm}$$
$$5 \text{ m} = \boxed{500} \text{ cm}$$
$$2 \text{ km} = \boxed{2000} \text{ m}$$

Try It

Check the equivalent measurement for each.

3 cm
- (A) 30 m
- (B) 30 mm

8 m
- (A) 800 mm
- (B) 8000 mm

Check the equivalent measurement for each.

① **6 km**
- (A) 6000 m
- (B) 60 cm

② **8 cm**
- (A) 800 m
- (B) 80 mm

③ **10 m**
- (A) 1000 cm
- (B) 100 cm

④ **0.9 m**
- (A) 0.009 cm
- (B) 90 cm

⑤ **30 cm**
- (A) 300 mm
- (B) 3 m

⑥ **500 m**
- (A) 5000 cm
- (B) 0.5 km

⑦ **20 mm**
- (A) 2 cm
- (B) 0.2 m

⑧ **40 m**
- (A) 4000 cm
- (B) 0.4 km

Do the conversions.

⑨ 12 cm = _____ mm

⑩ 6 m = _____ cm

⑪ 4 km = _____ m

⑫ 2 m = _____ cm

⑬ 3.5 km = _____ m

⑭ 0.5 m = _____ cm

⑮ 10.1 cm = _____ mm

⑯ 2.17 m = _____ cm

⑰ 0.826 km = _____ m

⑱ 4.52 km = _____ m

⑲ 0.5 cm = _____ mm

⑳ 12.09 m = _____ cm

Find the shortest routes between the places. Fill in the blanks.

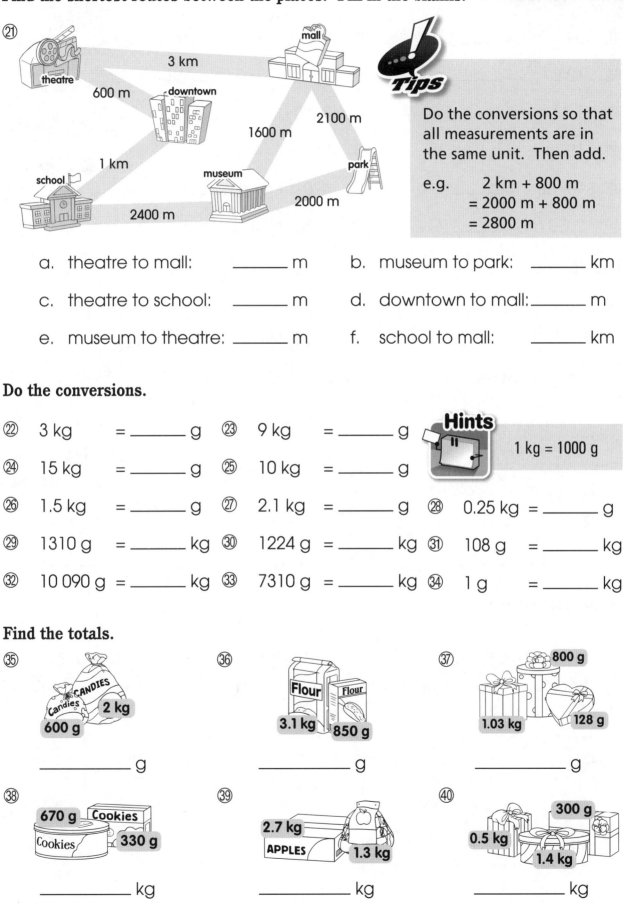

Tips

Do the conversions so that all measurements are in the same unit. Then add.

e.g.   2 km + 800 m
= 2000 m + 800 m
= 2800 m

a.   theatre to mall: _____ m   b.   museum to park: _____ km

c.   theatre to school: _____ m   d.   downtown to mall: _____ m

e.   museum to theatre: _____ m   f.   school to mall: _____ km

Do the conversions.

㉒   3 kg   = _____ g   ㉓   9 kg   = _____ g

Hints

1 kg = 1000 g

㉔   15 kg   = _____ g   ㉕   10 kg   = _____ g

㉖   1.5 kg   = _____ g   ㉗   2.1 kg   = _____ g   ㉘   0.25 kg = _____ g

㉙   1310 g   = _____ kg   ㉚   1224 g   = _____ kg   ㉛   108 g   = _____ kg

㉜   10 090 g = _____ kg   ㉝   7310 g   = _____ kg   ㉞   1 g   = _____ kg

Find the totals.

㉟

CANDIES
Candies   **2 kg**
600 g

_____ g

㊱

Flour   Flour
3.1 kg   **850 g**

_____ g

㊲

800 g

1.03 kg   **128 g**

_____ g

㊳

670 g   Cookies

Cookies   **330 g**

_____ kg

㊴

2.7 kg

APPLES   **1.3 kg**

_____ kg

㊵

300 g

0.5 kg

1.4 kg

_____ kg

Do the conversions.

(41) 6 L = ______ mL
(42) 4 L = ______ mL
(43) 12 L = ______ mL
(44) 20 L = ______ mL
(45) 1.3 L = ______ mL
(46) 3.2 L = ______ mL
(47) 180 mL = ______ L
(48) 860 mL = ______ L
(49) 96 mL = ______ L
(50) 470 mL = ______ L
(51) 2050 mL = ______ L
(52) 1450 mL = ______ L

Hints

1 L = 1000 mL

L → x 1000 → mL

mL → ÷ 1000 → L

Find the totals.

(53)

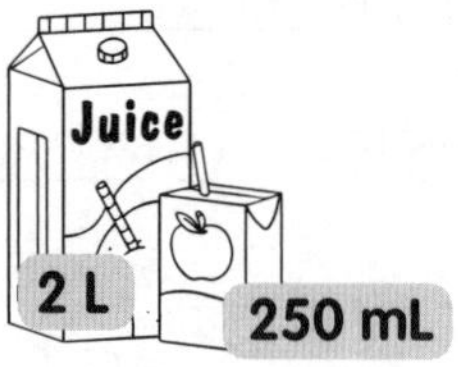
Juice
2 L
250 mL

______ mL

(54)

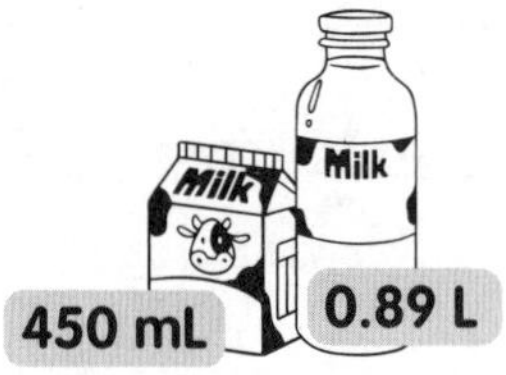
Milk
Milk
450 mL
0.89 L

______ mL

(55)

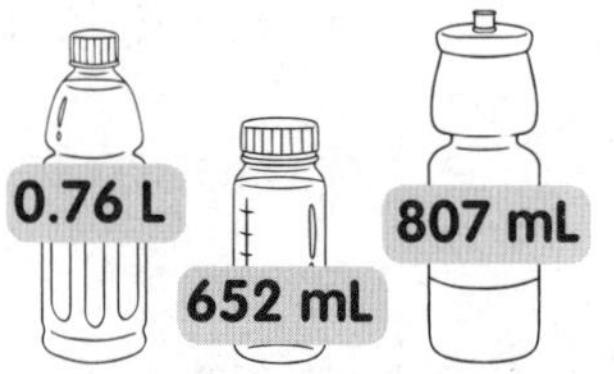
0.76 L
652 mL
807 mL

______ mL

(56)

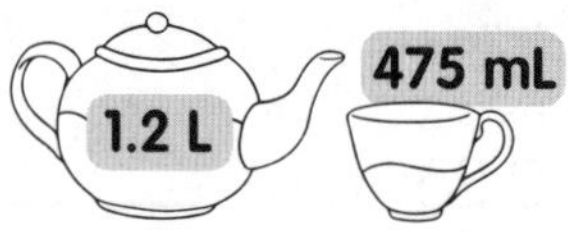
1.2 L
475 mL

______ L

(57)

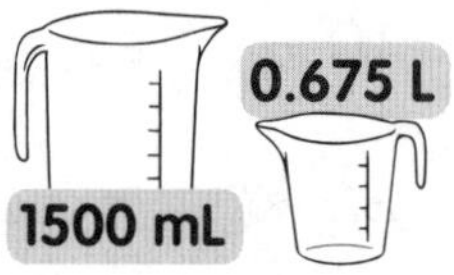
0.675 L
1500 mL

______ L

(58)

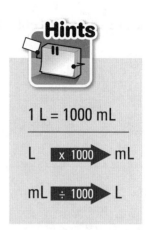

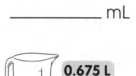

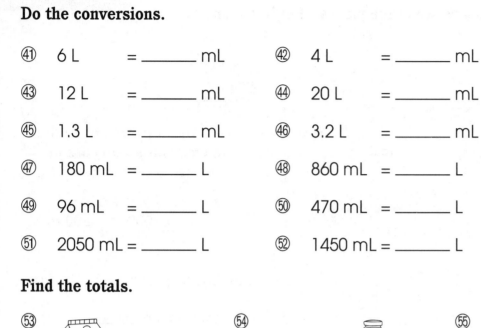

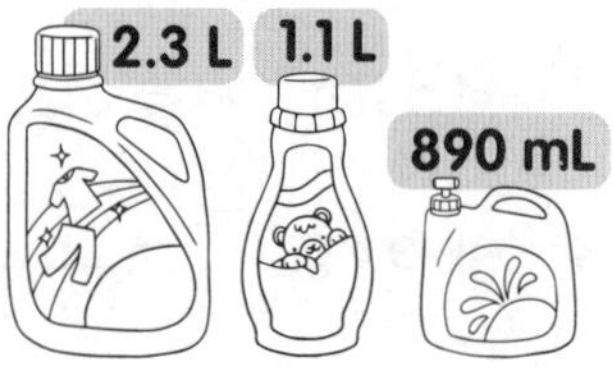
2.3 L
1.1 L
890 mL

______ L

Do the conversions.

(59)

Length

km	m	cm
3		
0.5		
		9000
1.5		
	700	

Weight

kg	g
2	
1.5	
	5000
	10 000
0.123	

Capacity

L	mL
5	
0.3	
	4000
	2500
1.05	

Write the times in 24-hour notation.

⑥⓪   4:35 p.m.   _____

⑥①   6:12 a.m.   _____

⑥②   11:25:46 a.m.   _____

⑥③   10:42:11 p.m.   _____

⑥④   6:27:53 p.m.   _____

Hints

Time can be converted between 12-hour notation and 24-hour notation.

e.g.

12-hour notation	24-hour notation
2:43:55 a.m. ⟷	02:43:55
2:43:55 p.m. ⟷	14:43:55

Write the times in 12-hour notation. Draw clock hands to show each time.

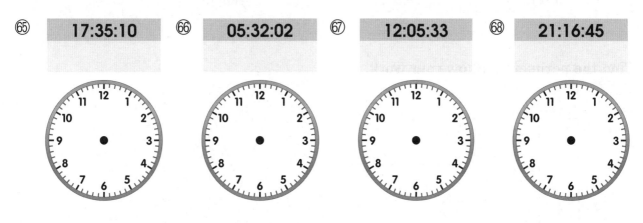

⑥⑤   17:35:10   ⑥⑥   05:32:02   ⑥⑦   12:05:33   ⑥⑧   21:16:45

Write each time in the specified notation.

⑥⑨   12-hour notation

a. 1 h before 9:30 a.m. _____

b. 5 h after 8:25:40 a.m. _____

c. 3 h before 14:11:20 _____

d. 2 h after 11:06:17 _____

⑦⓪   24-hour notation

a. 3 h before 10:39 _____

b. 2 h after 05:12:37 _____

c. 4 h before 2:24:01 p.m. _____

d. 1 h after 12:00:07 a.m. _____

Answer the questions.

⑦①   A movie started at 2:45 p.m. and ended at 16:55.
     How long did it last?   _____

⑦②   Joshua went to bed at 23:15 and got up at
     8:00 a.m. the next morning. How long did he sleep?   _____

14 Length and Perimeter

- determining length and perimeter

Use formulas to determine the perimeter of different polygons.

> Perimeter of a Rectangle: 2 x length + 2 x width
> Perimeter of a Square: 4 x length

Example Find the perimeter.

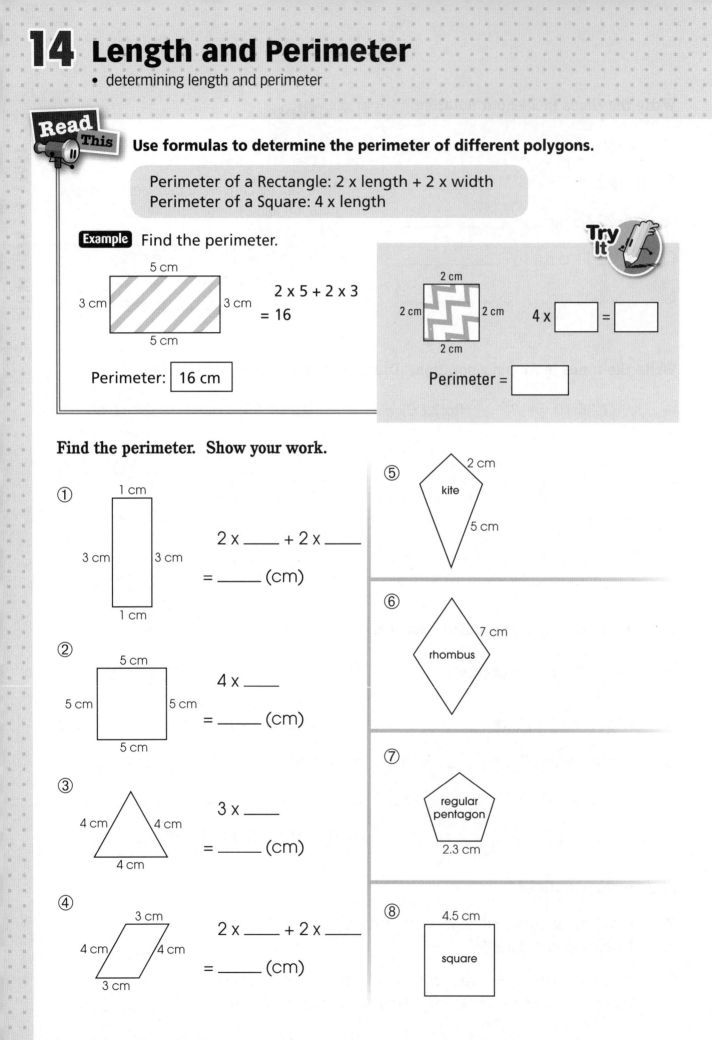

5 cm

3 cm   3 cm

5 cm

2 x 5 + 2 x 3
= 16

Perimeter: 16 cm

Try It

2 cm

2 cm   2 cm

2 cm

4 x ☐ = ☐

Perimeter = ☐

Find the perimeter. Show your work.

①
1 cm

3 cm   3 cm

1 cm

2 x ____ + 2 x ____

= ____ (cm)

②
5 cm

5 cm   5 cm

5 cm

4 x ____

= ____ (cm)

③
4 cm   4 cm

4 cm

3 x ____

= ____ (cm)

④
3 cm

4 cm   4 cm

3 cm

2 x ____ + 2 x ____

= ____ (cm)

⑤
2 cm

kite

5 cm

⑥
7 cm

rhombus

⑦
regular pentagon

2.3 cm

⑧
4.5 cm

square

Use the given measurements to find the perimeter.

⑨

rectangles

Length (cm)	Width (cm)	Perimeter (cm)
8	5	
13.5	2	
1.8	7	
4	3.5	
2.6	10.4	

⑩

squares

Length (cm)	Perimeter (cm)
12	
10.1	
2.5	
0.3	
1.15	

Measure the sides with a ruler and find the perimeter of each shape.

⑪

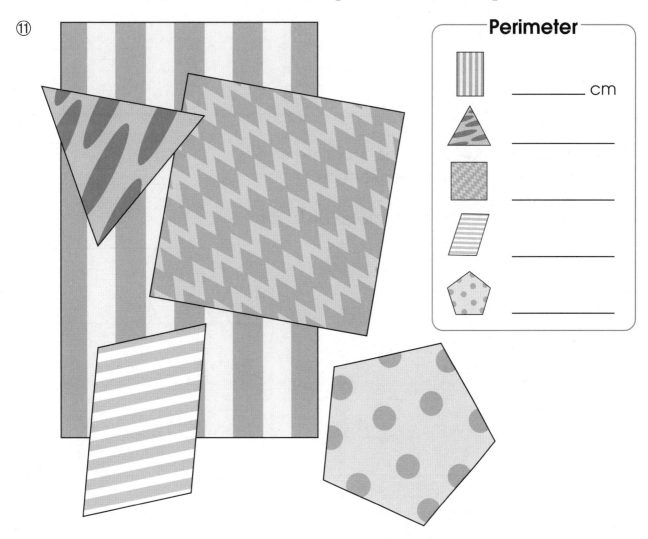

Perimeter

_____ cm

_____

_____

_____

_____

Draw the rectangles with whole number measurements. Then answer the questions.

⑫ Draw all possible rectangles that have a perimeter of 12 cm.
(Hint: A square is a special kind of rectangle.)

1 cm

1 cm

How many different rectangles can be drawn?

_____

List the length and width of all the rectangles.

Length (cm)	Width (cm)

⑬ Draw a rectangle that has a perimeter of 20 cm. What can its dimensions be?

_____

⑭ Draw a square with a perimeter of 16 cm. What is its side length?

_____

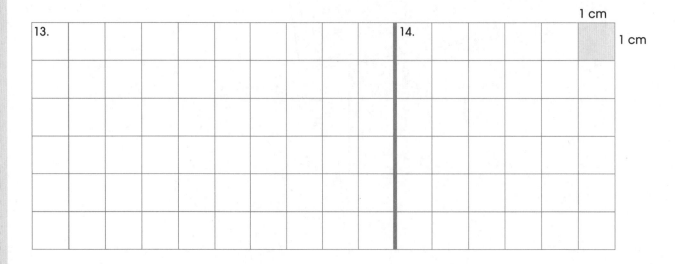

13.

14.

1 cm

1 cm

Look at the dimensions of each rectangle. Match the rectangle with the place or object that it represents. Then find the perimeter of each.

⑮   Top View of Place/Object

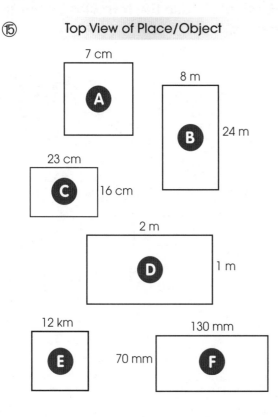

Place/Object	Length	Width	Perimeter
◯ phone			
◯ tablet			
◯ town			
◯ mug coaster			
◯ desk			
◯ tennis court			

Find the length of the side in bold.

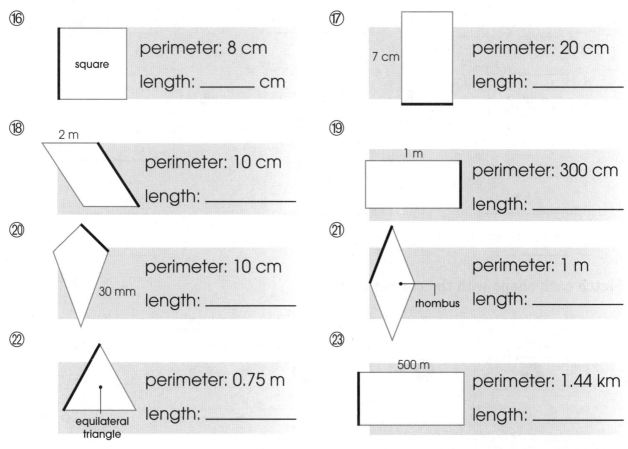

⑯ square   perimeter: 8 cm   length: _____ cm

⑰ 7 cm   perimeter: 20 cm   length: _____

⑱ 2 m   perimeter: 10 cm   length: _____

⑲ 1 m   perimeter: 300 cm   length: _____

⑳ 30 mm   perimeter: 10 cm   length: _____

㉑ rhombus   perimeter: 1 m   length: _____

㉒ equilateral triangle   perimeter: 0.75 m   length: _____

㉓ 500 m   perimeter: 1.44 km   length: _____

15 Area

• determining area

Read This

Area is measured in square units (cm², m², etc.). Use the formulas below to find the area of squares and rectangles.

> Area of a Square: length x length
> Area of a Rectangle: length x width

Example Find the area.

5 cm

2 cm

5 x 2 = 10

Area: | 10 cm² |

Try It

3 cm

[ ] x [ ] = [ ]

Area: [ ]

Find the area. Show your work.

① 6 cm

_____ X _____

= _____ (cm²)

② 9 km

3 km

_____

= _____

③ 3 m

5 m

_____

= _____

④ 5 km

6 km

_____

= _____

⑤ 4 mm

_____

= _____

⑥ 8 mm

2 mm

_____

= _____

Match each shape with the correct area.

⑦

2 cm 4.5 cm **A**

9 cm **B**

3.5 cm 10 cm **C**

6 cm **D**

Area

○ 81 cm²

○ 35 cm²

○ 9 cm²

○ 36 cm²

Find the area of each parallelogram. Show your work.

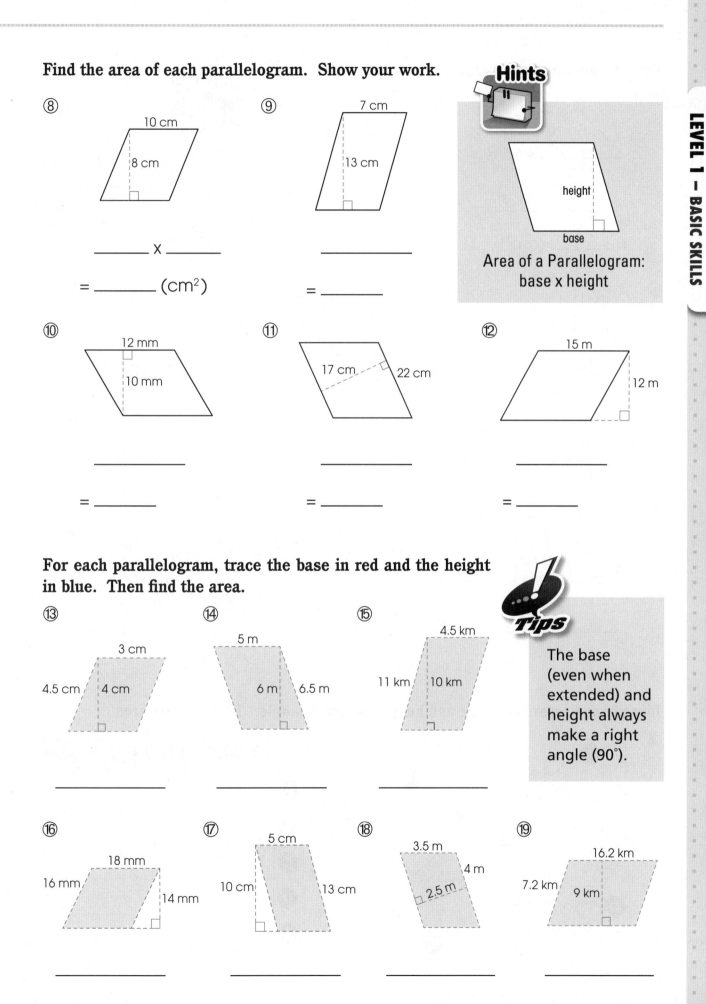

⑧ 10 cm 8 cm

_____ x _____

= _____ (cm²)

⑨ 7 cm 13 cm

_____

= _____

Hints

height

base

Area of a Parallelogram:
base x height

⑩ 12 mm 10 mm

_____

= _____

⑪ 17 cm 22 cm

_____

= _____

⑫ 15 m 12 m

_____

= _____

For each parallelogram, trace the base in red and the height in blue. Then find the area.

Tips

The base (even when extended) and height always make a right angle (90°).

⑬ 3 cm 4.5 cm 4 cm

_____

⑭ 5 m 6 m 6.5 m

_____

⑮ 4.5 km 11 km 10 km

_____

⑯ 18 mm 16 mm 14 mm

_____

⑰ 5 cm 10 cm 13 cm

_____

⑱ 3.5 m 4 m 2.5 m

_____

⑲ 16.2 km 7.2 km 9 km

_____

LEVEL 1 – BASIC SKILLS

Find the area of each triangle. Show your work.

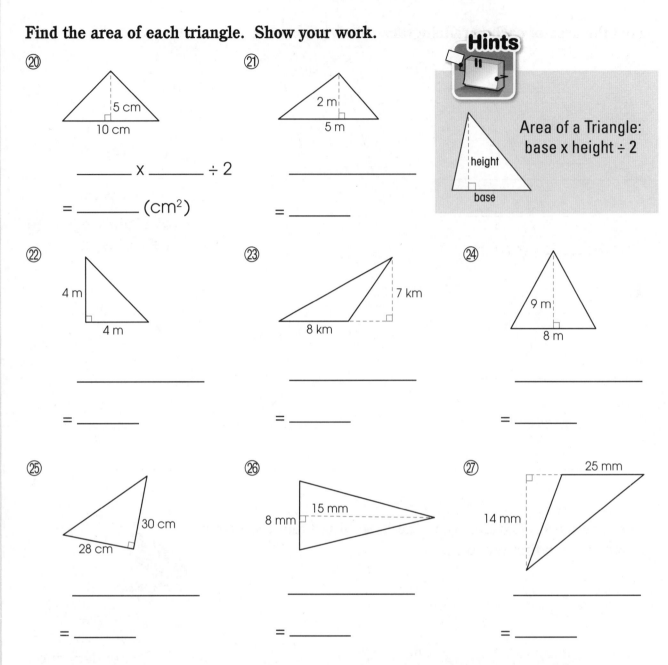

⑳
_____ x _____ ÷ 2

= _____ (cm²)

㉑
_____

= _____

㉒
_____

= _____

㉓
_____

= _____

㉔
_____

= _____

㉕
_____

= _____

㉖
_____

= _____

㉗
_____

= _____

Identify and record the base and height of each triangle. Then find its area.

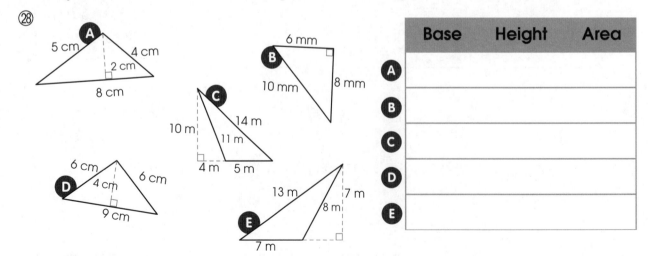

㉘

	Base	Height	Area
A			
B			
C			
D			
E			

Draw the shapes that the boy describes. Then record the measurements.

㉙ 1 cm

1 cm

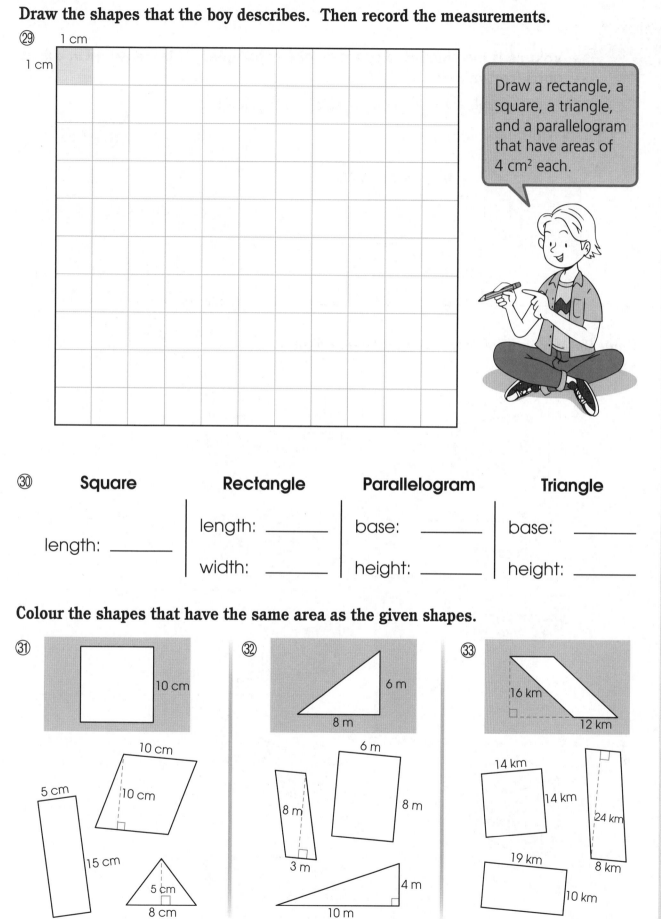

> Draw a rectangle, a square, a triangle, and a parallelogram that have areas of 4 cm² each.

㉚

Square	Rectangle	Parallelogram	Triangle
length: _____	length: _____ width: _____	base: _____ height: _____	base: _____ height: _____

Colour the shapes that have the same area as the given shapes.

㉛   10 cm

10 cm   10 cm

5 cm   15 cm

5 cm   8 cm

㉜   6 m   8 m

6 m   8 m

8 m   3 m

4 m   10 m

㉝   16 km   12 km

14 km   14 km

24 km   8 km

19 km   10 km

16 Volume

- determining volumes

Read This

Volume is the amount of space an object occupies. It is measured in cubed units (cm³, m³, etc.).

Volume of a Prism: area of base x height

Example Find the volume.

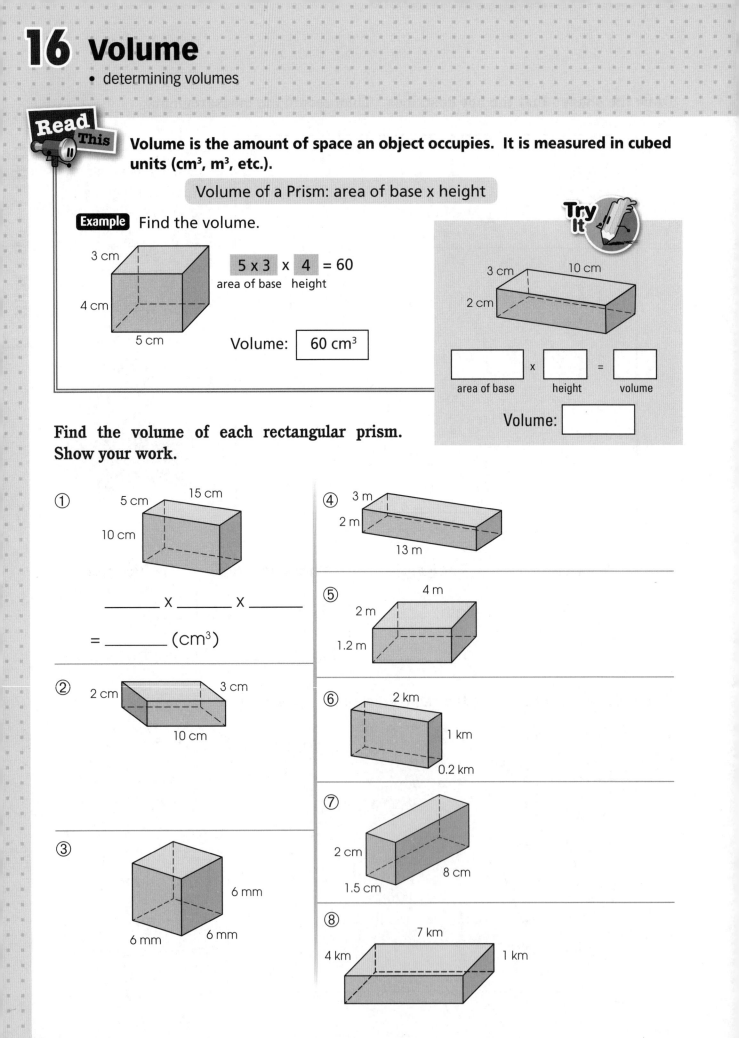

3 cm
4 cm
5 cm

$$5 \times 3 \times 4 = 60$$
area of base   height

Volume: 60 cm³

Try It

3 cm   10 cm
2 cm

[ ] x [ ] = [ ]
area of base   height   volume

Volume: [ ]

Find the volume of each rectangular prism. Show your work.

① 5 cm 15 cm
10 cm

_____ x _____ x _____

= _____ (cm³)

② 2 cm   3 cm
10 cm

③ 6 mm
6 mm   6 mm

④ 3 m
2 m
13 m

⑤ 4 m
2 m
1.2 m

⑥ 2 km
1 km
0.2 km

⑦ 2 cm
8 cm
1.5 cm

⑧ 7 km
4 km   1 km

Ann has the following items. Find the volumes and answer the questions.

⑨
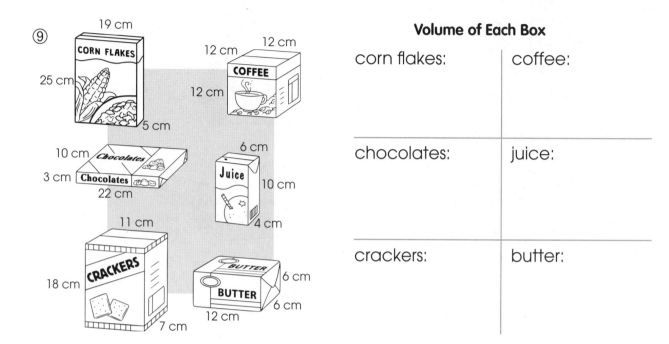

Volume of Each Box

corn flakes:	coffee:
chocolates:	juice:
crackers:	butter:

⑩ Ann has two boxes of crackers. See how they are put together in two different ways. Find the volumes and answer the question.

Volume

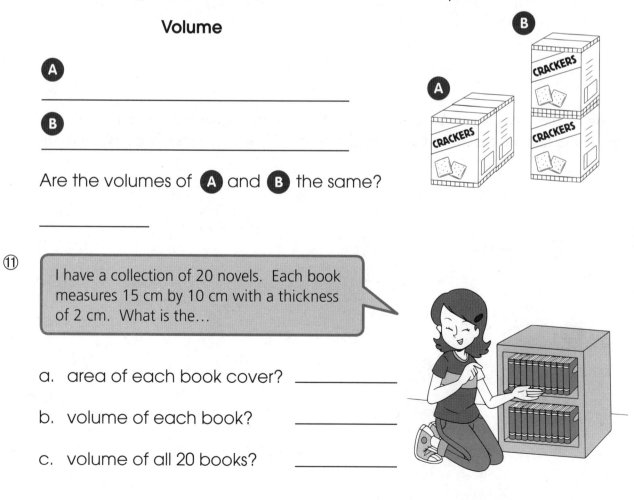

Ⓐ _____

Ⓑ _____

Are the volumes of Ⓐ and Ⓑ the same?

_____

⑪

I have a collection of 20 novels. Each book measures 15 cm by 10 cm with a thickness of 2 cm. What is the...

a. area of each book cover? _____

b. volume of each book? _____

c. volume of all 20 books? _____

Find the volume of each triangular prism. Show your work.

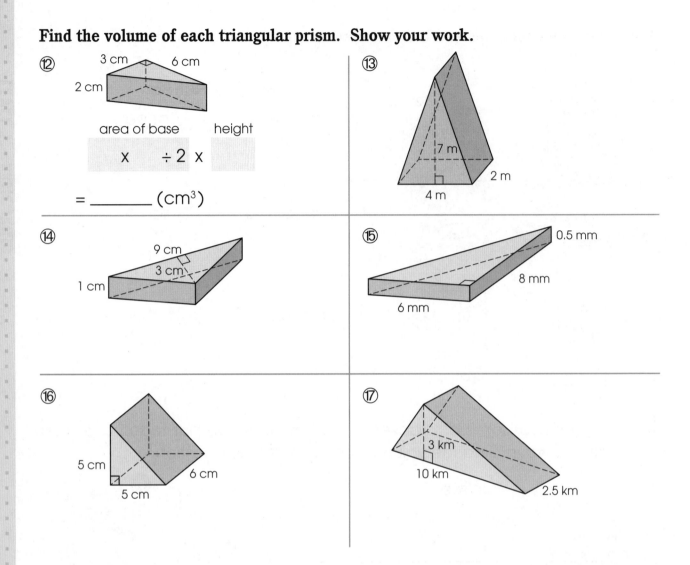

⑫

3 cm   6 cm

2 cm

area of base   height

___ x ___ ÷ 2 x ___

= _____ (cm³)

⑬

7 m

2 m

4 m

⑭

9 cm

3 cm

1 cm

⑮

0.5 mm

8 mm

6 mm

⑯

5 cm

6 cm

5 cm

⑰

3 km

10 km

2.5 km

Look at the measurements of each triangular prism. Circle the measurements that are needed to find the volume of the triangular prism. Then do the matching. Write the letters.

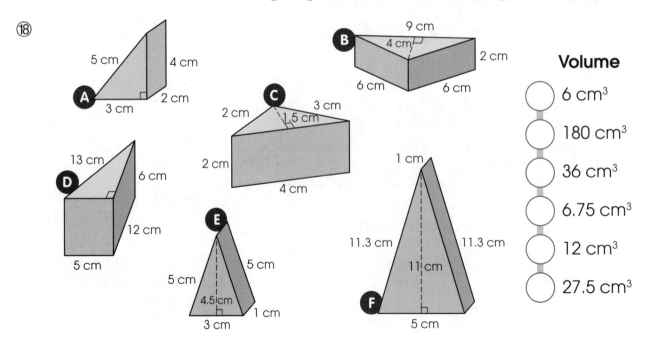

⑱

A   5 cm   4 cm   3 cm   2 cm

B   9 cm   4 cm   2 cm   6 cm   6 cm

C   2 cm   3 cm   1.5 cm   2 cm   4 cm

D   13 cm   6 cm   12 cm   5 cm

E   5 cm   5 cm   4.5 cm   1 cm   3 cm

F   1 cm   11.3 cm   11.3 cm   11 cm   5 cm

Volume

○ 6 cm³

○ 180 cm³

○ 36 cm³

○ 6.75 cm³

○ 12 cm³

○ 27.5 cm³

Complete the tables. Then do the matching. Write the letters.

⑲ **Rectangular Prism**

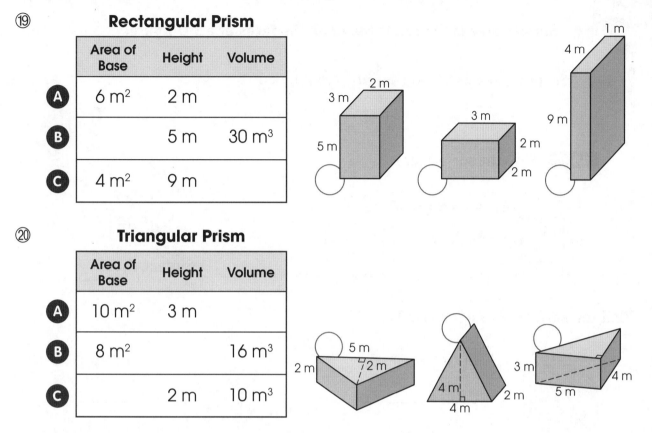

	Area of Base	Height	Volume
A	6 m²	2 m	
B		5 m	30 m³
C	4 m²	9 m	

⑳ **Triangular Prism**

	Area of Base	Height	Volume
A	10 m²	3 m	
B	8 m²		16 m³
C		2 m	10 m³

Find the volume of each composed solid.

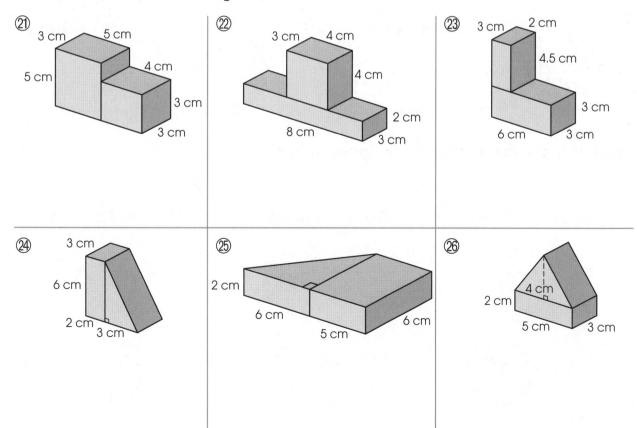

17 Surface Area

- determining surface areas

Surface area is the total area of all the faces of a 3-D figure.

Surface Area of a Cube: length x length x 6

area of 1 face   6 faces

Example Find the surface area.

4 cm
4 cm
4 cm

4 x 4 x 6 = 96

Surface Area: 96 cm²

Try It

1 m
1 m
1 m

Surface Area: _____

Find the surface area of each cube.

① 5 cm

Surface Area:

_____ x _____ x 6

= _____ (cm²)

② 2 km

Surface Area:

_____

= _____

③ 3 m

Surface Area:

_____

= _____

④ 6 mm

Surface Area:

_____

= _____

Check the cube that match with the given surface area.

⑤ Surface Area: 24 cm²

(A) 2 cm

(B) 3 cm

⑥ Surface Area: 600 m²

(A) 6 m

(B) 10 m

⑦ Surface Area: 54 m²

(A) 3 m

(B) 9 m

Check the correct expression to find the surface area of each prism. Then find the surface area.

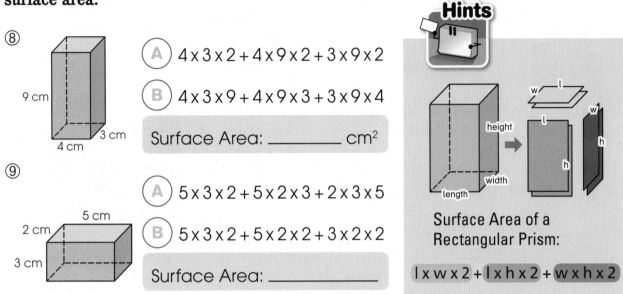

⑧

(A) 4 x 3 x 2 + 4 x 9 x 2 + 3 x 9 x 2

(B) 4 x 3 x 9 + 4 x 9 x 3 + 3 x 9 x 4

Surface Area: _____ cm²

⑨

(A) 5 x 3 x 2 + 5 x 2 x 3 + 2 x 3 x 5

(B) 5 x 3 x 2 + 5 x 2 x 2 + 3 x 2 x 2

Surface Area: _____

Hints

Surface Area of a Rectangular Prism:

l x w x 2 + l x h x 2 + w x h x 2

Find the surface area of each rectangular prism. Show your work.

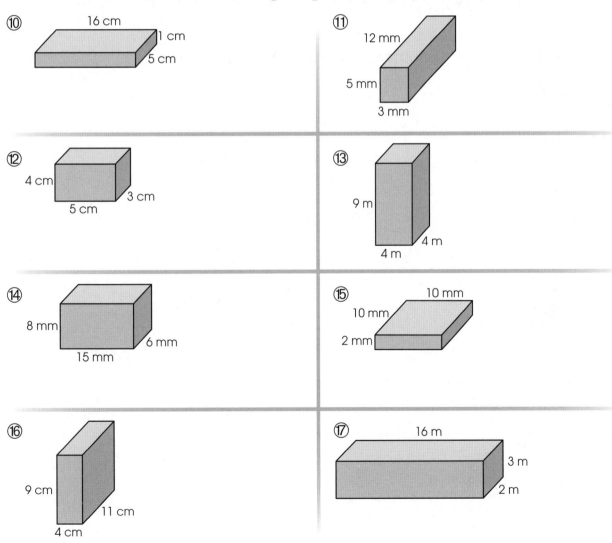

⑩ 16 cm, 1 cm, 5 cm

⑪ 12 mm, 5 mm, 3 mm

⑫ 4 cm, 3 cm, 5 cm

⑬ 9 m, 4 m, 4 m

⑭ 8 mm, 6 mm, 15 mm

⑮ 10 mm, 10 mm, 2 mm

⑯ 9 cm, 11 cm, 4 cm

⑰ 16 m, 3 m, 2 m

Check the correct expression to find the surface area of each triangular prism. Then find the surface area.

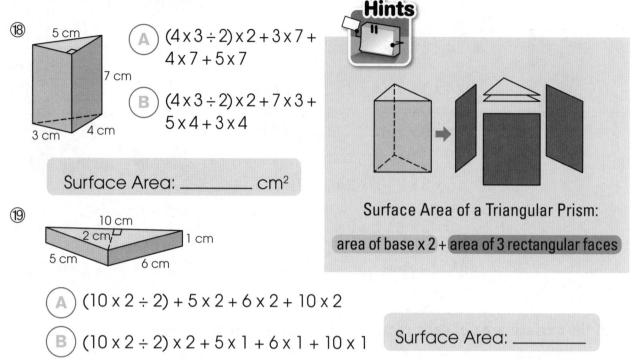

⑱ 5 cm, 7 cm, 3 cm, 4 cm

(A) $(4 \times 3 \div 2) \times 2 + 3 \times 7 + 4 \times 7 + 5 \times 7$

(B) $(4 \times 3 \div 2) \times 2 + 7 \times 3 + 5 \times 4 + 3 \times 4$

Surface Area: _____ cm²

Surface Area of a Triangular Prism:

area of base x 2 + area of 3 rectangular faces

⑲ 10 cm, 2 cm, 1 cm, 5 cm, 6 cm

(A) $(10 \times 2 \div 2) + 5 \times 2 + 6 \times 2 + 10 \times 2$

(B) $(10 \times 2 \div 2) \times 2 + 5 \times 1 + 6 \times 1 + 10 \times 1$

Surface Area: _____

Find the surface area of each triangular prism. Show your work.

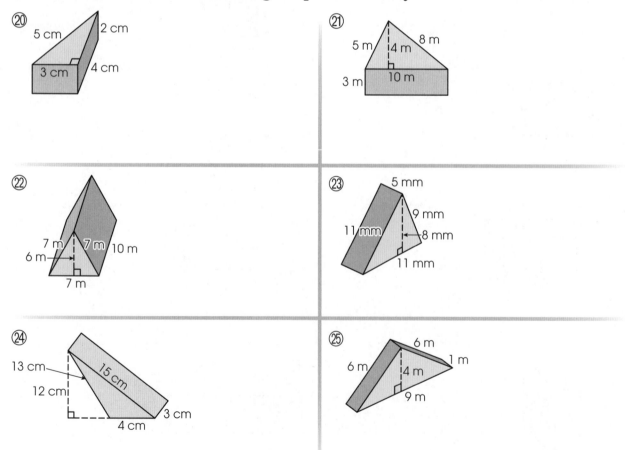

⑳ 5 cm, 2 cm, 3 cm, 4 cm

㉑ 5 m, 4 m, 8 m, 3 m, 10 m

㉒ 7 m, 7 m, 10 m, 6 m, 7 m

㉓ 5 mm, 9 mm, 11 mm, 8 mm, 11 mm

㉔ 13 cm, 12 cm, 15 cm, 3 cm, 4 cm

㉕ 6 m, 1 m, 6 m, 4 m, 9 m

Find the surface area of each prism. Show your work.

㉖

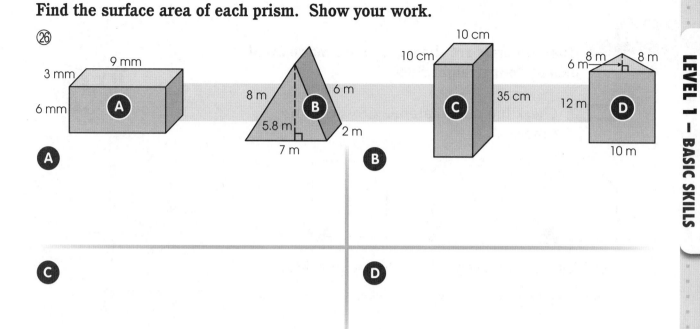

A

B

C

D

Timmy has to wrap some gift boxes. Answer the questions to help him.

㉗

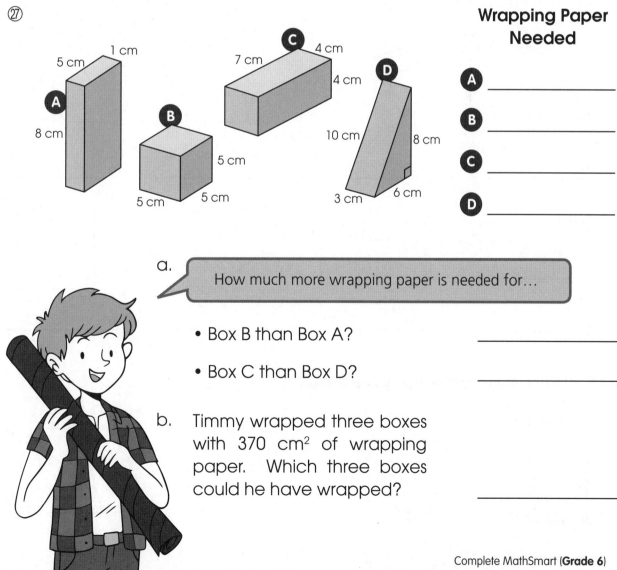

Wrapping Paper Needed

A _____

B _____

C _____

D _____

a. How much more wrapping paper is needed for…

• Box B than Box A?   _____

• Box C than Box D?   _____

b. Timmy wrapped three boxes with 370 cm² of wrapping paper. Which three boxes could he have wrapped?   _____

18 Shapes

- sorting quadrilaterals

Read This

Quadrilaterals are shapes that are made up of exactly four straight sides.

Example Check the quadrilateral. Cross out the others.

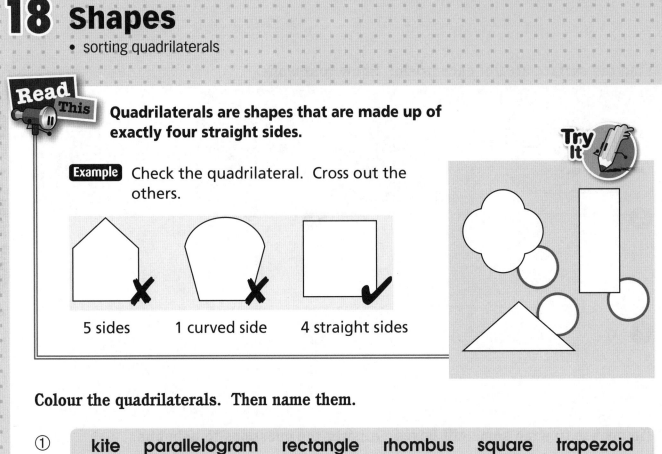

5 sides   1 curved side   4 straight sides

Try It

Colour the quadrilaterals. Then name them.

① kite   parallelogram   rectangle   rhombus   square   trapezoid

a. _____   b. _____   c. _____   d. _____

e. _____   f. _____   g. _____   h. _____

Draw all lines of symmetry where applicable.

②

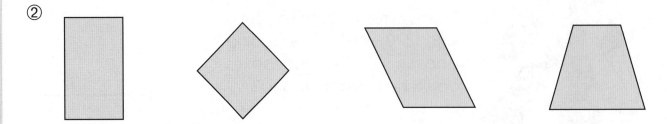

Fill in the blanks with the correct numbers to show the properties of the quadrilaterals.

③

_____ equal sides

_____ pair(s) of parallel sides

_____ right angles

④

_____ equal sides

_____ pair(s) of parallel sides

_____ right angles

⑤

_____ equal sides

_____ pair(s) of parallel sides

_____ right angles

Hints

The markings below are used to indicate some properties of shapes.

| : sides that are equal in length

2 pairs of equal sides

〉 : sides that are parallel

2 pairs of parallel sides

⌐ : a right angle

2 right angles

⑥

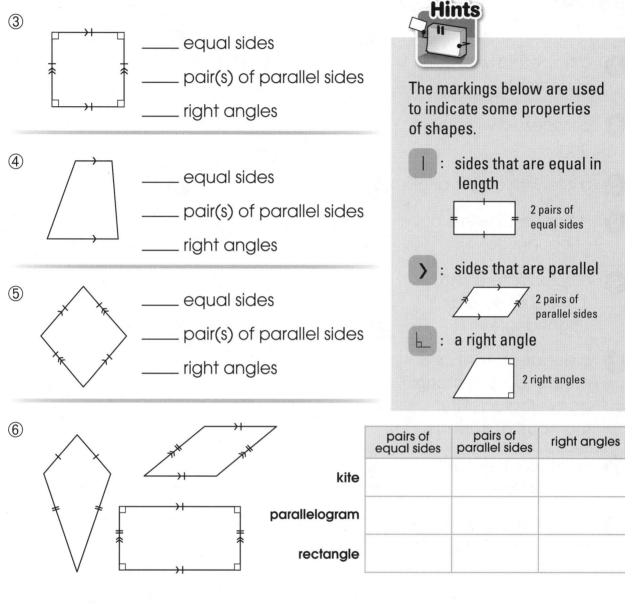

	pairs of equal sides	pairs of parallel sides	right angles
kite			
parallelogram			
rectangle			

Sort the quadrilaterals. Write the letters.

⑦ **Quadrilaterals that have**

- no parallel sides: _____

- no equal sides: _____

- no right angles: _____

- 1 pair of parallel sides:

_____

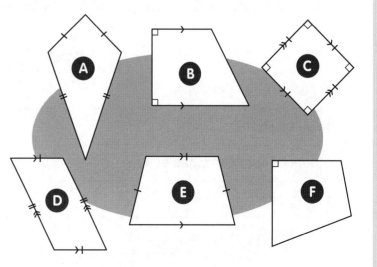

Complete MathSmart (**Grade 6**)   **75**

LEVEL 1 – BASIC SKILLS

Draw the quadrilaterals with the given descriptions. Then add markings to show their properties.

⑧

A a trapezoid with 1 line of symmetry

B a trapezoid with 2 right angles

C a kite with a right angle

D a trapezoid with 1 pair of equal sides

E a quadrilateral with 4 unequal sides and 1 right angle

F a quadrilateral that is not a square, rectangle, parallelogram, kite, rhombus, or trapezoid

G a quadrilateral with 3 equal sides

H a quadrilateral with an angle greater than 180°

A ·   ·   ·   ·   ·   ·   ·   ·   B ·   ·   ·   ·   ·   ·   ·   ·   ·

C ·   ·   ·   ·   ·   ·   ·   ·   D ·   ·   ·   ·   ·   ·   ·   ·   ·

E ·   ·   ·   ·   ·   ·   ·   ·   F ·   ·   ·   ·   ·   ·   ·   ·   ·

G ·   ·   ·   ·   ·   ·   ·   ·   H ·   ·   ·   ·   ·   ·   ·   ·   ·

Check the boxes to show the properties of the shapes.

⑨

	rectangle	rhombus	parallelogram	square
opposite sides parallel				
all sides equal				
2 pairs of opposite sides equal				
all angles 90°				
2 pairs of opposite angles equal				

Sort the quadrilaterals into the Venn diagrams. Write the letters.

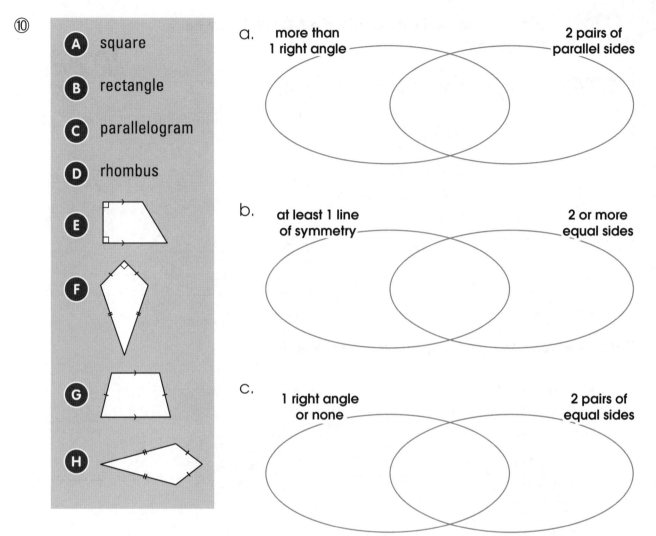

⑩

- Ⓐ square
- Ⓑ rectangle
- Ⓒ parallelogram
- Ⓓ rhombus
- Ⓔ
- Ⓕ
- Ⓖ
- Ⓗ

a. more than 1 right angle — 2 pairs of parallel sides

b. at least 1 line of symmetry — 2 or more equal sides

c. 1 right angle or none — 2 pairs of equal sides

Circle "T" for the true statements and "F" for the false ones.

⑪ All squares are rectangles. T / F

⑫ All trapezoids have 1 right angle. T / F

⑬ A kite can have no lines of symmetry. T / F

⑭ All parallelograms are rhombuses. T / F

⑮ If a shape is not a square, rectangle, parallelogram, rhombus, kite, or trapezoid, it cannot be a quadrilateral. T / F

⑯ A trapezoid that has 1 pair of equal sides must be symmetrical. T / F

19 Solids

• drawing solids

Read This

The front, top, and side views of a 3-D solid may be very different.

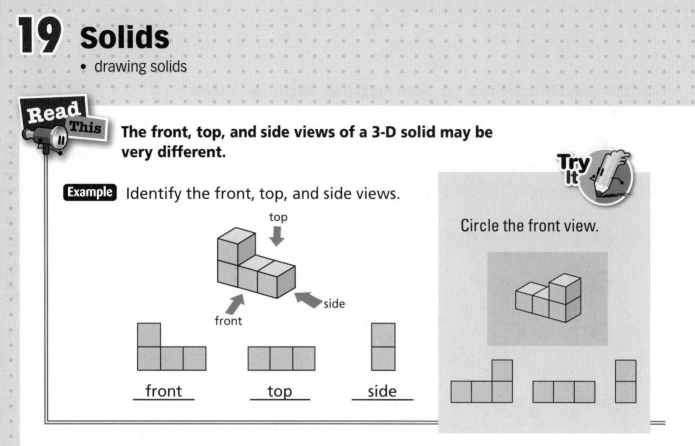

Example Identify the front, top, and side views.

front   top   side

Circle the front view.

Label the front, top, and side views for each solid.

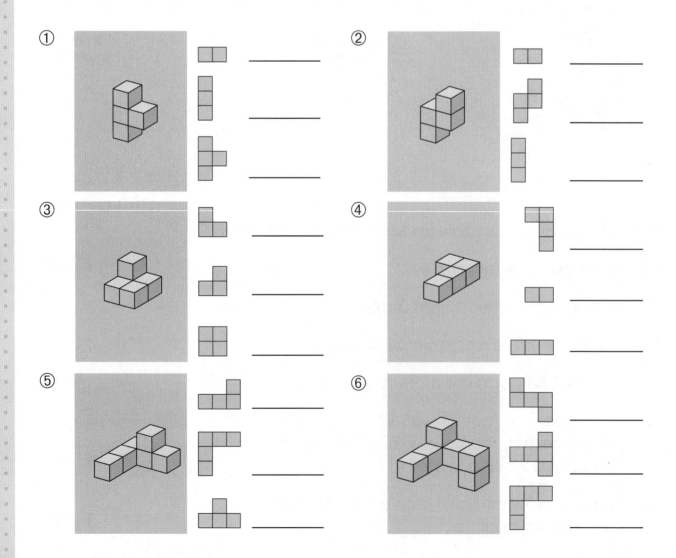

① ② ③ ④ ⑤ ⑥

Circle the correct view as specified for each solid.

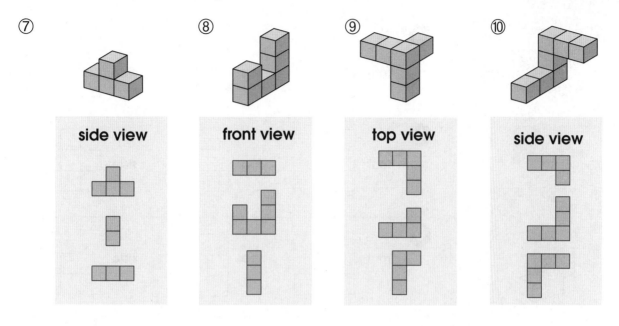

For each solid, colour the front blue, the top yellow, and the side red. Then draw them on the grid.

⑪

front view	top view	side view

⑫

front view	top view	side view

⑬

front view	top view	side view

⑭

front view

top view

side view

Match each solid with the correct set of views. Write the letters.

⑮

A

front ⬜ top ⬜ side ⬜

B

front ⬜ top ⬜ side ⬜

C

front ⬜ top ⬜ side ⬜

D

front ⬜ top ⬜ side ⬜

E

front ⬜ top ⬜ side ⬜

Draw each solid on the isometric grid.

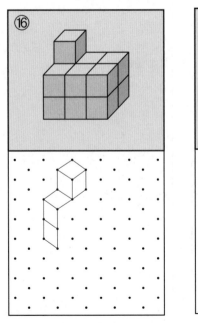

⑯

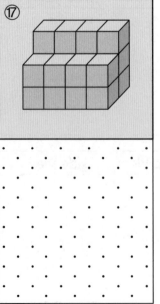

⑰

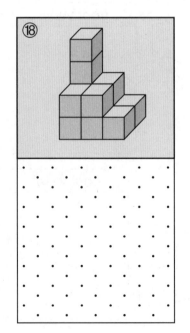

⑱

Draw the solid on the isometric grid for each given set of views.

⑲ front   top   side

⑳ front   top   side

㉑ front   top   side

㉒ front   top   side

㉓ front   top   side

Check to show the set of views that are possible for a solid. Draw and label the possible solids.

㉔

A   front   top   side

B   front   top   side

C   front   top   side

20 Patterning

• representing patterns

Each number in a pattern is called a term. In a growing or shrinking pattern, each term is related to the previous term by following the pattern rule.

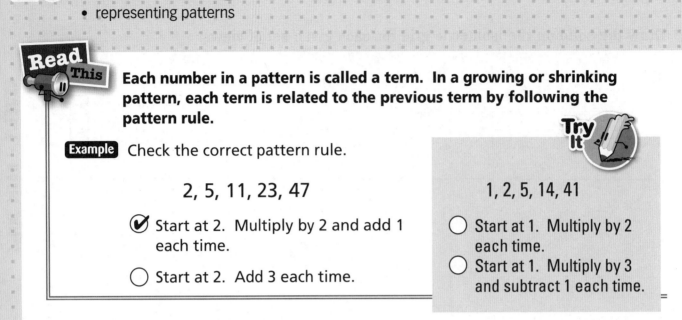

Example Check the correct pattern rule.

2, 5, 11, 23, 47

☑ Start at 2. Multiply by 2 and add 1 each time.

○ Start at 2. Add 3 each time.

1, 2, 5, 14, 41

○ Start at 1. Multiply by 2 each time.

○ Start at 1. Multiply by 3 and subtract 1 each time.

Try It

For each pattern, write "growing" or "shrinking". Then match each pattern with its pattern rule. Write the letter.

Pattern Rule

① **2, 3, 5, 9, 17**   Pattern Rule

a _____ pattern

② **132, 68, 36, 20**   Pattern Rule

a _____ pattern

③ **2, 7, 22, 67, 202**   Pattern Rule

a _____ pattern

④ **132, 64, 30, 13**   Pattern Rule

a _____ pattern

Ⓐ Start at 2. Multiply by 3 and add 1 each time.

Ⓑ Start at 2. Multiply by 2 and subtract 1 each time.

Ⓒ Start at 132. Divide by 2 and add 2 each time.

Ⓓ Start at 132. Divide by 2 and subtract 2 each time.

Write the next four terms for each pattern using the given pattern rule.

⑤ Start at 2. Add 2 each time.

2, _____

⑥ Start at 3. Multiply by 2 and add 1 each time.

3, _____

⑦ Start at 201. Divide by 3 and subtract 1 each time.

201, _____

Check the correct pattern rule for each pattern. Then find the next term.

⑧ 5, 8, 7, 10, 9, _____

A) Start at 5. Add 3 each time.

B) Start at 5. Add 3 and subtract 1 alternately.

⑨ 4, 5, 7, 11, 19, _____

A) Start at 4. Subtract 2 and multiply by 3 each time.

B) Start at 4. Multiply by 2 and subtract 3 each time.

⑩ 1, 4, 10, 22, 46, _____

A) Start at 1. Add 1 and multiply by 2 each time.

B) Start at 1. Multiply by 5 and subtract 1 each time.

⑪ 2, 5, 8, 11, 14, _____

A) Start at 2. Multiply by 2 and add 1 each time.

B) Start at 2. Add 3 each time.

⑫ 3, 7, 19, 55, 163, _____

A) Start at 3. Multiply by 2 and add 1 each time.

B) Start at 3. Multiply by 3 and subtract 2 each time.

⑬ 1, 3, 9, 27, 81, _____

A) Start at 1. Multiply by 3 each time.

B) Start at 1. Add 2 and multiply by 3 alternately.

Complete each pattern. Write the pattern rule.

⑭ 19, 18, 17, _____ , _____

Pattern Rule

⑮ 512, 256, 128, _____ , _____

Pattern Rule

⑯ 10, 25, 55, _____ , _____

Pattern Rule

⑰ 5, 12, 26, _____ , _____

Pattern Rule

⑱ 3, 6, 15, _____ , _____

Pattern Rule

⑲ 243, 81, 27, _____ , _____

Pattern Rule

Follow each pattern to draw Frame 4. Count and write the number of sticks. Then answer the questions.

⑳

	Frame 1	Frame 2	Frame 3	Frame 4
Pattern A				
no. of sticks	4	7	10	_____
Pattern B				
no. of sticks	5	12	19	_____
Pattern C				
no. of sticks	3	6	9	_____

㉑ What is the pattern rule for each pattern?

Pattern A: _____

Pattern B: _____

Pattern C: _____

㉒ How many sticks are there in Frame 5 of each pattern? Sketch the frame and write the number.

Pattern A	Pattern B	Pattern C
_____	_____	_____

Write the pattern rule for each pattern. Then draw the next two figures.

㉓ Rotate the figure [ ]° clockwise each time.

Tips

Geometric patterns can be created through rotations.

㉔ Rotate the figure _____ each time.

㉕ Rotate _____ .

The first figure of each pattern is in the box. Read the pattern rule. Then check the correct answer.

㉖ Rotate the figure 180° each time. Check the 3rd figure.

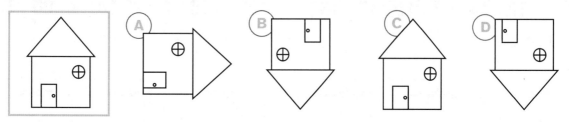

A   B   C   D

㉗ Rotate the figure 90° counterclockwise each time. Check the 4th figure.

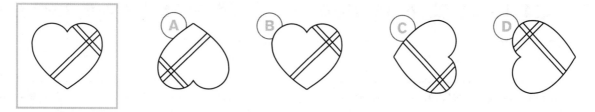

A   B   C   D

Mean, Median, and Mode

• finding and comparing mean, median, and mode

Read This

A measure of central tendency is a value that describes a set of data. There are three measures of central tendency: mean, median, and mode.

Example Find the mean, median, and mode of the data set: 7, 7, 4, 3, 3, 6, 7, 7, 1.

In order: | 1 | 3 | 3 | 4 | 6 | 7 | 7 | 7 | 7 |

Mean: | 5 | ← the sum of all the data values divided by the number of data values

Median: | 6 | ← the middle data value in an ordered set

Mode: | 7 | ← the data value that occurs most often

Try It

2   5
6   5   5   5   7

In order:

_____

Mean: ☐

Median: ☐

Mode: ☐

Find the mean, median, and mode of each set of data.

①
```
5   9   4   8   4
```
In order:

_____

mean ─ ☐   median ─ ☐   mode ─ ☐

Tips
To find the median of a set of data, first put the values in order. If there are two middle values, add them and divide the sum by 2 to find the median.

②
```
12   15   17   16   17   13
```
In order:

_____

mean ─ ☐   median ─ ☐   mode ─ ☐

③
```
25   2   9   14   7   20   14
```
In order:

_____

mean ─ ☐   median ─ ☐   mode ─ ☐

④
```
24   16   31   13   6   16   10   8
```
In order:

_____

mean ─ ☐   median ─ ☐   mode ─ ☐

⑤
```
25   9   16   26   2   9   13   13   31
```
In order:

_____

mean ─ ☐   median ─ ☐   mode ─ ☐

The children are given 10 bags of marbles. The number of marbles in each bag is shown. Complete the table and answer the questions.

⑥

Chris

17   26   18
25   28   57   31
31   28   19

Anna

21   36   2
28   24   23   32
68   45   21

Joseph

5   24   29
16   26   28   27
25   26   34

Eric

15   9   30
15   25   17   44
30   21   14

Sylvia

14   17   45
25   16   31   26
27   32   27

Olivia

20   26   22
18   24   37   25
25   38   25

	Chris	Anna	Joseph	Eric	Sylvia	Olivia
mean						
median						
mode						

a.   "If you pick a bag of marbles randomly from me, it is more likely that you will pick a bag with 25 marbles than any other amount." Which child said this? How do you know?

_____

b.   "I put my bags of marbles in order from the one with the most marbles to the one with the fewest. The bag in the middle has 19 marbles." Which child said this? How do you know?

_____

c.   Which child has the most marbles? Determine the answer based on the mean. How did you find the answer? Explain.

_____

_____

_____

Find the mean, median, and mode of each set of data. Then answer the questions.

⑦ **Ages of People in Two Parks**

Park A

4	11	13	9	15
14	4	9	8	10
8	9	4	3	11
11	4	10	15	8

_____   _____   _____
mean   median   mode

Park B

6	10	8	9	10
9	7	9	8	9
11	9	10	10	12
6	12	7	9	9

_____   _____   _____
mean   median   mode

⑧ Why is the mode of the data set of Park A not a good representation of the data?

Ⓐ The mode is not the same as the median.

Ⓑ The difference between the mode and the mean is greater than 2.

Ⓒ The data is mostly concentrated on the 8 to 11 range. To use the mode to describe the data set would be misleading.

⑨ As a central tendency, is "9" a good representation of the data in Park B? Explain.

_____

_____

⑩ Which park is being described in each case below?

a. More than a quarter of the people are 9 years old.   _____

b. The age range of the set is 3 to 15 years old.   _____

c. The difference between the mean age and every other age in the set is 3 or less.   _____

The graph shows the number of bags of candy that two machines packaged. Complete the tables and find the answers.

⑪

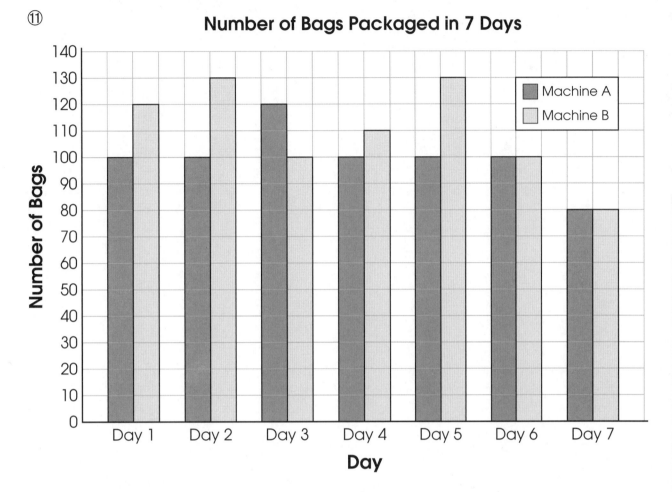

Number of Bags Packaged in 7 Days

a.

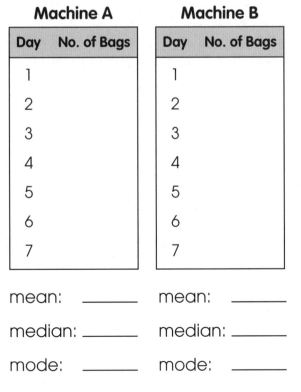

Machine A

Day	No. of Bags
1	
2	
3	
4	
5	
6	
7	

mean: _____

median: _____

mode: _____

Machine B

Day	No. of Bags
1	
2	
3	
4	
5	
6	
7	

mean: _____

median: _____

mode: _____

b. Janice wants to purchase one of the machines to package candy.

- Which machine is more consistent with the number of bags it packages?

  _____

- Which machine packages more bags of candy?

  _____

LEVEL 2
FURTHER YOUR UNDERSTANDING

1 Order of Operations

• solving addition, subtraction, multiplication, and division problems

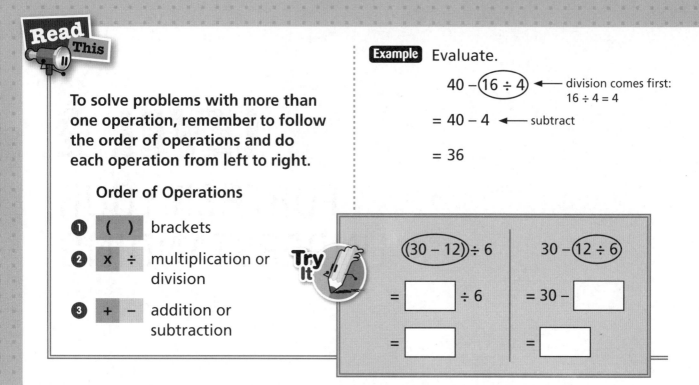

Read This

To solve problems with more than one operation, remember to follow the order of operations and do each operation from left to right.

Order of Operations

❶ **( )** brackets

❷ **x ÷** multiplication or division

❸ **+ −** addition or subtraction

Example Evaluate.

$40 - \boxed{16 \div 4}$ ⟵ division comes first: $16 \div 4 = 4$

$= 40 - 4$ ⟵ subtract

$= 36$

Try It

$\boxed{(30 - 12)} \div 6$

$= \boxed{} \div 6$

$= \boxed{}$

$30 - \boxed{12 \div 6}$

$= 30 - \boxed{}$

$= \boxed{}$

Circle the part that should be solved first. Then evaluate. Show the steps.

① $20 - 4 \times 2$

= _____

= _____

② $6 \times 5 - 9$

= _____

= _____

③ $8 \div 2 + 7$

= _____

= _____

④ $5 + 18 \div 9$

= _____

= _____

⑤ $11 - 15 \div 5$

= _____

= _____

⑥ $10 + 4 \times 6$

= _____

= _____

⑦ $(2 + 3) \times 5$

= _____

= _____

⑧ $8 \div (9 - 5)$

= _____

= _____

⑨ $(15 - 7) \times 3$

= _____

= _____

⑩ $(13 + 7) \div 5$

= _____

= _____

⑪ $7 \times (3 + 7)$

= _____

= _____

⑫ $45 \div (13 - 4)$

= _____

= _____

Apply the commutative property to solve the problems.

⑬   29 + 16 + 11

⑭   4 x 23 x 25

⑮   15 x 8 x 4

⑯   8 + 59 + 22

⑰   5 x 17 x 8

⑱   7 + 38 + 3

LEVEL 2 – FURTHER YOUR UNDERSTANDING

Match the expressions that have the same answers.

⑲

| 24 + 16 x 29 • | •   17 x 31 + 22 |

| 31 x 17 + 22 • | •   16 + 24 x 29 |

| 29 x 24 + 16 • | •   29 x 16 + 24 |

| 22 x 31 + 17 • | •   31 x 22 + 17 |

Use the distributive property to solve the problems.

㉕ $(8 + 5) \times 5$ ㉑ $4 \times (11 - 7)$

㉒ $(17 + 6) \times 7$ ㉓ $(6 + 8) \times 3$

> **Hints**
>
> **Distributive Property**
>
> By this property, numbers in brackets can be rewritten as separate multiplications.
>
> e.g. $2 \times (3 + 1)$
> $= 2 \times 3 + 2 \times 1$
> $= 6 + 2$
> $= 8$

㉔ $(12 - 7) \times 2$ ㉕ $6 \times (15 - 6)$ ㉖ $5 \times (8 + 11)$

Simplify the problem by using brackets. Then solve the problem.

㉗ $5 \times 36 - 5 \times 16$ ㉘ $12 \times 8 + 8 \times 18$ ㉙ $31 \times 9 - 9 \times 16$

$= 5 \times (\underline{\hspace{1cm}} - \underline{\hspace{1cm}})$

$= 5 \times \underline{\hspace{1cm}}$

$= \underline{\hspace{1cm}}$

㉚ $18 \times 7 + 3 \times 7$ ㉛ $23 \times 6 - 5 \times 6$ ㉜ $32 \times 6 + 28 \times 6$

Solve.

㉝ $15 + 3 \times 6 - 9$

㉞ $15 - 24 \div (5 + 3)$

㉟ $30 \times 5 \div 6 + 9$

㊱ $14 + 6 \times (3 + 17) - 12$

㊲ $3 \times 17 - 8 \times 3 \div 4$

㊳ $37 \times 6 - (18 - 11) \times 6$

㊴ $18 \div 3 - 4 + (5 + 7) \times 9$

㊵ $15 \times (16 - 9) - 7 \times (2 + 4)$

Write the symbols "+", "–", "x", or "÷" or add brackets to make the equations correct.

㊶ a. $3 \bigcirc 8 \bigcirc 1 = 25$

b. $4 \bigcirc 9 \bigcirc 3 = 7$

c. $13 \bigcirc 7 \bigcirc 11 = 31$

d. $26 \bigcirc 19 \bigcirc 4 = 11$

㊷ a. $2 \times 4 + 5 \div 3 = 6$

b. $4 \times 9 - 4 - 2 = 18$

c. $20 - 8 + 6 \div 2 = 9$

d. $11 + 3 \times 6 - 2 = 23$

2 Adding and Subtracting Decimals

• adding and subtracting decimals to thousandths

When adding or subtracting decimals, remember to align the decimal points first. Add zeros if needed.

e.g. 15.1 – 8.652 = _____

```
        ← Align.
  15.100  ← Add the zeros.
–  8.652
```

Example Add or subtract.

6.493 + 5.2 = _____

```
    6.493
+   5.200
  ───────
  11.693
```

15.46 – 3.916 = _____

```
  15.4600
–  3.916
  ───────
  11.544
```

Try It

```
    8.210
–   3.149
  ───────
```

```
    4.773
+   2.485
  ───────
```

Add or subtract.

①
```
    6.070
+   3.039
```

②
```
    7.453
+   8.498
```

③
```
    2.981
–   1.790
```

④
```
   59.307
+  28.838
```

⑤
```
    7.920
–   1.875
```

⑥
```
    8.000
–   3.998
```

⑦
```
    9.280
+   2.839
```

⑧
```
    0.799
+   0.958
```

⑨
```
   12.250
–   3.987
```

⑩
```
   10.080
–   9.289
```

⑪
```
  300.000
– 194.509
```

⑫
```
  106.423
+ 218.650
```

Find the answers.

Do your work here.

⑬ 15.12 + 9.297 = _____

⑭ 3.412 + 2.798 = _____

⑮ 18.04 – 7.816 = _____

⑯ 20 – 14.19   = _____

⑰ 0.58 + 18.417 = _____

⑱ 16.041 + 5.79 = _____

⑲ 0.98 – 0.026 = _____

Find the sum and difference of each pair of numbers.

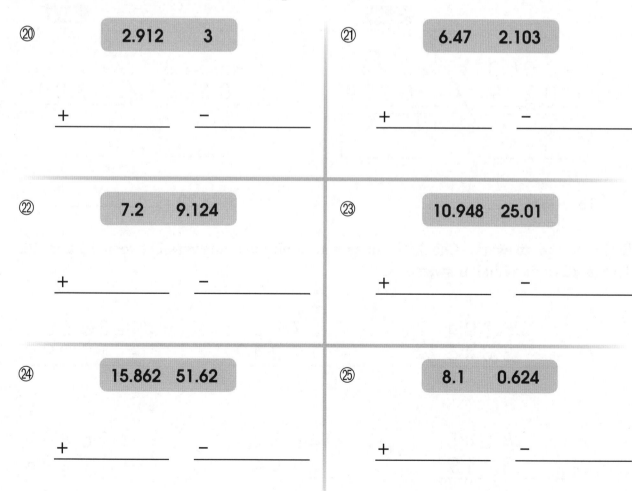

⑳   **2.912   3**

+ _____   – _____

㉑   **6.47   2.103**

+ _____   – _____

㉒   **7.2   9.124**

+ _____   – _____

㉓   **10.948   25.01**

+ _____   – _____

㉔   **15.862   51.62**

+ _____   – _____

㉕   **8.1   0.624**

+ _____   – _____

LEVEL 2 – FURTHER YOUR UNDERSTANDING

For each question, find the answer. Then use the opposite operation to check your answer.

㉖ Use **addition** to check your answers.

a.

```
   1 2.4 8 0        Check
 -    6.2 5 7    + 6.2 5 7
 [          ]    [          ]
```

If it is **12.48**, then your answer is correct.

12.48 – 6.257 = _____

b.

```
   1 3.0 0 0        Check
 -    0.2 0 9    + 0.2 0 9
 [          ]    [          ]
```

13 – 0.209 = _____

㉗ Use **subtraction** to check your answers.

a.

```
   9.2 0 0          Check
 + 0.4 7 1      -  0.4 7 1
 [          ]    [          ]
```

If it is **9.2**, then your answer is correct.

9.2 + 0.471 = _____

b.

```
   6.3 1 3          Check
 + 8.2 9 0      -  8.2 9 0
 [          ]    [          ]
```

6.313 + 8.29 = _____

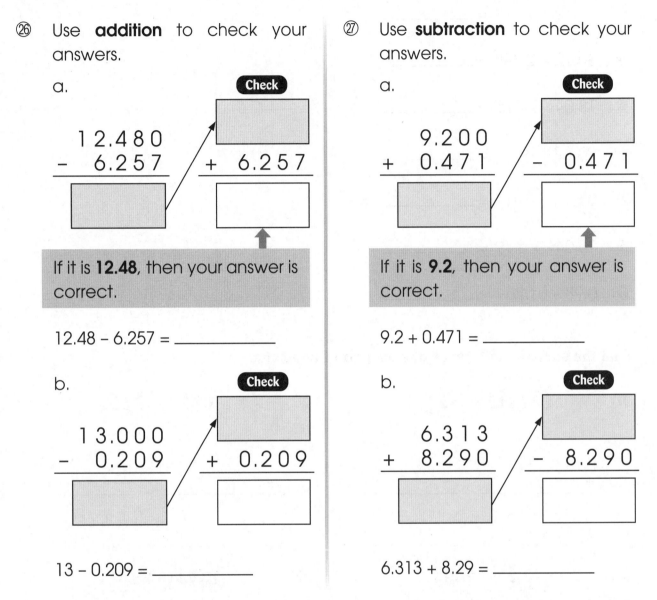

Estimate the answers. Check the ones you think have answers between 10 and 20. Then find their actual answers.

㉘

A.
```
     8.2 9 4
 +   3.8 4 6
```

B.
```
   3 7.9 8 1
 - 1 9.2 4 9
```

C.
```
   3 5.5 5 5
 - 1 0.9 9 9
```

D.
```
     8.2 4 8
 +   2.6 1 9
```

E.
```
   4 8.1 2 3
 - 2 9.8 4 3
```

F.
```
   2 6.8 4 9
 - 1 9.2 9 8
```

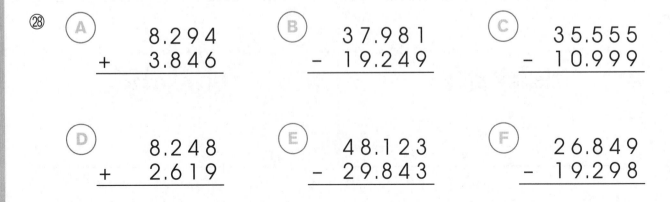

See how heavy each toy is. Answer the questions.

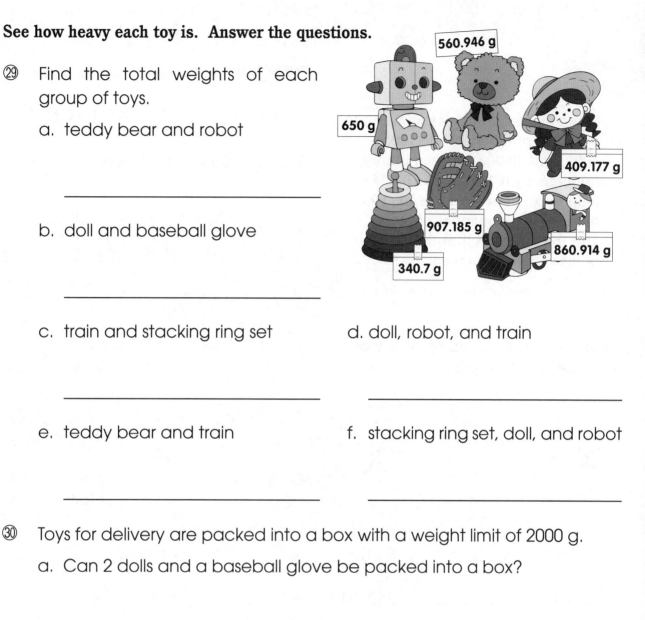

㉙ Find the total weights of each group of toys.

a. teddy bear and robot

_____

b. doll and baseball glove

_____

c. train and stacking ring set

_____

d. doll, robot, and train

_____

e. teddy bear and train

_____

f. stacking ring set, doll, and robot

_____

㉚ Toys for delivery are packed into a box with a weight limit of 2000 g.

a. Can 2 dolls and a baseball glove be packed into a box?

_____

b. Can a teddy bear, a stacking ring set, and a train be packed into a box?

_____

c. A robot and a train are packed into a box. Which toy can be packed into the same box without exceeding the weight limit?

_____

3 Multiplying and Dividing Decimals

- multiplying and dividing decimals using a variety of methods

Using mental strategies to multiply or divide numbers by 10, 100, 1000, and 10 000 and to multiply numbers by 0.1, 0.01, and 0.001 can help make your work easier. First determine the number of places and the direction that the decimal point should be moved.

Example Multiply and divide the decimals.

$7.6 \times 10 = 76$

$7.6 \times 0.1 = 0.76$

$7.6 \div 10 = 0.76$

$7.6 \times 0.01 = 0.076$

Try It

$451 \times 0.01 = $ _____

$5.4 \div 10 = $ _____

$2.01 \times 100 = $ _____

Read the notes. Multiply or divide using mental strategies.

①

X	by 10, 100, 1000, or 10 000
	move "." to the **right**

$0.25 \times 10 = $ _____

$0.09 \times 100 = $ _____

$1.7 \times 10\,000 = $ _____

$8.3 \times 1000 = $ _____

$6.1 \times 100 = $ _____

$0.007 \times 10 = $ _____

$9.01 \times 10 = $ _____

$2.08 \times 1000 = $ _____

$0.1 \times 10\,000 = $ _____

②

X	by 0.1, 0.01, or 0.001
	move "." to the **left**

$5 \times 0.1 = $ _____

$340 \times 0.1 = $ _____

$71 \times 0.01 = $ _____

$0.4 \times 0.1 = $ _____

$6 \times 0.001 = $ _____

$2.011 \times 0.1 = $ _____

$1.61 \times 0.001 = $ _____

$20 \times 0.001 = $ _____

$14.2 \times 0.1 = $ _____

③

÷	by 10, 100, 1000, or 10 000
	move "." to the **left**

$19 \div 100 = $ _____

$340 \div 1000 = $ _____

$7 \div 10\,000 = $ _____

$28 \div 1000 = $ _____

$0.79 \div 100 = $ _____

$2.1 \div 1000 = $ _____

$92 \div 10\,000 = $ _____

$0.01 \div 10 = $ _____

$7.5 \div 100 = $ _____

Find the answers.

④
$$2.39$$
$$\times \qquad 5$$

⑤
$$3.92$$
$$\times \qquad 7$$

⑥
$$2.56$$
$$\times \qquad 9$$

⑦
$$0.89$$
$$\times \qquad 6$$

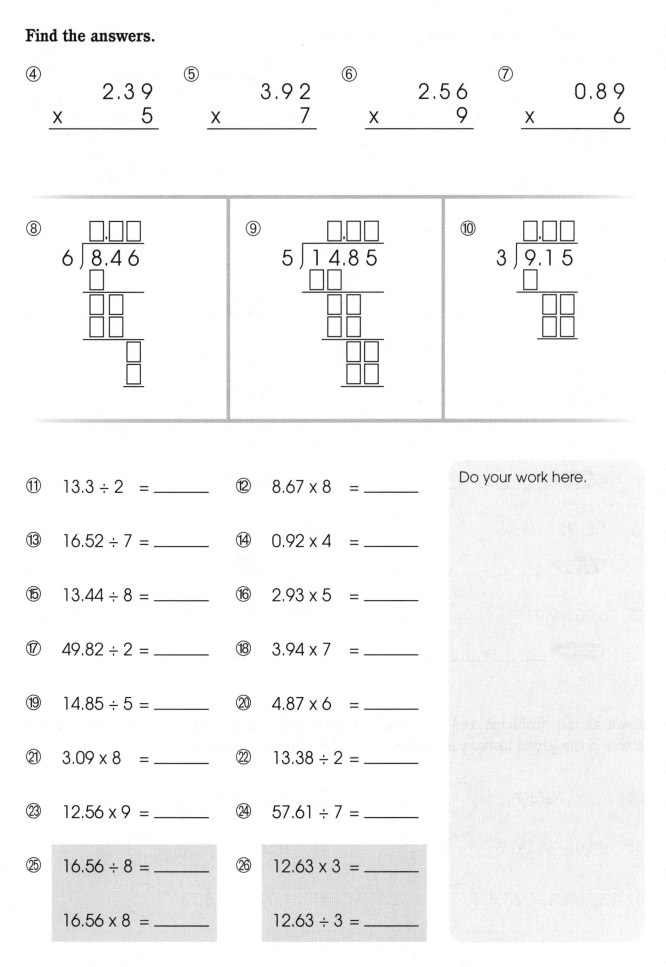

⑧
$$6 \overline{)8.46}$$

⑨
$$5 \overline{)14.85}$$

⑩
$$3 \overline{)9.15}$$

⑪ $13.3 \div 2 =$ _____

⑫ $8.67 \times 8 =$ _____

⑬ $16.52 \div 7 =$ _____

⑭ $0.92 \times 4 =$ _____

⑮ $13.44 \div 8 =$ _____

⑯ $2.93 \times 5 =$ _____

⑰ $49.82 \div 2 =$ _____

⑱ $3.94 \times 7 =$ _____

⑲ $14.85 \div 5 =$ _____

⑳ $4.87 \times 6 =$ _____

㉑ $3.09 \times 8 =$ _____

㉒ $13.38 \div 2 =$ _____

㉓ $12.56 \times 9 =$ _____

㉔ $57.61 \div 7 =$ _____

㉕ $16.56 \div 8 =$ _____

$16.56 \times 8 =$ _____

㉖ $12.63 \times 3 =$ _____

$12.63 \div 3 =$ _____

Do your work here.

Estimate the answer to each problem to the nearest whole number.

Tips

Estimate an answer by rounding each decimal to the nearest whole number. Then do the operation.

㉗   59.82 ÷ 19.89

    estimate _____ ÷ _____ = _____

㉘   3.24 x 89.98

    estimate _____ x _____ = _____

㉙   3.92 x 1.89

    estimate _____ x _____ = _____

㉚   3.92 ÷ 1.89

    estimate _____ ÷ _____ = _____

㉛   15.8 ÷ 3.9

    estimate _____ ÷ _____ = _____

㉜   36.25 ÷ 5.83

    estimate _____ ÷ _____ = _____

㉝   12.14 ÷ 3.98

    estimate _____ ÷ _____ = _____

㉞   100.48 ÷ 25.01

    estimate _____ ÷ _____ = _____

㉟   143.72 ÷ 11.98

    estimate _____ ÷ _____ = _____

㊱   225.2 ÷ 8.91

    estimate _____ ÷ _____ = _____

㊲   5.98 x 9.91

    estimate _____ x _____ = _____

㊳   19.65 x 2.73

    estimate _____ x _____ = _____

Look at the problems and estimate the answer for each. Put a check mark in the circle if the given answer is reasonable; otherwise, put a cross.

㊳   5.8 x 7 = 406   ◯

㊴   83.7 ÷ 6 = 13.95   ◯

㊶   30.9 ÷ 6 = 51.5   ◯

㊷   10.4 ÷ 4 = 20.6   ◯

㊸   53.8 x 3 = 161.4   ◯

㊹   1.09 x 8 = 8.72   ◯

Fill in the blanks.

㊺ ________ x 100 = 52.8

㊻ ________ x 2 = 0.34

㊼ ________ x 3 = 7.2

㊽ ________ ÷ 2 = 5.1

㊾ ________ ÷ 5 = 1.2

㊿ 12.93 ÷ ________ = 1.293

(51) 5.8 ÷ ________ = 2

(52) 7.3 x ________ = 73

For each number in bold, put the decimal point in the right place and add the correct number of zeros if necessary to make each number sentence true.

(53) **3 2** x 10 = 3.2

(54) **3 5** x 8 = 0.28

(55) 1.45 x 7 = **1 0 1 5**

(56) **2 1 2** x 5 = 1.06

(57) 5 ÷ 2 = **2 5**

(58) 5.1 ÷ 4 = **1 2 7 5**

(59) **9 1 3** ÷ 4 = 2.2825

(60) **1 3 6** ÷ 8 = 0.017

Estimate the answer to each question. Complete only those questions with an estimated answer between 5 and 10.

(61)
$$\begin{array}{r} 1.98 \\ \times \quad 3 \\ \hline \end{array}$$

(62)
$$\begin{array}{r} 3.19 \\ \times \quad 5 \\ \hline \end{array}$$

(63)
$$\begin{array}{r} 0.89 \\ \times \quad 6 \\ \hline \end{array}$$

(64)
$$\begin{array}{r} 3.99 \\ \times \quad 4 \\ \hline \end{array}$$

(65)
$$\begin{array}{r} 0.72 \\ \times \quad 8 \\ \hline \end{array}$$

(66)
$$\begin{array}{r} 0.71 \\ \times \quad 9 \\ \hline \end{array}$$

(67)
$$3\overline{)19.86}$$

(68)
$$5\overline{)23.45}$$

(69)
$$8\overline{)55.12}$$

4 Fractions

- representing, comparing, and ordering fractions

Follow the steps below to compare fractions with different denominators.

1. Find their common denominator.

2. Write equivalent fractions.*

3. The one with a greater numerator is greater.

* If the fraction is a mixed number, change it to an improper fraction before finding the equivalent fraction.

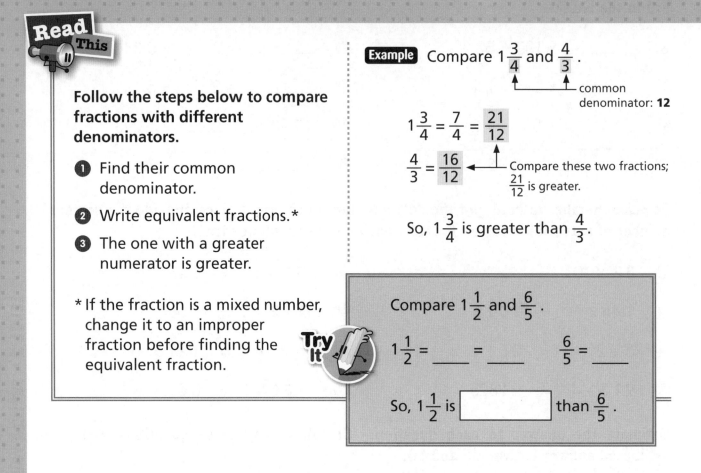

Example Compare $1\frac{3}{4}$ and $\frac{4}{3}$.

common denominator: **12**

$$1\frac{3}{4} = \frac{7}{4} = \frac{21}{12}$$

$$\frac{4}{3} = \frac{16}{12}$$

Compare these two fractions; $\frac{21}{12}$ is greater.

So, $1\frac{3}{4}$ is greater than $\frac{4}{3}$.

Try It

Compare $1\frac{1}{2}$ and $\frac{6}{5}$.

$$1\frac{1}{2} = \underline{\qquad} = \underline{\qquad} \qquad \frac{6}{5} = \underline{\qquad}$$

So, $1\frac{1}{2}$ is $\boxed{}$ than $\frac{6}{5}$.

Compare each pair of fractions in two ways: using diagrams and using equivalent fractions. Write "<" or ">" in the circles.

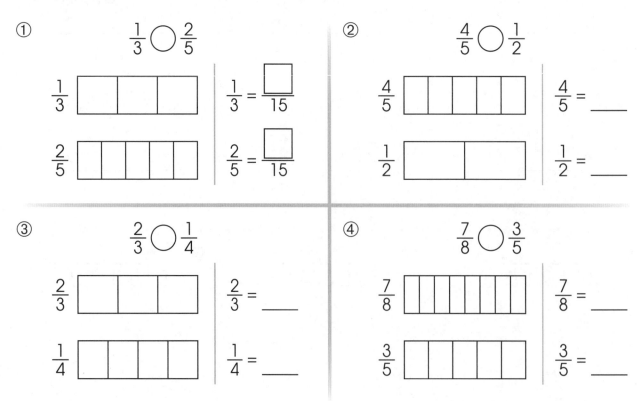

① $\frac{1}{3} \bigcirc \frac{2}{5}$

$\frac{1}{3}$

$\frac{2}{5}$

$\frac{1}{3} = \frac{\square}{15}$

$\frac{2}{5} = \frac{\square}{15}$

② $\frac{4}{5} \bigcirc \frac{1}{2}$

$\frac{4}{5}$

$\frac{1}{2}$

$\frac{4}{5} = \underline{\qquad}$

$\frac{1}{2} = \underline{\qquad}$

③ $\frac{2}{3} \bigcirc \frac{1}{4}$

$\frac{2}{3}$

$\frac{1}{4}$

$\frac{2}{3} = \underline{\qquad}$

$\frac{1}{4} = \underline{\qquad}$

④ $\frac{7}{8} \bigcirc \frac{3}{5}$

$\frac{7}{8}$

$\frac{3}{5}$

$\frac{7}{8} = \underline{\qquad}$

$\frac{3}{5} = \underline{\qquad}$

SCAN IT!

Write each improper fraction as a mixed number in simplest form.
Then compare and write "<", ">", or "=" in the circles.

⑤ $\dfrac{10}{6} = $ _____

$\dfrac{28}{21} = $ _____

$\dfrac{10}{6}$ ◯ $\dfrac{28}{21}$

⑥ $\dfrac{22}{7} = $ _____

$\dfrac{37}{12} = $ _____

$\dfrac{22}{7}$ ◯ $\dfrac{37}{12}$

⑦ $\dfrac{20}{16} = $ _____

$\dfrac{38}{36} = $ _____

$\dfrac{20}{16}$ ◯ $\dfrac{38}{36}$

⑧ $\dfrac{29}{9} = $ _____

$\dfrac{23}{7} = $ _____

$\dfrac{29}{9}$ ◯ $\dfrac{23}{7}$

⑨ $\dfrac{9}{5} = $ _____

$\dfrac{11}{7} = $ _____

$\dfrac{9}{5}$ ◯ $\dfrac{11}{7}$

⑩ $\dfrac{19}{8} = $ _____

$\dfrac{23}{10} = $ _____

$\dfrac{19}{8}$ ◯ $\dfrac{23}{10}$

⑪ $\dfrac{9}{4}$ ◯ $\dfrac{17}{6}$

⑫ $\dfrac{8}{4}$ ◯ $\dfrac{4}{2}$

⑬ $\dfrac{4}{3}$ ◯ $\dfrac{10}{9}$

⑭ $\dfrac{40}{15}$ ◯ $2\dfrac{2}{3}$

⑮ $\dfrac{15}{20}$ ◯ $\dfrac{4}{3}$

⑯ $\dfrac{16}{10}$ ◯ $\dfrac{3}{2}$

⑰ $\dfrac{24}{7}$ ◯ $3\dfrac{3}{7}$

⑱ $\dfrac{22}{6}$ ◯ $\dfrac{14}{3}$

LEVEL 2 – FURTHER YOUR UNDERSTANDING

Put the fractions in order.

⑲ $\dfrac{6}{7}$ $\dfrac{6}{9}$ $\dfrac{6}{11}$ $\dfrac{6}{5}$

_____ < _____ < _____ < _____

⑳ $\dfrac{2}{5}$ $\dfrac{3}{7}$ $\dfrac{5}{8}$ $\dfrac{6}{4}$

_____ < _____ < _____ < _____

㉑ $2\dfrac{1}{2}$ $\dfrac{10}{8}$ $\dfrac{4}{3}$ $1\dfrac{6}{7}$

_____ > _____ > _____ > _____

㉒ $\dfrac{19}{8}$ $1\dfrac{3}{5}$ $\dfrac{12}{7}$ $\dfrac{20}{9}$

_____ > _____ > _____ > _____

㉓ $3\dfrac{1}{4}$ $\dfrac{16}{5}$ $\dfrac{19}{6}$ $\dfrac{10}{3}$

_____ < _____ < _____ < _____

㉔ $\dfrac{11}{4}$ $\dfrac{12}{3}$ $2\dfrac{5}{8}$ $\dfrac{15}{7}$

_____ > _____ > _____ > _____

Write the fractions as mixed numbers in simplest form. Then put them in order from smallest to greatest and write the letters to find out what the boy says.

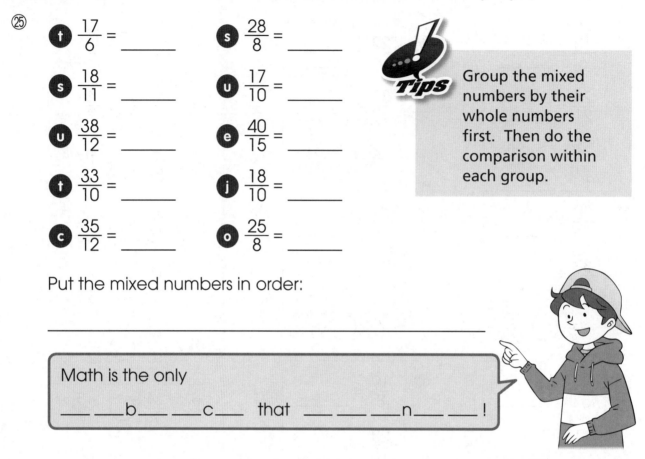

㉕

(t) $\frac{17}{6}$ = _____   (s) $\frac{28}{8}$ = _____

(s) $\frac{18}{11}$ = _____   (u) $\frac{17}{10}$ = _____

(u) $\frac{38}{12}$ = _____   (e) $\frac{40}{15}$ = _____

(t) $\frac{33}{10}$ = _____   (j) $\frac{18}{10}$ = _____

(c) $\frac{35}{12}$ = _____   (o) $\frac{25}{8}$ = _____

Tips Group the mixed numbers by their whole numbers first. Then do the comparison within each group.

Put the mixed numbers in order:

_____

Math is the only

___ ___b___ ___c___ that ___ ___ ___n___ ___ !

Cross out the set of fractions that is not listed in order from smallest to greatest. Then reorder it in the box.

㉖

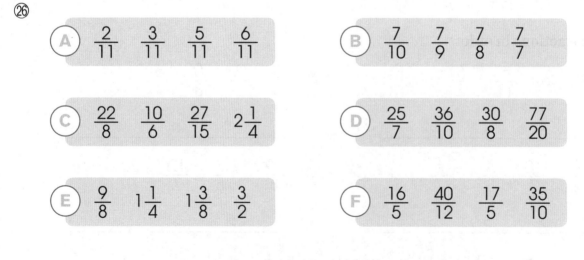

(A) $\frac{2}{11}$ $\frac{3}{11}$ $\frac{5}{11}$ $\frac{6}{11}$

(B) $\frac{7}{10}$ $\frac{7}{9}$ $\frac{7}{8}$ $\frac{7}{7}$

(C) $\frac{22}{8}$ $\frac{10}{6}$ $\frac{27}{15}$ $2\frac{1}{4}$

(D) $\frac{25}{7}$ $\frac{36}{10}$ $\frac{30}{8}$ $\frac{77}{20}$

(E) $\frac{9}{8}$ $1\frac{1}{4}$ $1\frac{3}{8}$ $\frac{3}{2}$

(F) $\frac{16}{5}$ $\frac{40}{12}$ $\frac{17}{5}$ $\frac{35}{10}$

the reordered set (smallest to greatest)

Find the sum of the fractions with the help of the diagrams.

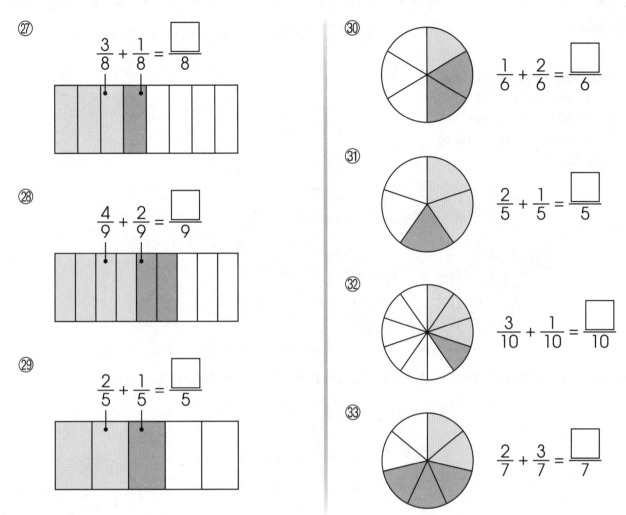

㉗ $\dfrac{3}{8} + \dfrac{1}{8} = \dfrac{\square}{8}$

㉚ $\dfrac{1}{6} + \dfrac{2}{6} = \dfrac{\square}{6}$

㉘ $\dfrac{4}{9} + \dfrac{2}{9} = \dfrac{\square}{9}$

㉛ $\dfrac{2}{5} + \dfrac{1}{5} = \dfrac{\square}{5}$

㉙ $\dfrac{2}{5} + \dfrac{1}{5} = \dfrac{\square}{5}$

㉜ $\dfrac{3}{10} + \dfrac{1}{10} = \dfrac{\square}{10}$

㉝ $\dfrac{2}{7} + \dfrac{3}{7} = \dfrac{\square}{7}$

Colour and cross out the parts to do the subtraction.

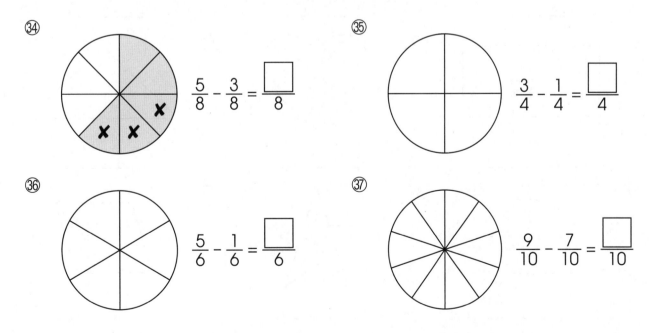

㉞ $\dfrac{5}{8} - \dfrac{3}{8} = \dfrac{\square}{8}$

㉟ $\dfrac{3}{4} - \dfrac{1}{4} = \dfrac{\square}{4}$

㊱ $\dfrac{5}{6} - \dfrac{1}{6} = \dfrac{\square}{6}$

㊲ $\dfrac{9}{10} - \dfrac{7}{10} = \dfrac{\square}{10}$

5 Percents

• estimating using percents

Read This

Benchmark percents are 10%, 25%, 50%, 75%, and 100%. They are helpful when estimating quantities.

Example Estimate using benchmark percents.

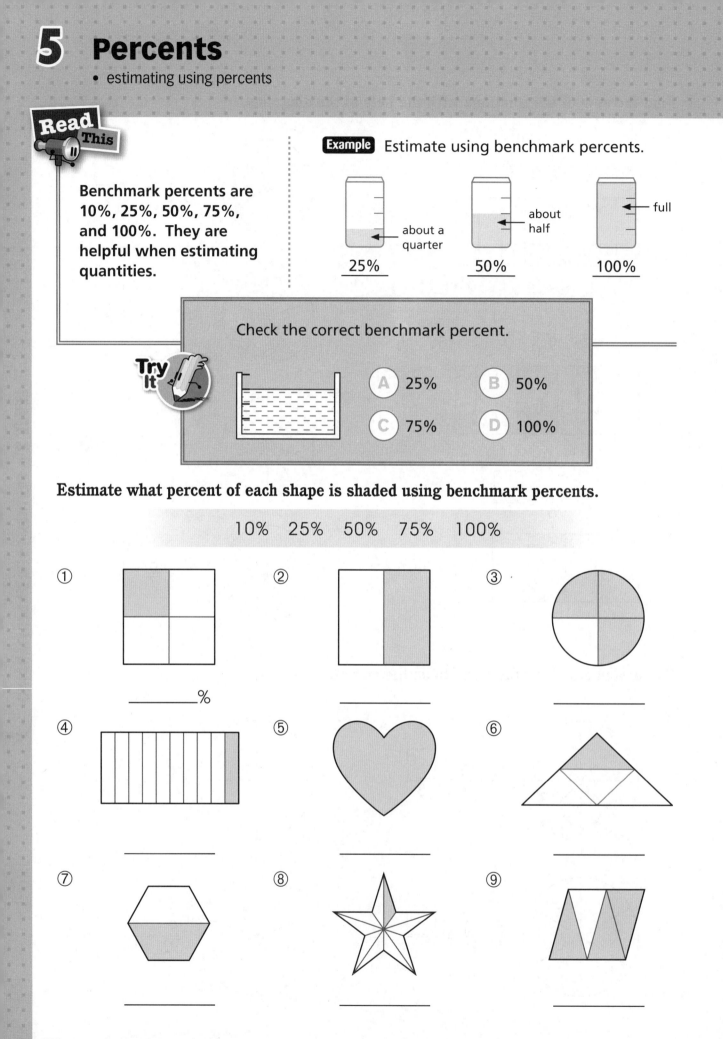

about a quarter
25%

about half
50%

full
100%

Try It

Check the correct benchmark percent.

A) 25%   B) 50%
C) 75%   D) 100%

Estimate what percent of each shape is shaded using benchmark percents.

10%   25%   50%   75%   100%

① _____%

②

③

④

⑤

⑥

⑦

⑧

⑨

Look at the shaded section of each circle and match it with a percent. Write the letter.

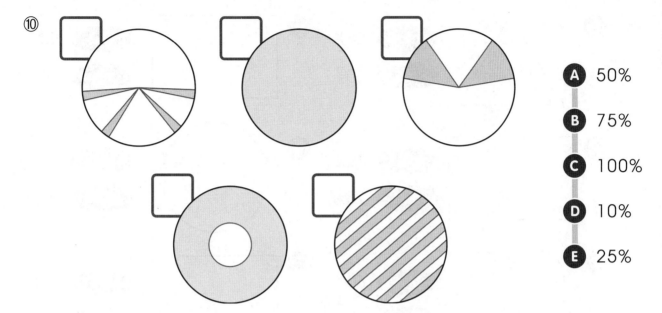

A 50%

B 75%

C 100%

D 10%

E 25%

Circle to estimate how full each container is.

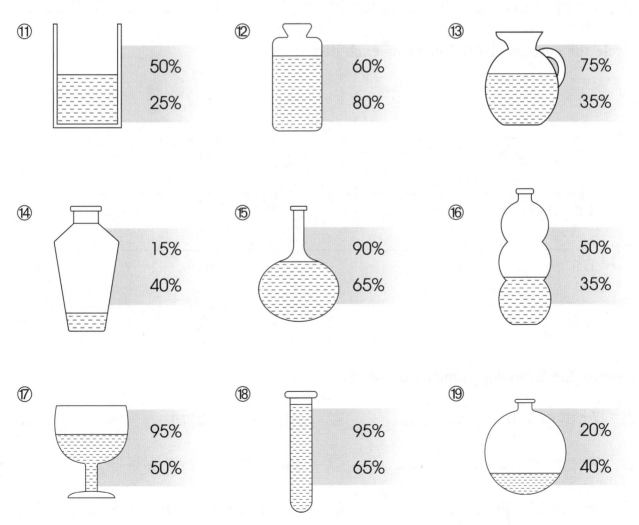

⑪ 50% 25%

⑫ 60% 80%

⑬ 75% 35%

⑭ 15% 40%

⑮ 90% 65%

⑯ 50% 35%

⑰ 95% 50%

⑱ 95% 65%

⑲ 20% 40%

Colour the shapes with the correct colours. Then answer the question.

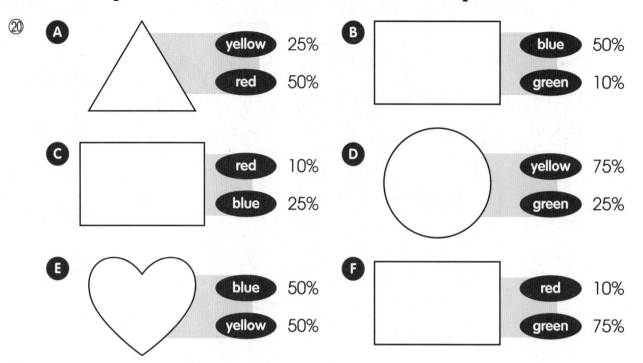

㉠ **A**   yellow 25%   red 50%

B   blue 50%   green 10%

C   red 10%   blue 25%

D   yellow 75%   green 25%

E   blue 50%   yellow 50%

F   red 10%   green 75%

㉑   Which shapes are 100% coloured?   _____

Circle the correct "100%" mark on each line.

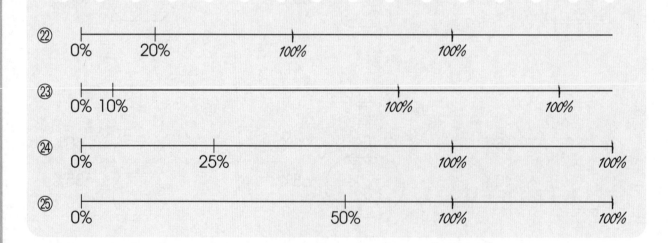

㉒   0%   20%   100%   100%

㉓   0% 10%   100%   100%

㉔   0%   25%   100%   100%

㉕   0%   50%   100%   100%

Rewrite the following percents using "%".

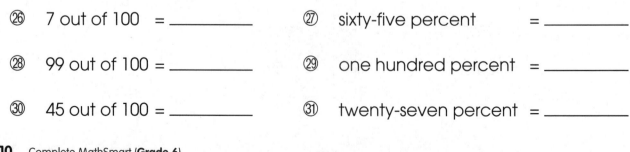

㉖   7 out of 100   = _____

㉗   sixty-five percent   = _____

㉘   99 out of 100 = _____

㉙   one hundred percent   = _____

㉚   45 out of 100 = _____

㉛   twenty-seven percent   = _____

Answer the questions.

㉜ There are 72 boys and 28 girls in the school yard. What percent of the students are girls? _____

㉝ 60 out of 100 participants are female. What percent is this? _____

㉞ 47 out of 100 students are girls.

a. What percent of the students are girls? _____

b. What percent of the students are not girls? _____

㉟ 38 students have a computer at home and 62 do not.

a. What percent of the students have a computer? _____

b. What percent of the students do not have a computer? _____

㊱ All the clothes in a shop are sold at a 40% discount. What percent of the original price do you pay? _____

㊲ A bicycle is sold at 55% of the original price. What is the discount in percent? _____

㊳ 10 out of 50 apples in the basket are red. What percent of the apples are red? _____

㊴ In a photo album, 37% of the pictures were taken in Canada; 28% of the pictures were taken indoors; 13% of the pictures were taken in summer.

a. What percent of the pictures were taken outside of Canada? _____

b. What percent were taken outdoors? _____

c. What percent were not taken in summer? _____

- converting fractions, decimals, and percents

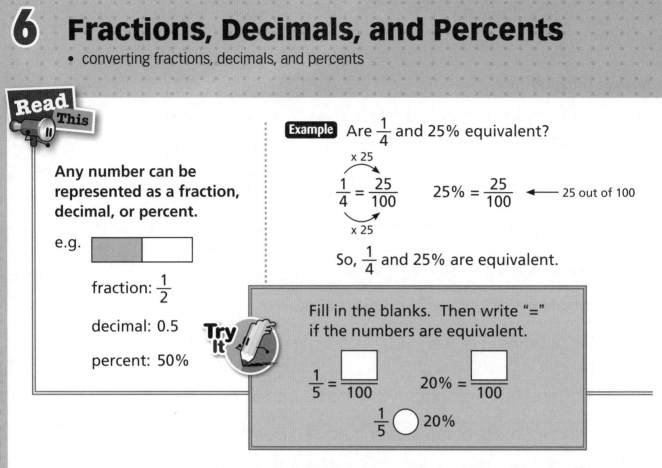

Read This

Any number can be represented as a fraction, decimal, or percent.

e.g.

fraction: $\frac{1}{2}$

decimal: 0.5

percent: 50%

Example Are $\frac{1}{4}$ and 25% equivalent?

$$\frac{1}{4} = \frac{25}{100} \qquad 25\% = \frac{25}{100} \longleftarrow 25 \text{ out of } 100$$

x 25

So, $\frac{1}{4}$ and 25% are equivalent.

Try It

Fill in the blanks. Then write "=" if the numbers are equivalent.

$$\frac{1}{5} = \frac{\boxed{}}{100} \qquad 20\% = \frac{\boxed{}}{100}$$

$$\frac{1}{5} \bigcirc 20\%$$

Read the tips for converting fractions, decimals, and percents. Then do the conversions.

① **fraction to decimal**

Divide the numerator by the denominator.

$\frac{1}{2} = 0.5 \longleftarrow 1 \div 2 = 0.5$

decimal to fraction

Drop the decimal point and write as a numerator with a denominator of 10, 100, etc., depending on how many 0s are in the decimal.

$0.5 = \frac{5}{10} = \frac{1}{2}$

fraction	decimal
$\frac{1}{5}$	
$\frac{3}{4}$	
	0.25
	0.4

② **decimal to percent**

Move the decimal point 2 places to the right. Add "%".

$0.5 = 50\%$

percent to decimal

Drop the "%". Move the decimal point 2 places to the left.

$50\% = 0.5$

decimal	percent
0.15	
0.2	
	40%
	65%

③ **percent to fraction**

Drop the "%" and write as a numerator with a denominator of 100. Then simplify.

$50\% = \frac{50}{100} = \frac{1}{2}$

fraction to percent

Convert the fraction to a decimal. Then convert the decimal to a percent.

$\frac{1}{2} = 0.5 = 50\%$

percent	fraction
40%	
10%	
	$\frac{3}{5}$
	$\frac{7}{10}$

Describe the shaded parts of each diagram as a fraction, decimal, and percent.

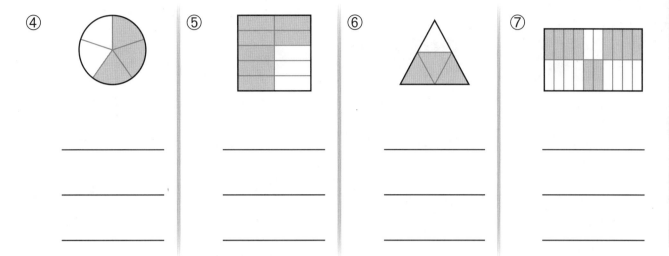

④   ⑤   ⑥   ⑦

_____   _____   _____   _____

_____   _____   _____   _____

_____   _____   _____   _____

Write each number in the form specified.

⑧

Percent

a. $\frac{9}{10}$ ____%   b. 0.24 _____   c. 0.35 _____

d. 0.7 _____   e. $\frac{4}{5}$ _____   f. 0.3 _____

g. $\frac{3}{20}$ _____   h. 0.05 _____   i. $\frac{19}{25}$ _____

⑨

Decimal

a. $\frac{19}{100}$ _____   b. 18% _____   c. $\frac{3}{25}$ _____

d. 15% _____   e. $\frac{8}{25}$ _____   f. 60% _____

g. $\frac{7}{10}$ _____   h. 8% _____   i. $\frac{4}{200}$ _____

⑩

Fraction

a. 0.55 _____   b. 35% _____   c. 0.6 _____

d. 70% _____   e. 0.28 _____   f. 40% _____

g. 0.85 _____   h. 60% _____   i. 5% _____

Complete the table. Then match each diagram with the set of numbers it represents. Write the letter.

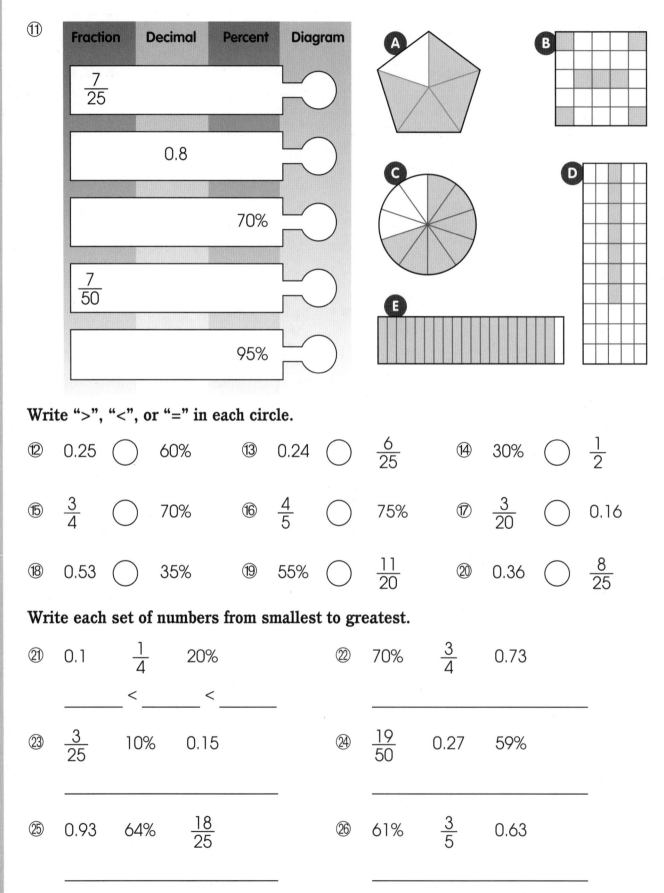

⑪

Fraction	Decimal	Percent	Diagram
$\frac{7}{25}$			◯
	0.8		◯
		70%	◯
$\frac{7}{50}$			◯
		95%	◯

A   B   C   D   E

Write ">", "<", or "=" in each circle.

⑫ 0.25 ◯ 60%

⑬ 0.24 ◯ $\frac{6}{25}$

⑭ 30% ◯ $\frac{1}{2}$

⑮ $\frac{3}{4}$ ◯ 70%

⑯ $\frac{4}{5}$ ◯ 75%

⑰ $\frac{3}{20}$ ◯ 0.16

⑱ 0.53 ◯ 35%

⑲ 55% ◯ $\frac{11}{20}$

⑳ 0.36 ◯ $\frac{8}{25}$

Write each set of numbers from smallest to greatest.

㉑ 0.1 $\frac{1}{4}$ 20%

_____ < _____ < _____

㉒ 70% $\frac{3}{4}$ 0.73

_____

㉓ $\frac{3}{25}$ 10%   0.15

_____

㉔ $\frac{19}{50}$ 0.27   59%

_____

㉕ 0.93   64% $\frac{18}{25}$

_____

㉖ 61% $\frac{3}{5}$ 0.63

_____

Each pair of numbers represents a range. Write the correct number from the set between each pair.

㉗

| 0.96 | 0.55 | 0.86 | 0.25 | 0.8 | 0.08 |

a. $\frac{1}{2}$ _____ 70%

b. 90% _____ $\frac{4}{5}$

c. 85% _____ $\frac{3}{4}$

d. $\frac{1}{10}$ _____ 30%

e. $\frac{5}{100}$ _____ 10%

f. 99% _____ $\frac{9}{10}$

㉘

| 7% | 78% | 26% | 52% | 86% | 11% |

a. 0.13 _____ $\frac{2}{5}$

b. 0.8 _____ $\frac{3}{4}$

c. $\frac{4}{5}$ _____ 0.92

d. $\frac{2}{3}$ _____ 0.45

e. $\frac{2}{25}$ _____ 0.2

f. $\frac{1}{20}$ _____ 0.09

㉙

| $\frac{3}{20}$ | $\frac{23}{25}$ | $\frac{1}{4}$ | $\frac{7}{10}$ | $\frac{4}{5}$ | $\frac{18}{25}$ |

a. 20% _____ 0.1

b. 0.8 _____ 95%

c. 0.7 _____ 80%

d. 0.3 _____ 20%

e. 72% _____ 68%

f. 73% _____ 0.9

Circle "T" for the true statements and "F" for the false ones.

㉚ 100% is equivalent to 1. T / F

㉛ The only percent that is greater than 99% is 100%. T / F

㉜ 100% is greater than 2. T / F

7 Ratios

- solving problems with ratios

Read This

The order of the terms in a ratio is important because it represents the order of the items listed.

Example Jerry has 5 markers and 8 crayons. What is the ratio of markers to crayons?

$$\underset{\text{1st term}}{\underline{\text{markers}}} \text{ to } \underset{\text{2nd term}}{\underline{\text{crayons}}} = \underset{\text{1st term}}{\underline{\textbf{5}}} \text{ to } \underset{\text{2nd term}}{\underline{\textbf{8}}}$$

So, the ratio is 5:8.

Try It

There are 3 apples and 9 oranges. What is the ratio of apples to oranges?

A 3 to 1   **B** $\frac{1}{3}$ **C** 9:3

Write each ratio in two other forms.

① $\frac{3}{4}$ ___ to ___   ___ : ___   ② 1:2   _____ _____

③ 3 to 5 _____ _____   ④ 6:5   _____ _____

⑤ 7:2 _____ _____   ⑥ 8 to 5 _____ _____

Write two equivalent ratios for each given ratio.

⑦ 5:7   ___ : ___   ___ : ___   ⑧ 4:9   _____ _____

⑨ 10:15 _____ _____   ⑩ 12:20 _____ _____

⑪ 9:6 _____ _____   ⑫ 30:24 _____ _____

Write each ratio in simplest form.

⑬ 14:21 _____   ⑭ 75:25 _____

⑮ 20:80 _____   ⑯ 85:15 _____

⑰ 28:72 _____   ⑱ 32:48 _____

Hints

To write a ratio in simplest form, divide both terms by the same number until their common factor is 1.

Lucy has a sheet of stickers. Find the ratios in simplest form and answer the questions.

⑲ Find the ratios.

a. pig:fish _____

b. monkey:giraffe _____

c. fish:giraffe _____

d. pig:monkey _____

e. monkey:fish _____

f. fish:monkey _____

g. pig:giraffe _____

h. monkey:pig _____

i. fish:pig _____

j. pig:all _____

k. fish:all _____

l. giraffe:all _____

⑳ If Lucy trades 1 pig sticker and 2 monkey stickers for 1 fish sticker and 2 giraffe stickers, what will the new ratios be?

a. pig:fish _____   b. monkey:giraffe _____

c. fish:monkey _____   d. pig:giraffe _____

㉑ If Lucy uses the last 2 rows of the sticker sheet, what will the ratios for the remaining stickers be?

a. pig:giraffe _____   b. fish:giraffe _____

c. monkey:all _____   d. giraffe:all _____

Match each group of items with the correct ratio. Write the letter in the circle.

Tips

Remember that a ratio shows a comparison between quantities. It does not indicate the exact quantities.

e.g. ● to ▲ = __2:1__

The ratio "2:1" means that there are 2 circles for every 1 triangle present.

㉒

A

B

C

D

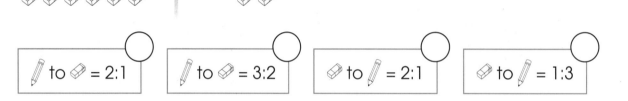

✎ to ▱ = 2:1   ✎ to ▱ = 3:2   ▱ to ✎ = 2:1   ▱ to ✎ = 1:3

Complete the ratios. Then answer the questions.

㉓

rice		water
1	:	2
2	:	
3	:	
4	:	
5	:	
6	:	
7	:	
8	:	

a. What is the ratio of water to rice in simplest form? _____

b. How many cups of water are needed to cook

   • 3 cups of rice? _____

   • 6 cups of rice? _____

   • 8 cups of rice? _____

c. Helen wants to cook 10 cups of rice. How much water is needed? _____

d. Jody used 18 cups of water to cook some rice. How many cups of rice did she cook? _____

e. What is the ratio of rice to the mixture of water and rice? _____

Answer the questions. Write the answers in simplest form.

㉔ In a bag, there are 8 red balls, 4 green balls, and 12 yellow balls.

  a. What is the ratio of

  • red balls to green balls? _____

  • green balls to yellow balls? _____

  • red balls to yellow balls? _____

  • green balls to all balls? _____

  b. If 2 red balls are taken out and 4 green balls are added, what is the ratio of

  • red balls to green balls? _____

  • green balls to yellow balls? _____

  • red balls to yellow balls? _____

  • green balls to all balls? _____

Tips

Draw pictures to illustrate the problem to help yourself visualize it.

㉕ There are 4 girls, 6 boys, and 5 adults in a park.

  a. What is the ratio of

  • girls to boys? _____

  • boys to adults? _____

  • children to adults? _____

  • adults to all? _____

  b. 1 girl and 1 boy left the park, and 3 adults arrived. What is the ratio of

  • girls to boys? _____

  • boys to adults? _____

  • children to adults? _____

  • adults to all? _____

8 Rates

• comparing rates

A rate is a ratio that compares the quantities of different units of measure. A unit rate compares the amount to its unit of measure.

e.g $5/book ◄——

1 book costs $5.

Example Store A sells 3 cookies for $3.99 while Store B sells 4 cookies for $5.20. Which is the better buy?

Store A: $3.99 ÷ 3 cookies = $1.33/cookie
Store B: $5.20 ÷ 4 cookies = $1.30/cookie ◄— costs less

So, Store B is the better buy.

Try It

Store C sells 5 cookies for $6.55. Does Store C offer the best buy?

Store C: $_____ / cookie

Store C _____ offer the best buy.
does/does not

Find the unit prices for the items. Then check the better buy.

Better Buy

① **Store A:** 3 for $1.74

_____ ÷ _____ = _____ $_____ /notebook ◯

Store B: 5 for $2.85

_____ ÷ _____ = _____   _____ ◯

② **Store A:** 2 for $2.40

_____ ÷ _____ = _____   _____ ◯

Store B: 4 for $9.60

_____ ÷ _____ = _____   _____ ◯

③ **Store A:** 3 for $6.30

_____ ÷ _____ = _____   _____ ◯

Store B: 2 for $4.30

_____ ÷ _____ = _____   _____ ◯

④ **Store A:** 5 for $27.95

_____ ÷ _____ = _____   _____ ◯

Store B: 4 for $22.40

_____ ÷ _____ = _____   _____ ◯

Find the unit price for each quantity. Round to the nearest cent if necessary. Then check for the better buy.

⑤

		Total Cost	Unit Price	Better Buy
A		3 cartons for $7.78	$_____ /carton	◯
		4 cartons for $10.48		◯
B		2 pots for $4.25		◯
		3 pots for $6.35		◯
C		3 cups for $8.97		◯
		5 cups for $13.75		◯
D		6 bars for $5.35		◯
		10 bars for $8.55		◯

Find the unit prices. Then answer the question.

⑥

	Store A	Store B	Store C
Drumsticks	3 kg for $19.80 $_____ /kg	4 kg for $25.80 _____	5 kg for $34.25 _____
Water	3 bottles for $3.57 _____	4 bottles for $5 _____	2 bottles for $2.84 _____
Cup Noodles	5 cups for $3.95 _____	2 cups for $1.36 _____	3 cups for $2.67 _____

⑦ Which store offers the best buy for each item?

drumsticks: Store _____   **water**: Store _____   **noodles**: Store _____

Answer the questions about rates. Show your work. Round your answers to the nearest hundredth if necessary.

⑧ Sue's hair grows 1.66 cm in 2 months. How long does it grow in 5 months?

> unit rate

_____ ÷ _____ = _____

> hair growth in 5 months

_____ x _____ = _____

It grows _____ cm in 5 months.

⑨ Peggy saves $62.50 in 5 weeks. How much does she save in 3 weeks?

> unit rate

_____ ÷ _____ = _____

> savings in 3 weeks

_____ x _____ = _____

She saves $_____ in 3 weeks.

⑩ 4 L of gas costs $3. How much does 5 L of gas cost?

_____

⑪ Brenda buys 6 L of water for $4.26. How much does 10 L of water cost?

_____

⑫ 6 amusement park tickets cost $187. How much do 4 amusement park tickets cost?

_____

⑬ Jody charges $109.50 for 5 h of cleaning. How much does she charge for
a. 3 h?

_____

b. 6 h?

_____

Solve the problems. Show your work.

Allen's Boutique
3 for $29.55

4 for $38.56
Outfit Store

⑭ 3 T-shirts are sold for $29.55 at Allen's Boutique and 4 T-shirts are sold for $38.56 at Outfit Store. Which store has the better buy?

_____

⑮ Sheila can read 9 books in 12 days and Karen can read 5 books in 8 days. Who reads faster?

_____

⑯ 6 apples are sold for $5.88 and 4 oranges are sold for $3.04. Which fruit is more expensive?

_____

⑰ A carton of 12 eggs costs $4.44 and a carton of 18 eggs costs $6.84. Which carton is the better buy?

_____

⑱ Susan earns $71.25 for 5 h of babysitting. Bob earns $13.80/h for babysitting.

a. Who is better paid?

_____

Tips

Make sure the rates are in the same unit before you compare them.

b. Janet earns $7 for each 30 min of babysitting. Who is paid best?

_____

9 Perimeter and Area

• relating perimeter and area

Remember that perimeter is measured in units of length (cm, m, etc.) while area is measured in square units (cm², m², etc.).

Example Find the perimeter and area.

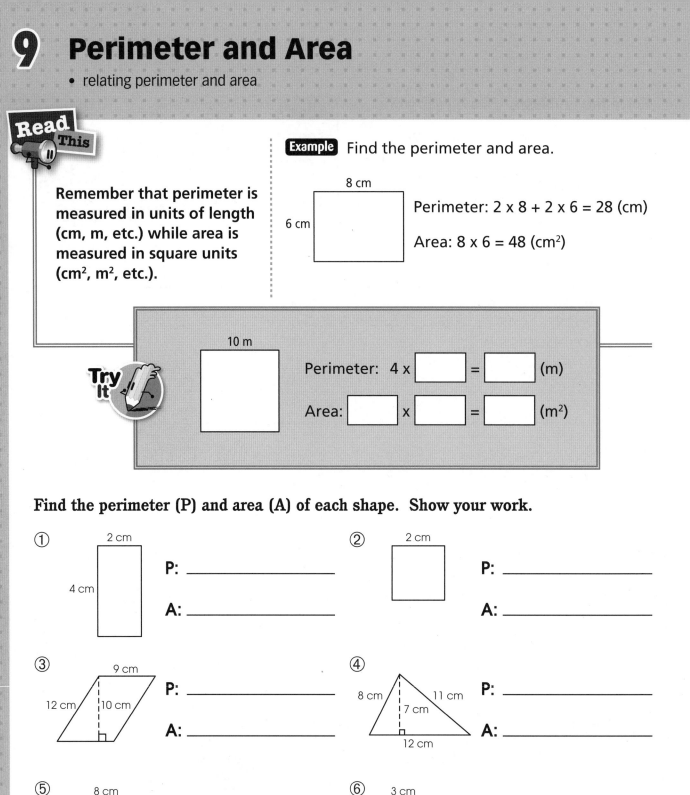

8 cm

6 cm

Perimeter: 2 x 8 + 2 x 6 = 28 (cm)

Area: 8 x 6 = 48 (cm²)

Try It

10 m

Perimeter: 4 x ☐ = ☐ (m)

Area: ☐ x ☐ = ☐ (m²)

Find the perimeter (P) and area (A) of each shape. Show your work.

① 2 cm

4 cm

P: _____

A: _____

② 2 cm

P: _____

A: _____

③ 9 cm

12 cm 10 cm

P: _____

A: _____

④ 8 cm   11 cm

7 cm

12 cm

P: _____

A: _____

⑤ 8 cm

P: _____

A: _____

⑥ 3 cm

7 cm   8.5 cm

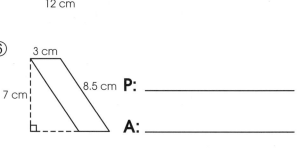

P: _____

A: _____

⑦

4 cm   6.5 cm

4.5 cm

3 cm

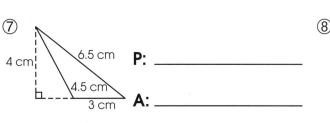

P: _____

A: _____

⑧ 0.5 cm

2 cm

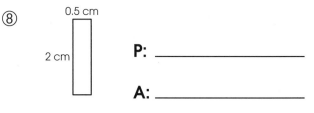

P: _____

A: _____

Find the perimeter and area of each shape. Complete the table.

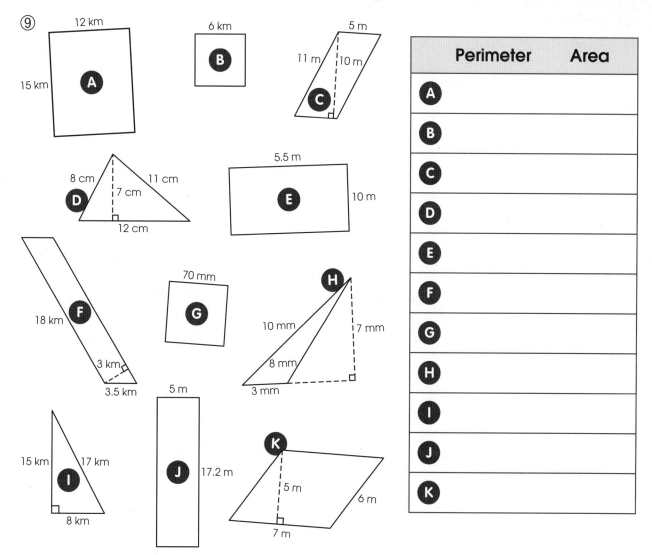

	Perimeter	Area
A		
B		
C		
D		
E		
F		
G		
H		
I		
J		
K		

With the given measurements of each shape, determine whether the perimeter, the area, or both can be found. Put a check mark in the circle and find the answer.

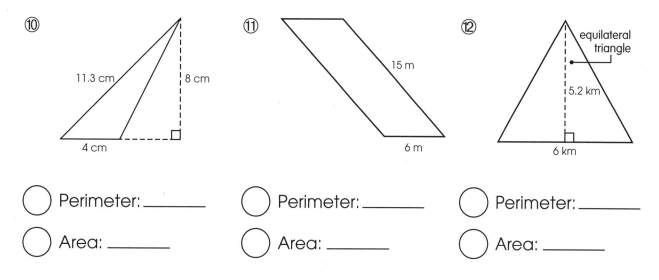

⑩ ◯ Perimeter:_____   ◯ Area: _____

⑪ ◯ Perimeter:_____   ◯ Area: _____

⑫ ◯ Perimeter:_____   ◯ Area: _____

Draw the shapes as specified. Then circle "T" for the true statements and "F" for the false ones.

⑬ Draw 3 different parallelograms, each with an area of 12 cm².

1 cm

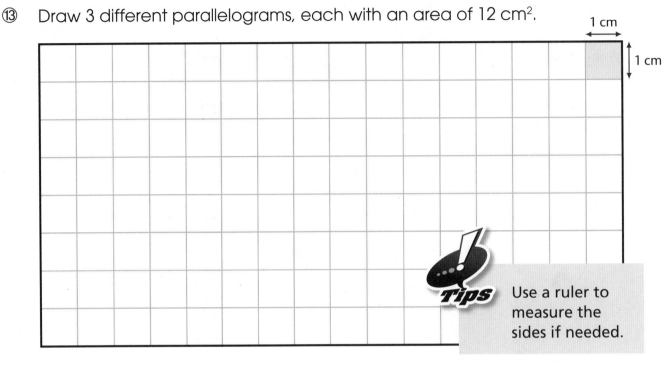

1 cm

Tips Use a ruler to measure the sides if needed.

a. There is only one way to draw a parallelogram with a given area. T / F

b. Parallelograms that have the same area must have the same perimeter. T / F

⑭ Draw 3 different triangles, each with a base of 6 cm and a height of 2 cm.

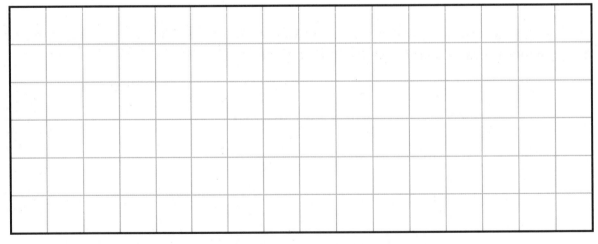

a. There is more than one way to draw a triangle with a given base and height. T / F

b. Triangles that have different perimeters must have different areas. T / F

Solve the problems. Show your work.

⑮ A rectangular field measures 8.5 m by 6 m.
   a. How many metres of fencing is needed to enclose the field?

   _____

   b. How many square metres of turf are needed to cover the whole field?

   _____

⑯ Sean has a poster with the dimensions of 27 cm by 21 cm and a baseball card with the dimensions of 9 cm by 7 cm. How many times is the poster as large as the card?

   _____

⑰ a. Calculate the area of the door.

   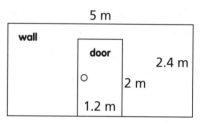

   _____

   b. Ava wants to paint the wall. Calculate the area of the wall that will be painted.

   _____

⑱ Antville is 13 km north of Beetown and Capeview is 20 km east of Beetown.

   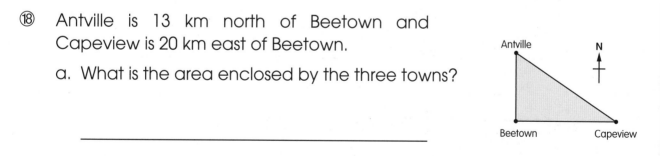

   a. What is the area enclosed by the three towns?

   _____

   b. The distance between Antville and Capeview is 24 km. If a route connecting the 3 towns is built as shown on the map, how long is the route?

   _____

10 Volume and Surface Area

• relating volume and surface area

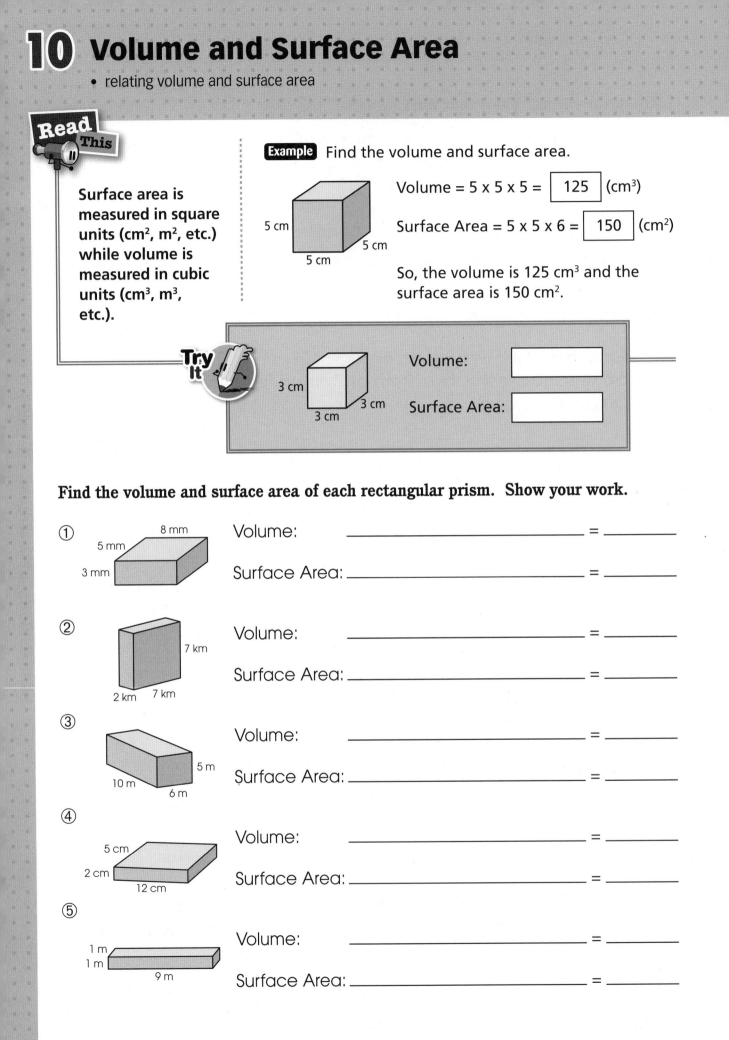

Read This

Surface area is measured in square units (cm², m², etc.) while volume is measured in cubic units (cm³, m³, etc.).

Example Find the volume and surface area.

5 cm
5 cm
5 cm

Volume = 5 x 5 x 5 = [125] (cm³)

Surface Area = 5 x 5 x 6 = [150] (cm²)

So, the volume is 125 cm³ and the surface area is 150 cm².

Try It

3 cm
3 cm
3 cm

Volume: [   ]

Surface Area: [   ]

Find the volume and surface area of each rectangular prism. Show your work.

① 8 mm, 5 mm, 3 mm

Volume: _____ = _____

Surface Area: _____ = _____

② 7 km, 2 km, 7 km

Volume: _____ = _____

Surface Area: _____ = _____

③ 5 m, 10 m, 6 m

Volume: _____ = _____

Surface Area: _____ = _____

④ 5 cm, 2 cm, 12 cm

Volume: _____ = _____

Surface Area: _____ = _____

⑤ 1 m, 1 m, 9 m

Volume: _____ = _____

Surface Area: _____ = _____

Find the volume and surface area of each triangular prism. Show your work.

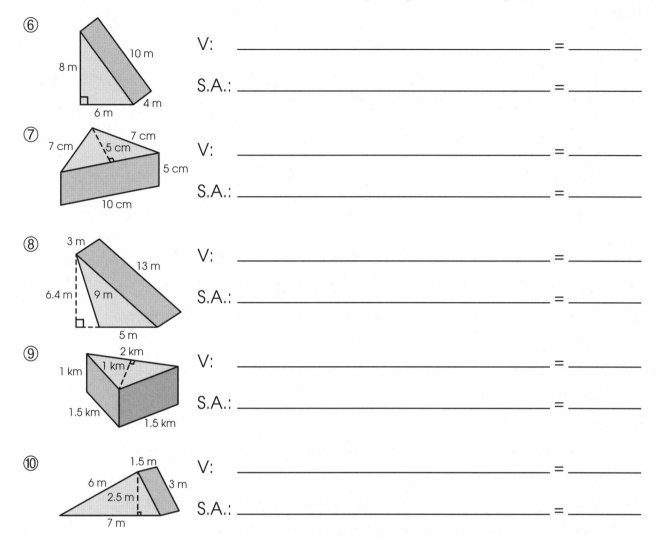

⑥

V: _____ = _____

S.A.: _____ = _____

⑦

V: _____ = _____

S.A.: _____ = _____

⑧

V: _____ = _____

S.A.: _____ = _____

⑨

V: _____ = _____

S.A.: _____ = _____

⑩

V: _____ = _____

S.A.: _____ = _____

Find the volume and surface area of each prism. Complete the table.

⑪

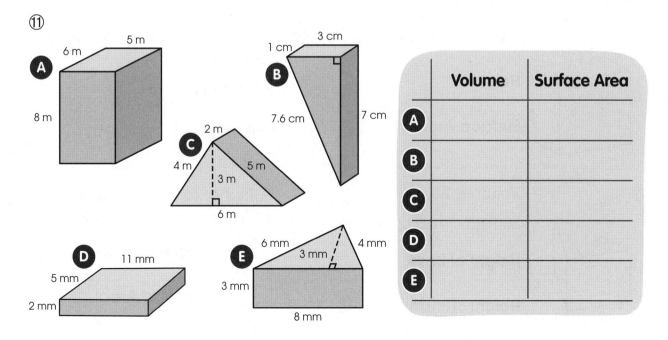

	Volume	Surface Area
A		
B		
C		
D		
E		

Find the volume and surface area of each prism. Then circle "T" for true and "F" for false.

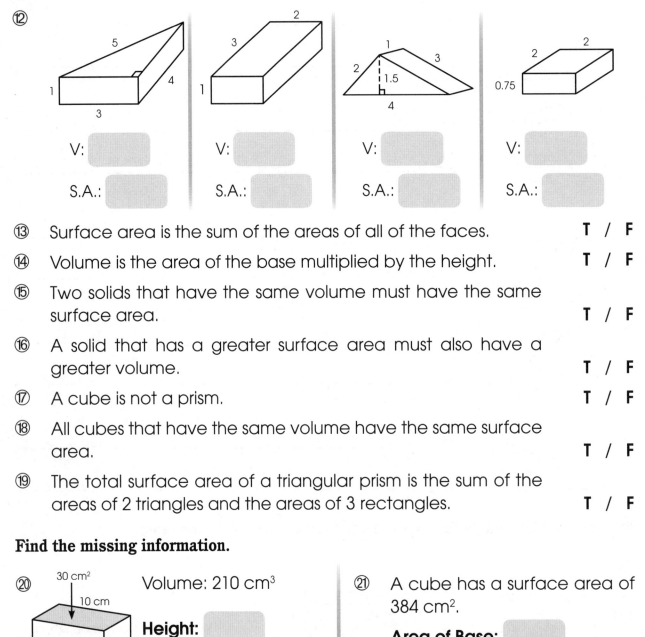

⑫

V: [ ]

S.A.: [ ]

V: [ ]

S.A.: [ ]

V: [ ]

S.A.: [ ]

V: [ ]

S.A.: [ ]

⑬ Surface area is the sum of the areas of all of the faces. **T / F**

⑭ Volume is the area of the base multiplied by the height. **T / F**

⑮ Two solids that have the same volume must have the same surface area. **T / F**

⑯ A solid that has a greater surface area must also have a greater volume. **T / F**

⑰ A cube is not a prism. **T / F**

⑱ All cubes that have the same volume have the same surface area. **T / F**

⑲ The total surface area of a triangular prism is the sum of the areas of 2 triangles and the areas of 3 rectangles. **T / F**

Find the missing information.

⑳ 30 cm² 10 cm

Volume: 210 cm³

Height: [ ]

Surface Area: [ ]

㉑ A cube has a surface area of 384 cm².

Area of Base: [ ]

Volume: [ ]

㉒ 27 cm² 7 cm 9 cm

Volume: 216 cm³

Surface Area: 246 cm²

Height of Base: [ ]

Height of Prism: [ ]

㉓ A triangular prism has a volume of 14 cm³. Its base is shown.

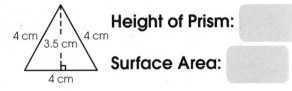

4 cm 3.5 cm 4 cm 4 cm

Height of Prism: [ ]

Surface Area: [ ]

Look at the measurements of each prism. Find the volume and surface area of the combined structures. Then answer the questions.

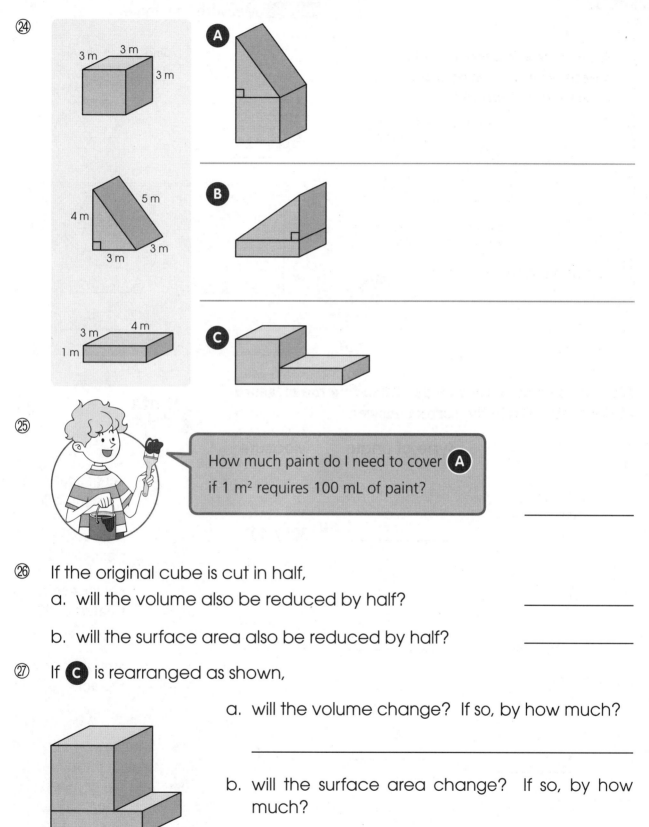

㉔

A

B

C

㉕ How much paint do I need to cover **A** if 1 m² requires 100 mL of paint?

_____

㉖ If the original cube is cut in half,

a. will the volume also be reduced by half? _____

b. will the surface area also be reduced by half? _____

㉗ If **C** is rearranged as shown,

a. will the volume change? If so, by how much?

_____

b. will the surface area change? If so, by how much?

_____

11 Angles

• measuring and drawing angles

A protractor is a tool used to measure angles. Angles are measured in degrees (°).

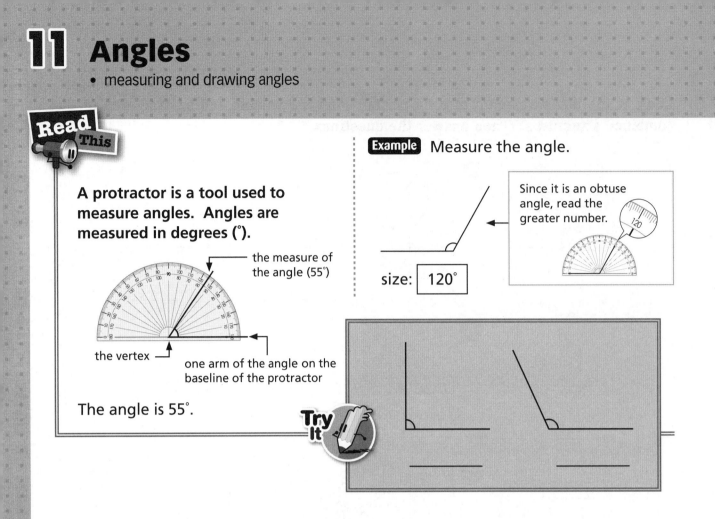

the measure of the angle (55°)

the vertex

one arm of the angle on the baseline of the protractor

The angle is 55°.

Example Measure the angle.

Since it is an obtuse angle, read the greater number.

size: 120°

Try It

Identify the type of each angle. Then find the measure of the angle. Circle the correct answer.

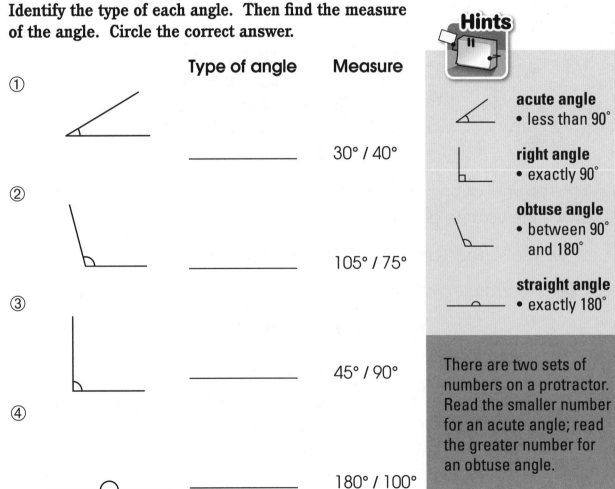

	Type of angle	Measure
①	_____	30° / 40°
②	_____	105° / 75°
③	_____	45° / 90°
④	_____	180° / 100°

Hints

acute angle
• less than 90°

right angle
• exactly 90°

obtuse angle
• between 90° and 180°

straight angle
• exactly 180°

There are two sets of numbers on a protractor. Read the smaller number for an acute angle; read the greater number for an obtuse angle.

Draw the angles using the given lines. Then write the letters to sort the angles.

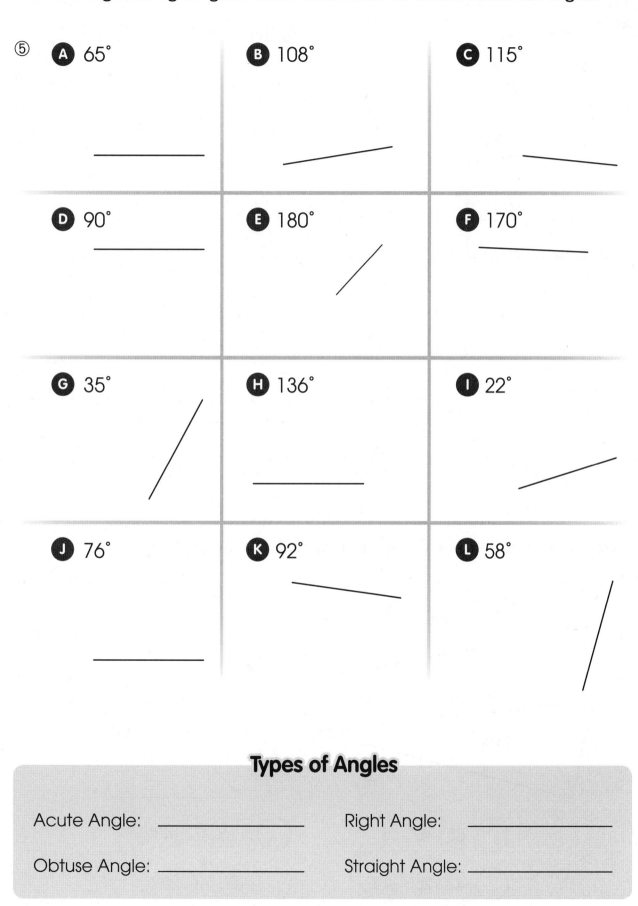

⑤ Ⓐ 65°   Ⓑ 108°   Ⓒ 115°

Ⓓ 90°   Ⓔ 180°   Ⓕ 170°

Ⓖ 35°   Ⓗ 136°   Ⓘ 22°

Ⓙ 76°   Ⓚ 92°   Ⓛ 58°

Types of Angles

Acute Angle: _____   Right Angle: _____

Obtuse Angle: _____   Straight Angle: _____

Measure and record the measures of the marked angles in each shape.

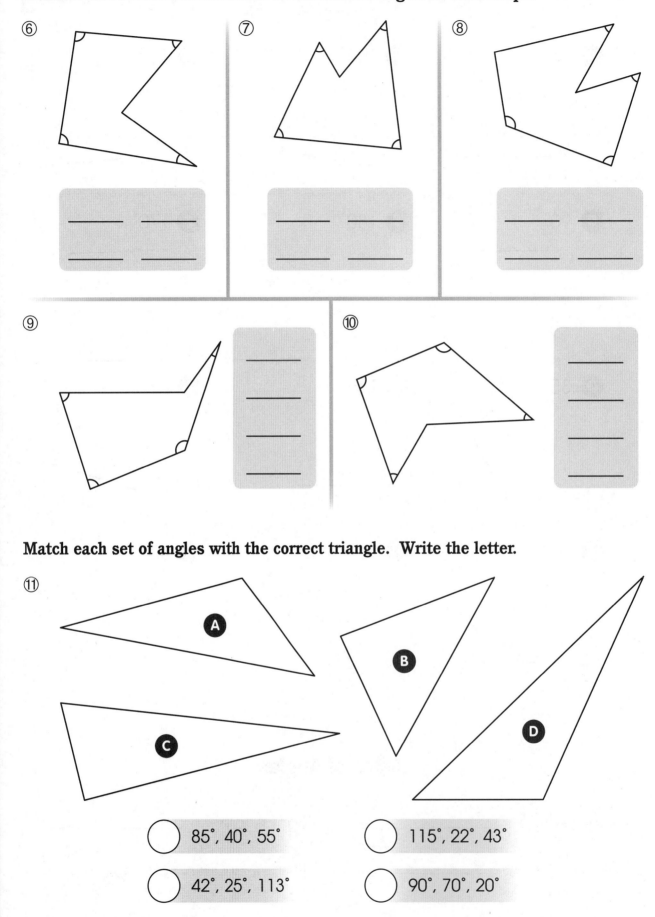

⑥

_____ _____

_____

⑦

_____ _____

_____

⑧

_____ _____

_____

⑨

_____

_____

_____

_____

⑩

_____

_____

_____

_____

Match each set of angles with the correct triangle. Write the letter.

⑪

Ⓐ

Ⓑ

Ⓒ

Ⓓ

◯ 85°, 40°, 55°   ◯ 115°, 22°, 43°

◯ 42°, 25°, 113°   ◯ 90°, 70°, 20°

Match the shapes with the descriptions. Write the letters.

⑫

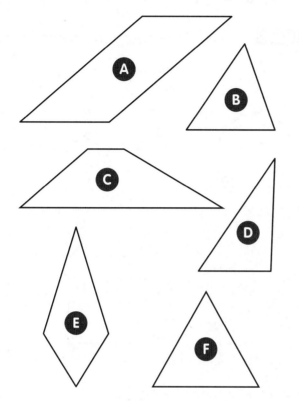

a. quadrilaterals with an angle of 40°:

_____

b. triangles with an angle of 55°:

_____

c. quadrilaterals with an angle greater than 125°:

_____

d. triangles with all angles less than 75°:

_____

Measure and record the measures of the angles. Then answer the question.

⑬

Angle a: _____

Angle m: _____

Angle n: _____

Sum of angles: _____

Angle x: _____

Angle y: _____

Angle z: _____

Sum of angles: _____

⑭ Compare Angle a with the sums of the other angles. What do you find?

_____

_____

12 Shapes
• sorting and drawing polygons

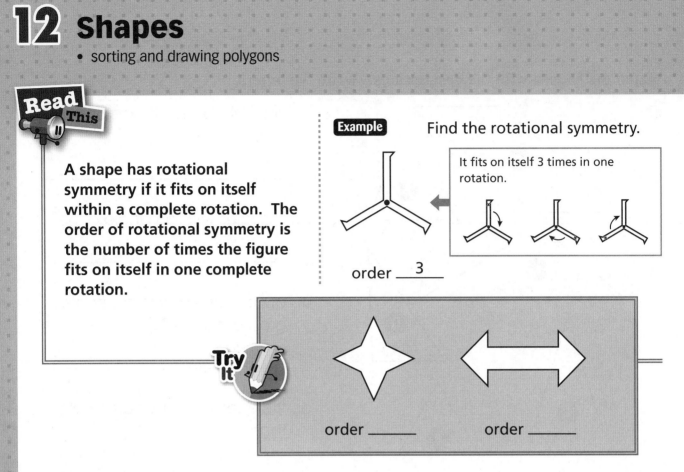

Read This

A shape has rotational symmetry if it fits on itself within a complete rotation. The order of rotational symmetry is the number of times the figure fits on itself in one complete rotation.

Example Find the rotational symmetry.

It fits on itself 3 times in one rotation.

order ___3___

Try It

order _____   order _____

Write the order of rotational symmetry for each shape in the circle.

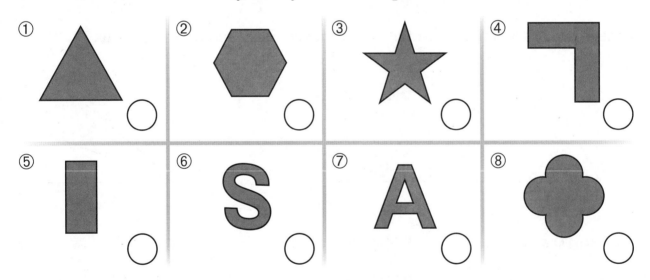

① ○

② ○

③ ○

④ ○

⑤ ○

⑥ S ○

⑦ A ○

⑧ ○

Complete the drawings to get the given order of rotational symmetry.

⑨ Order 2

⑩ Order 3

⑪ Order 4

Write the number of lines of symmetry for each shape.

⑫
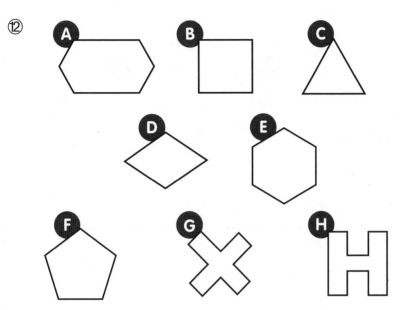

No. of Lines of Symmetry	
A _____	B _____
C _____	D _____
E _____	F _____
G _____	H _____

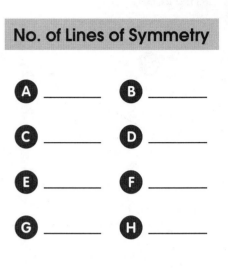

Use the lines of symmetry (dotted lines) to complete each shape.

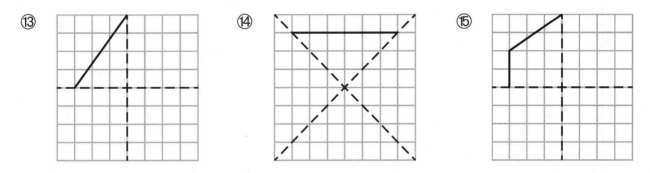

⑬   ⑭   ⑮

Write the number of lines of symmetry and the order of rotational symmetry for each shape.

⑯
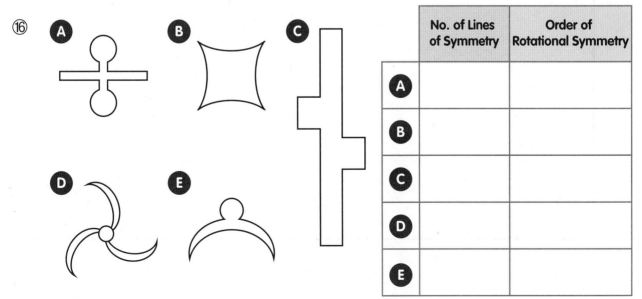

	No. of Lines of Symmetry	Order of Rotational Symmetry
A		
B		
C		
D		
E		

LEVEL 2 – FURTHER YOUR UNDERSTANDING

Draw the triangles with the given measurements on the centimetre grid using a protractor.

⑰

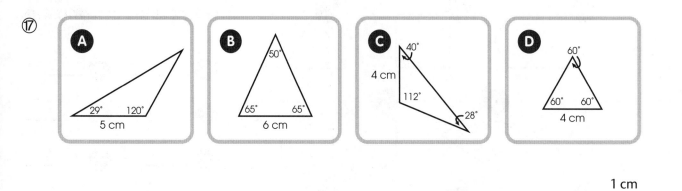

A
29° 120°
5 cm

B
50°
65° 65°
6 cm

C
40°
4 cm
112°
28°

D
60°
60° 60°
4 cm

1 cm

1 cm

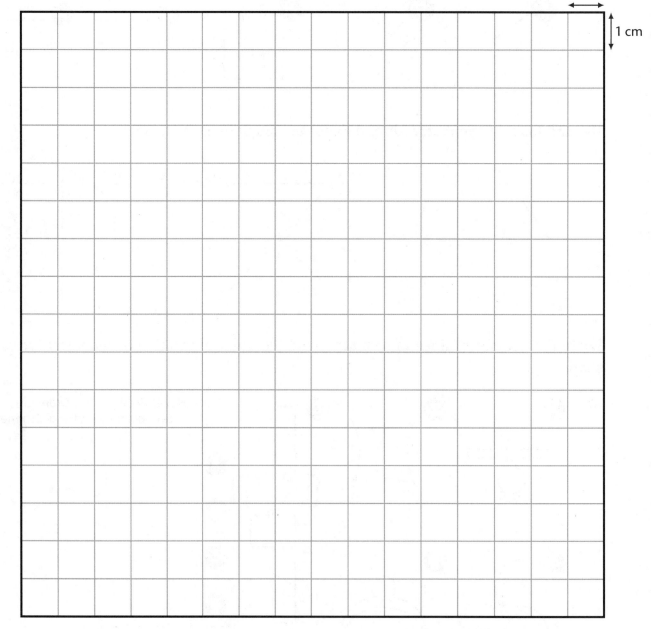

Draw the quadrilaterals with the given measurements using a protractor. Then answer the question.

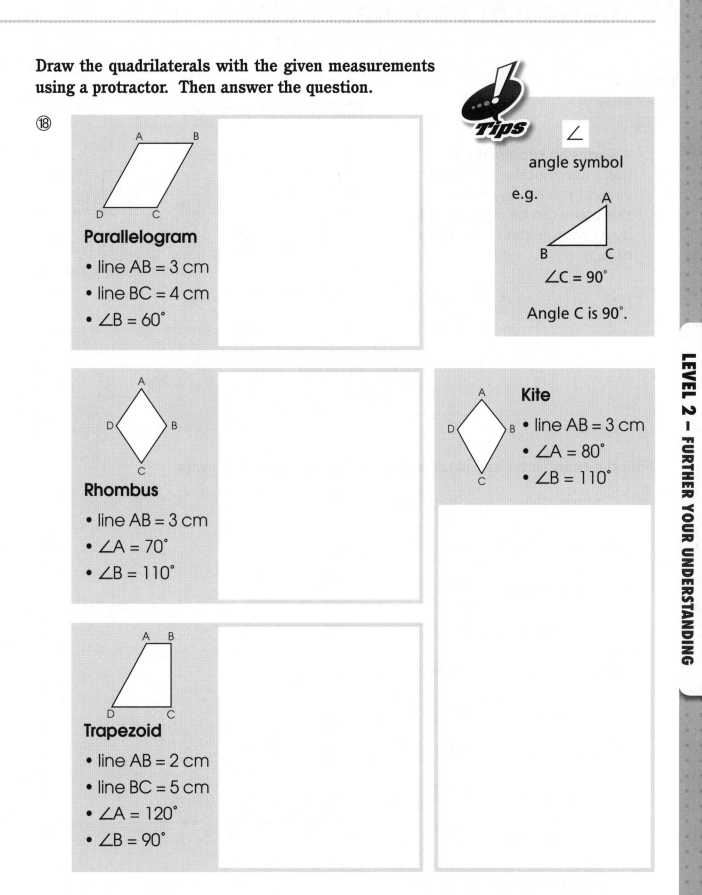

⑱

Parallelogram

- line AB = 3 cm
- line BC = 4 cm
- ∠B = 60°

Tips

∠

angle symbol

e.g.

∠C = 90°

Angle C is 90°.

Rhombus

- line AB = 3 cm
- ∠A = 70°
- ∠B = 110°

Kite

- line AB = 3 cm
- ∠A = 80°
- ∠B = 110°

Trapezoid

- line AB = 2 cm
- line BC = 5 cm
- ∠A = 120°
- ∠B = 90°

⑲ Measure and find the sum of the angles of each quadrilateral. What do you find?

_____

13 Cartesian Coordinate Plane

• describing location on a Cartesian coordinate plane

Read This

A Cartesian coordinate plane has a horizontal *x*-axis and a vertical *y*-axis. Any point on this plane can be represented by its coordinates in the form of (*x*,*y*).

$(x,y) = ($ | no. of units right | , | no. of units up | $)$

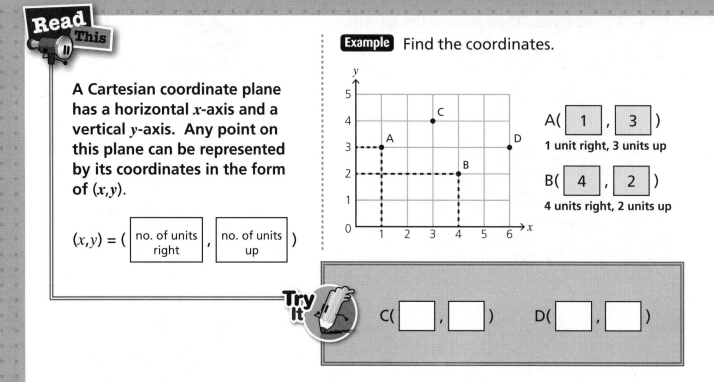

Example Find the coordinates.

A(1 , 3)
1 unit right, 3 units up

B(4 , 2)
4 units right, 2 units up

Try It

C(☐ , ☐)   D(☐ , ☐)

Find the coordinates and plot the points. Then write the answers.

① Coordinates of the Points

A(____ , ____)   S(5,8)

B _____   T(10,10)

C _____   U(1,6)

D _____   V(9,0)

E _____   W(3,11)

F _____   X(0,3)

G _____   Y(7,5)

H _____   Z(11,5)

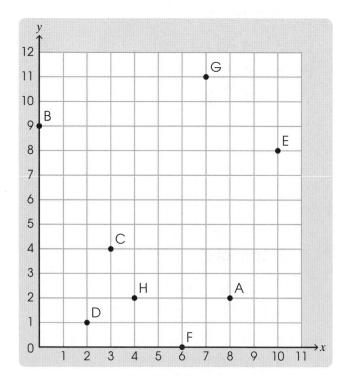

② Points that lie on the *x*-axis: _____

③ Points that lie on the *y*-axis: _____

④ Points that have a *y*-coordinate of 8: _____

Write the coordinates of the vertices of each triangle.

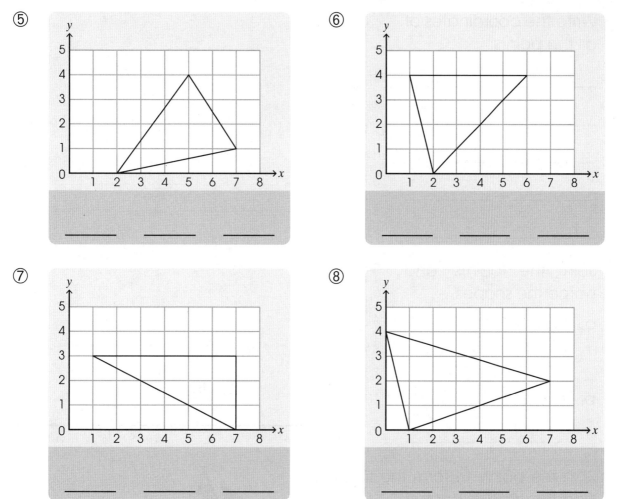

⑤

_____ _____ _____

⑥

_____ _____ _____

⑦

_____ _____ _____

⑧

_____ _____ _____

Plot each set of vertices. Join them in order and name the shape.

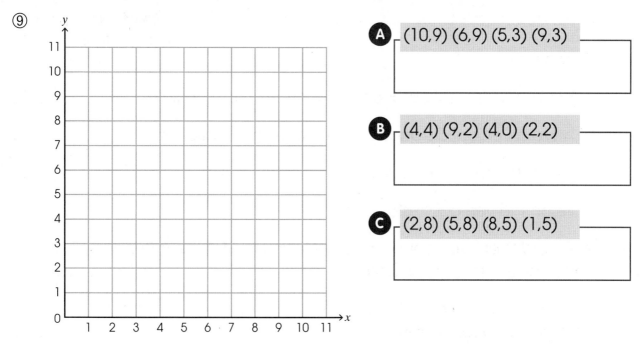

⑨

A (10,9) (6,9) (5,3) (9,3)

B (4,4) (9,2) (4,0) (2,2)

C (2,8) (5,8) (8,5) (1,5)

Find the answers.

⑩ Write the coordinates of
    all the points.

    _____ _____

    _____ _____

    _____ _____

    _____ _____

    _____ _____

⑪ Join the points and
    name the shapes.

    a. A, E, G, F

    _____

    b. A, E, C, H

    _____

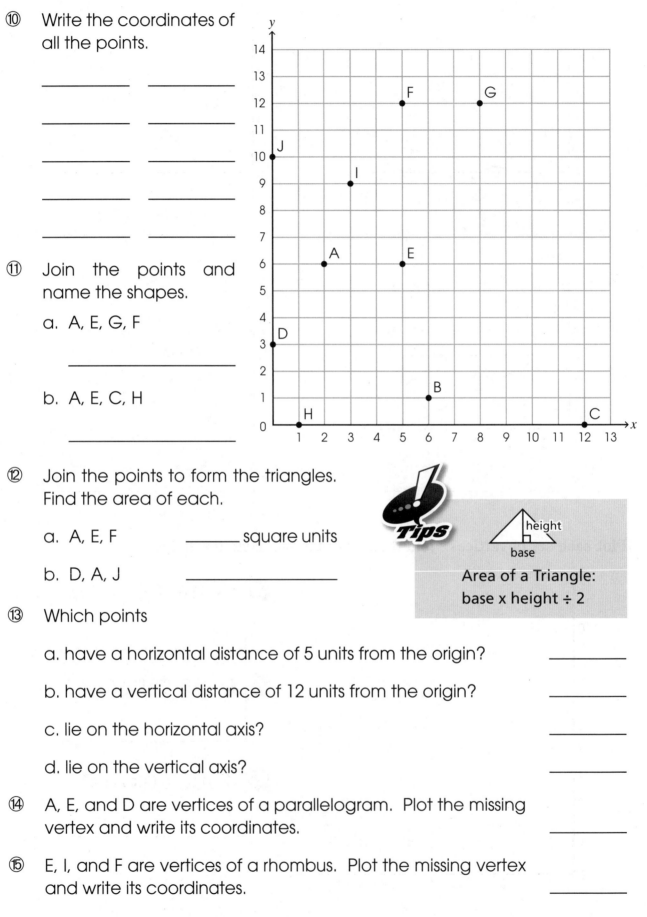

⑫ Join the points to form the triangles.
    Find the area of each.

    a. A, E, F   _____ square units

    b. D, A, J   _____

    Tips

    Area of a Triangle:
    base x height ÷ 2

⑬ Which points

    a. have a horizontal distance of 5 units from the origin?   _____

    b. have a vertical distance of 12 units from the origin?   _____

    c. lie on the horizontal axis?   _____

    d. lie on the vertical axis?   _____

⑭ A, E, and D are vertices of a parallelogram. Plot the missing
    vertex and write its coordinates.   _____

⑮ E, I, and F are vertices of a rhombus. Plot the missing vertex
    and write its coordinates.   _____

Look at the map of the St. Louis Zoo. Find the answers.

⑯ Write the coordinates of the places.

a. Gate _____

b. Petting Zoo _____

c. Butterfly House _____

d. Insect Dome _____

e. Restaurant _____

⑰ The coordinates of 4 washrooms are listed below. Plot and label them A, B, C, and D respectively.

(9,1) (8,7) (4,4) (0,0)

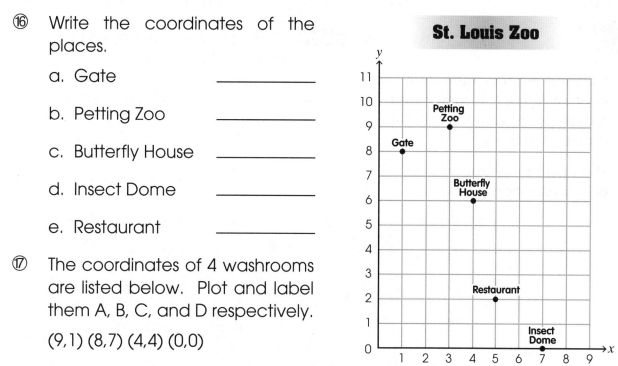

St. Louis Zoo

Look at the seating plan of Ms. Led's classroom. Answer the questions.

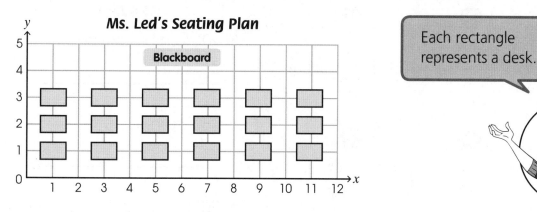

Ms. Led's Seating Plan

Blackboard

Each rectangle represents a desk.

⑱ Rebecca has weaker eyesight. If you were Ms. Led, would you assign Rebecca to sit at (1,2) or (7,3)? Explain.

_____

_____

⑲ Ms. Led did not want Olive, Gary, and Terry to sit close to one another. If Olive was assigned (1,3), which seats could the other two not sit at?

_____

14 Transformations

- describing and performing transformations

Rotation is a transformation in which a figure is turned about a fixed point, which is called a centre of rotation.

The turn can be clockwise (↻) or counterclockwise (↺).

Example Circle the correct description of the rotation shown.

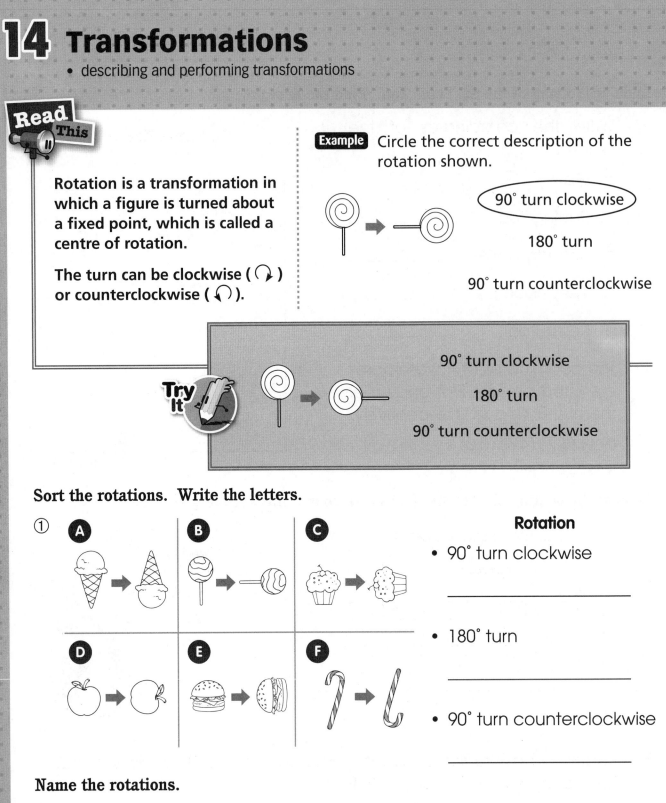

(90° turn clockwise)

180° turn

90° turn counterclockwise

Try It

90° turn clockwise

180° turn

90° turn counterclockwise

Sort the rotations. Write the letters.

① A   B   C

D   E   F

Rotation

- 90° turn clockwise

  _____

- 180° turn

  _____

- 90° turn counterclockwise

  _____

Name the rotations.

② centre of rotation

③

④

_____   _____   _____

Describe the rotations of the shaded shapes.

⑤

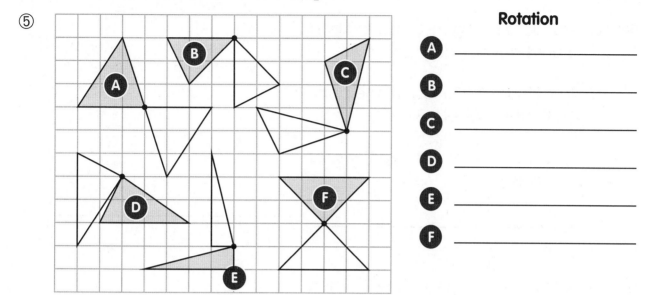

Rotation

A _____

B _____

C _____

D _____

E _____

F _____

Draw to show the rotations.

⑥ Rotate it 90° counterclockwise.

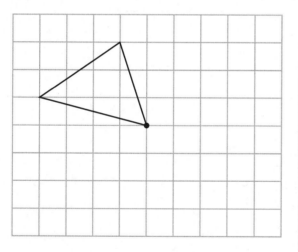

⑧ Rotate them 180°.

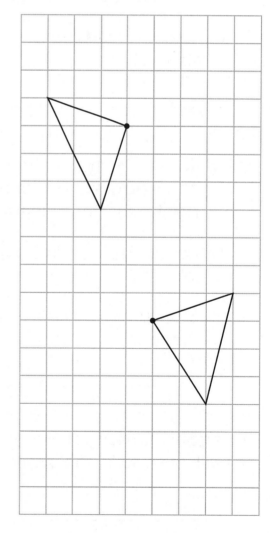

⑦ Rotate it 90° clockwise.

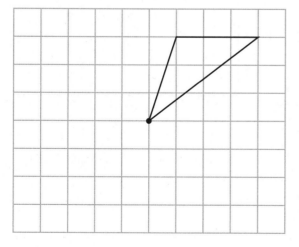

LEVEL 2 – FURTHER YOUR UNDERSTANDING

Draw the figures on the grids and solve the problems.

⑨ a. Translate the figure 3 units left and 3 units down. Then label it A.

   b. Turn Figure A 180° about the point (5,3). Then label it B.

   c. Coordinates of the vertices of Figure B:

   _____

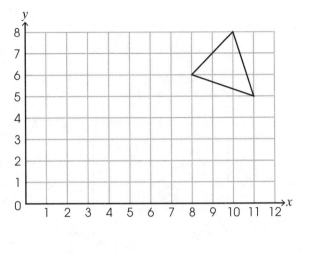

⑩ a. Reflect the figure in Line *I*. Then label it M.

   b. Translate Figure M 5 units right and 3 units up. Then label it N.

   c. Coordinates of the vertices of Figure N:

   _____

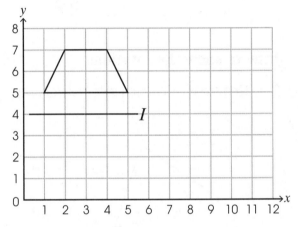

⑪ a. Rotate the figure 90° counterclockwise about the point (7,5) . Then label it X.

   b. Reflect Figure X in Line *I*. Then label it Y.

   c. Coordinates of the vertices of Figure Y:

   _____

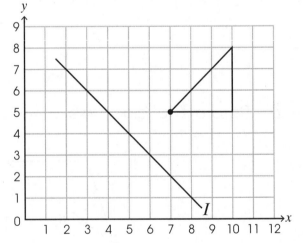

⑫ After translation, rotation, or reflection of a figure, is the image congruent with or similar to the original figure?

_____

One of the figures in each set can form a tiling pattern. Circle it and create a tiling pattern with it.

⑬

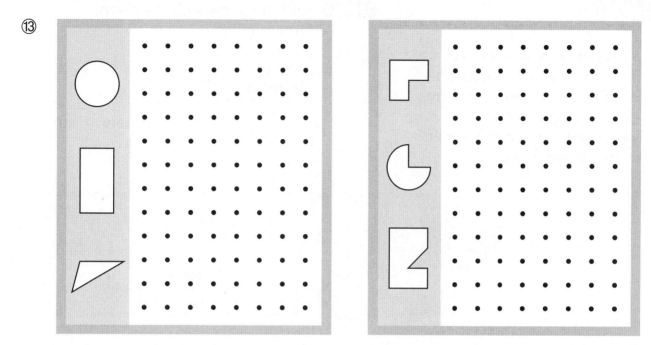

Complete the tiling pattern. Then fill in the blanks and answer the question.

⑭

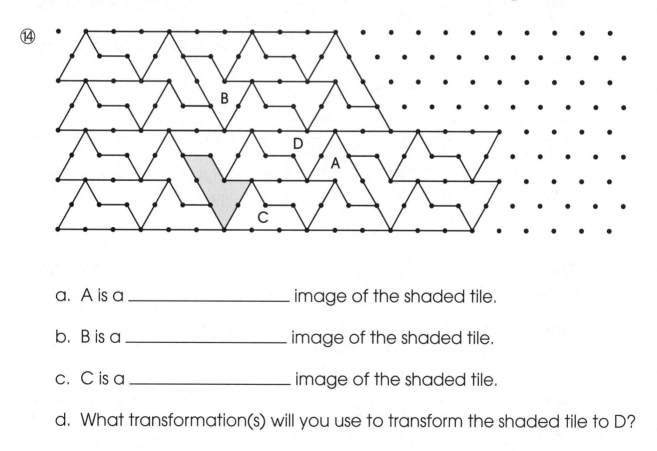

a. A is a _____ image of the shaded tile.

b. B is a _____ image of the shaded tile.

c. C is a _____ image of the shaded tile.

d. What transformation(s) will you use to transform the shaded tile to D?

_____

15 Patterning

- identifying pattern rules and extending patterns

Read This

A term is a number in a pattern and a term number tells the position of a term. Generally, a term can be related to its term number in a pattern rule.

Example Find the terms with the given term numbers.

Term Number	Term
1	4
2	7
3	10
4	13
5	16
6	19

3rd term: 10

Try It

5th term: ☐   6th term: ☐

For each pattern, check the correct pattern rule and complete the table.

①

Term Number	1	2	3	4	5
Term	6	7	8		

A) Add 5 to the term number.

B) Multiply the term number by 6.

②

Term Number	1	2	3	4	5
Term	2	4	6		

A) Add 1 to the term number.

B) Multiply the term number by 2.

③

Term Number	1	2	3	4	5
Term	2	3	4		

A) Add 1 to the term number.

B) Multiply the term number by 2.

④

Term Number	1	2	3	4	5
Term	3	6	9		

A) Add 2 to the term number.

B) Multiply the term number by 3.

Write a pattern rule that relates the terms to their term numbers for each pattern.

⑤

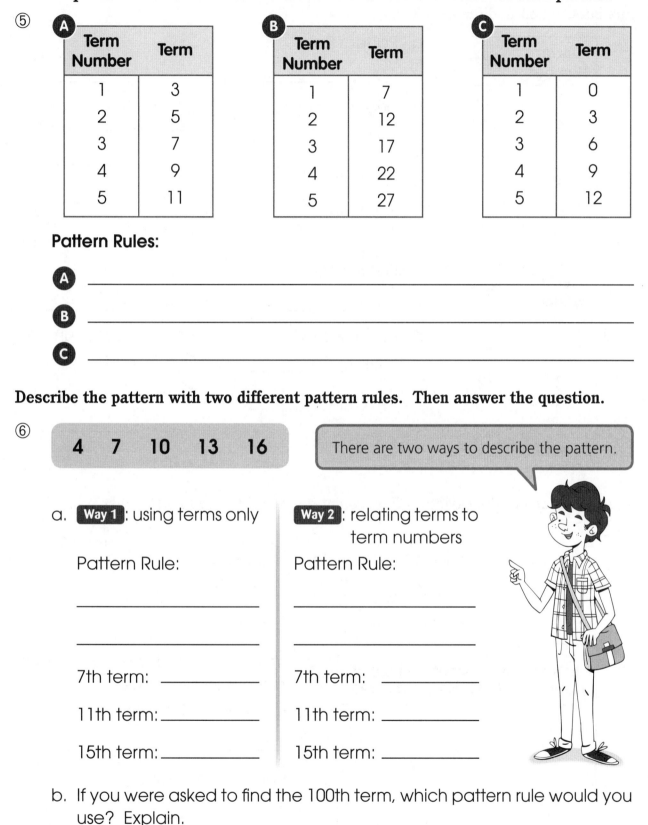

A

Term Number	Term
1	3
2	5
3	7
4	9
5	11

B

Term Number	Term
1	7
2	12
3	17
4	22
5	27

C

Term Number	Term
1	0
2	3
3	6
4	9
5	12

Pattern Rules:

Ⓐ _____

Ⓑ _____

Ⓒ _____

Describe the pattern with two different pattern rules. Then answer the question.

⑥

| 4 | 7 | 10 | 13 | 16 |

There are two ways to describe the pattern.

a. **Way 1**: using terms only

Pattern Rule:

_____

_____

7th term: _____

11th term: _____

15th term: _____

Way 2: relating terms to term numbers

Pattern Rule:

_____

_____

7th term: _____

11th term: _____

15th term: _____

b. If you were asked to find the 100th term, which pattern rule would you use? Explain.

_____

_____

Complete each pattern. Write the pattern rule that relates the terms and the term numbers. Then find the answers.

⑦

Term Number	Term
1	2
2	4
3	6
4	
5	

a. Pattern Rule:

_____

b. Find the terms.
- 7th term: _____
- 12th term: _____
- 25th term: _____

c. Find the term numbers of the given terms.
- 18: _____
- 36: _____
- 70: _____

⑧

Term Number	Term
1	4
2	8
3	12
4	
5	

a. Pattern Rule:

_____

b. Find the terms.
- 8th term: _____
- 15th term: _____
- 30th term: _____

c. Find the term numbers of the given terms.
- 28: _____
- 40: _____
- 100: _____

Draw to complete the pattern. Then complete the table and find the answers.

⑨

Frame 1   Frame 2   Frame 3   Frame 4   Frame 5

a.

Frame Number	Number of Triangles	Number of Sticks
1		
2		
3		
4		
5		

b. Write the pattern rule relating the frame number to the
- number of triangles.

_____

- number of sticks.

_____

c. How many triangles and sticks are there in Frame 10?

_____

Follow the pattern to complete each table. Find the pattern rule and list the ordered pairs. Then plot the points on the Cartesian coordinate plane.

⑩

Set A					
x-coordinate	1	2	3	4	5
y-coordinate	1	3	5	7	

Pattern Rule: _____

Ordered Pairs: (1, ___), _____

_____

Tips

Ordered Pair
(x,y)
_____

e.g.

(**2** , **1**)
↑ ↑
x-coordinate y-coordinate

⑪

Set B					
x-coordinate	1	2	3	4	5
y-coordinate	0	2	4	6	

Pattern Rule: _____

Ordered Pairs: _____

⑫ Plot the ordered pairs from Set A in red and the ones from Set B in blue.

⑬ Extend the sets by adding 2 more points for each. List the ordered pairs and plot them.

Set A	Set B
_____	_____
_____	_____

⑭ Plot (8,14). Which set does the point belong to?

_____

LEVEL 2 – FURTHER YOUR UNDERSTANDING

16 Simple Equations

• solving equations and substituting values into equations

Read This

A constant is a quantity that does not change, such as numbers (2, 5, etc.). A variable is a quantity that can change, usually represented by letters (x, y, etc.). An equation can contain constants and/or variables.

Example Identify the constants and variables in the equation.

$$15 + a \div 2 = b$$

Constants: $\boxed{15, 2}$ Variables: $\boxed{a, b}$

Try It

$$(3 + x) \times y = 18$$

Constants: ☐   Variables: ☐

For each equation, identify the constants and variables. Do what the boy says and fill in the blanks.

Draw a square around each constant and a triangle around each variable.

① $$p + 3 = q$$

If the value of p is changed, the value of q _____ change.
<u>will/will not</u>

② $$(x + y) \times 2 = a$$

If the value of y is changed, the value of a _____ change.
<u>will/will not</u>

③ $$t = m \times n \div 9$$

If the value of n is changed, the constant _____ change.
<u>will/will not</u>

④ $$5 + d = 10 - e$$

If the value of d is changed, the constants _____ change.
<u>will/will not</u>

Solve the equations.

⑤ $h + 4 = 18$

$h = $ _____

⑥ $17 = g + 8$

$g = $ _____

⑦ $13 - a = 6$

$a = $ _____

⑧ $28 \div d = 4$

$d = $ _____

⑨ $x - 17 = 98$

$x = $ _____

⑩ $4 \times j = 24$

$j = $ _____

⑪ $i \div 5 = 10$

$i = $ _____

⑫ $12 + k = 21$

$k = $ _____

⑬ $2 \times w = 31 - 1$

$w = $ _____

⑭ $r \times 9 = 59 - 5$

$r = $ _____

⑮ $30 - 9 = h \times 3$

$h = $ _____

⑯ $13 + k = 220 \div 11$

$k = $ _____

Use the guess-and-check method to solve for the variables.

⑰ $10 - 2x = 6$

$x = $ _____

Guess	Check

⑱ $5y + 1 = 16$

$y = $ _____

Guess	Check

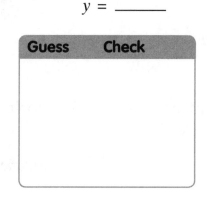

In a guess-and-check method, try to make the most reasonable guess about the value of the variable. Then do the math.

e.g. $(a + 1) \div 2 = 5$

Guess	Check
7	$(7 + 1) \div 2 = 4$
8	$(8 + 1) \div 2 = 4.5$
9	$(9 + 1) \div 2 = 5$ ✔

So, a is 9.

⑲ $(6 + a) \div 3 = 3$

$a = $ _____

Guess	Check

⑳ $14 \div (b + 1) = 2$

$b = $ _____

Guess	Check

Match each number puzzle with the correct equation. Then solve the number puzzles and write the answers in the boxes.

㉑
☐   Increase this number by 7 and then double it to get 70. •

☐   This number is halved and then reduced by 20 to get 30. •

☐   Half of this number is 7 more than 37. •

☐   Add 25 to this number and then multiply it by 3 to get 120. •

☐   Divide this number by 2 and then reduce it by 3 to get 11. •

- $x \div 2 - 3 = 11$
- $x \div 2 - 7 = 37$
- $(x + 25) \times 3 = 120$
- $x \div 2 - 20 = 30$
- $(x + 7) \times 2 = 70$

For each sentence, write an equation to represent it. Then solve for the number.

Use "x" to represent the unknown.

㉒ This number is doubled and then reduced by 5 to get 7.

Equation

Number

㉓ Subtract 3 from this number. Then multiply it by 2 to get 14.

Equation

Number

㉔ Divide this number by 3. Then add 4 to it to get 6.

Equation

Number

㉕ Decrease this number by 2 and then triple it to get 3.

Equation

Number

Substitute the given value of the variable into each equation. Then solve the equation.

㉖
$$x = 7$$

a. $x + y = 11$

$$\boxed{} + y = 11$$

$$y = \boxed{}$$

b. $x - z = 2$

㉗
$$x = 2$$

a. $3 \times x + y = 7$

b. $z - 2x = 1$

㉘
$$x = 5$$

a. $(x + y) \times 2 = 20$

b. $(z - x) \div 2 = 3$

Solve for x in each equation by substituting the given equation.

㉙
$$m + 5 = 6$$

$m + 5 + x = 11$

$6 + x = 11$

$x = \underline{}$

㉚
$$v - 2 = 9$$

$x + v - 2 = 13$

㉛
$$p + 3 = 5$$

$x \div (p + 3) = 2$

㉜
$$q - 1 = 8$$

$x \div (q - 1) = 2$

㉝
$$s \div 3 = 3$$

$s \div 3 \times x = 12$

㉞
$$t \times 2 = 6$$

$t \times 2 \times x = 18$

㉟
$$k \div 3 = 2$$

$x \times k \div 3 = 8$

㊱
$$8 + j = 9$$

$8 + j - x = 2$

㊲
$$4 \times m = 20$$

$4 \times m - x = 8$

17 Graphs

- creating and interpreting graphs

Graphs help present data in meaningful ways. Different types of graphs are used for different situations. For example, bar graphs are used for data comparison, line graphs for showing changes over time, and circle graphs for showing parts of a whole.

Example How many more students like blue than red?

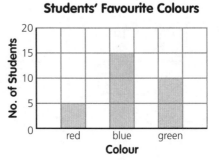

Students' Favourite Colours

10 more students like blue than red.

Try It

Which colour is the most popular?

_____

The children recorded the amount of water they drank each day. Match the data sets with the correct bar graphs. Write the letters. Then answer the questions.

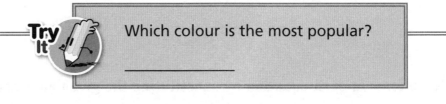

A Glasses of Water Drank

B Glasses of Water Drank

①

Jenny ⬤	
Day	No. of Glasses
M	4
T	3
W	4
Th	3
F	5

Kenny ⬤	
Day	No. of Glasses
M	3
T	4
W	5
Th	6
F	7

② On which day did the children
- drink the most water?

_____

- drink the least water?

_____

③ Which child drank more and more water each day?

_____

The graph shows the amount of time the students spent reading and jogging. Answer the questions.

④

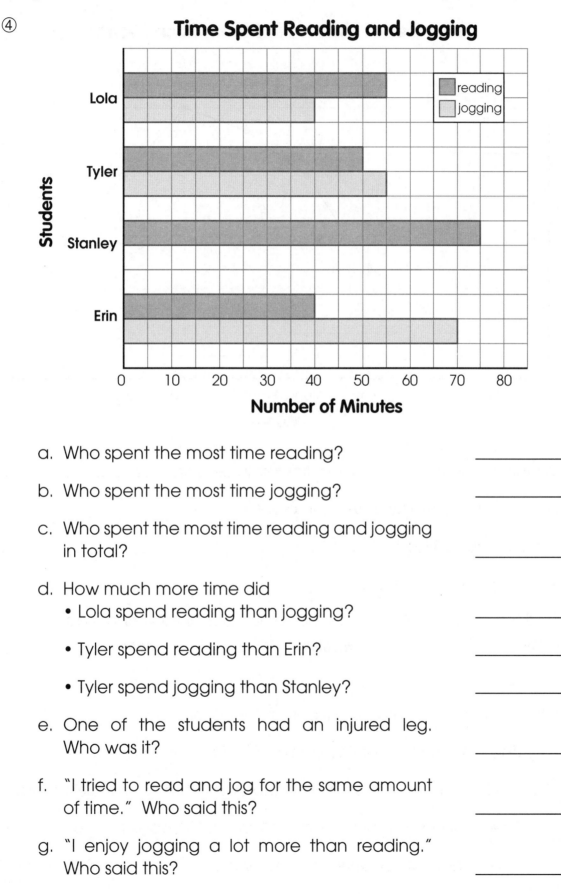

Time Spent Reading and Jogging

Students

Number of Minutes

a. Who spent the most time reading? _____

b. Who spent the most time jogging? _____

c. Who spent the most time reading and jogging in total? _____

d. How much more time did
   • Lola spend reading than jogging? _____

   • Tyler spend reading than Erin? _____

   • Tyler spend jogging than Stanley? _____

e. One of the students had an injured leg. Who was it? _____

f. "I tried to read and jog for the same amount of time." Who said this? _____

g. "I enjoy jogging a lot more than reading." Who said this? _____

Mr. Gloom planted some flowers in his backyard and recorded the number of flowers in bloom at the end of each month in the line graph. Answer the questions.

⑤

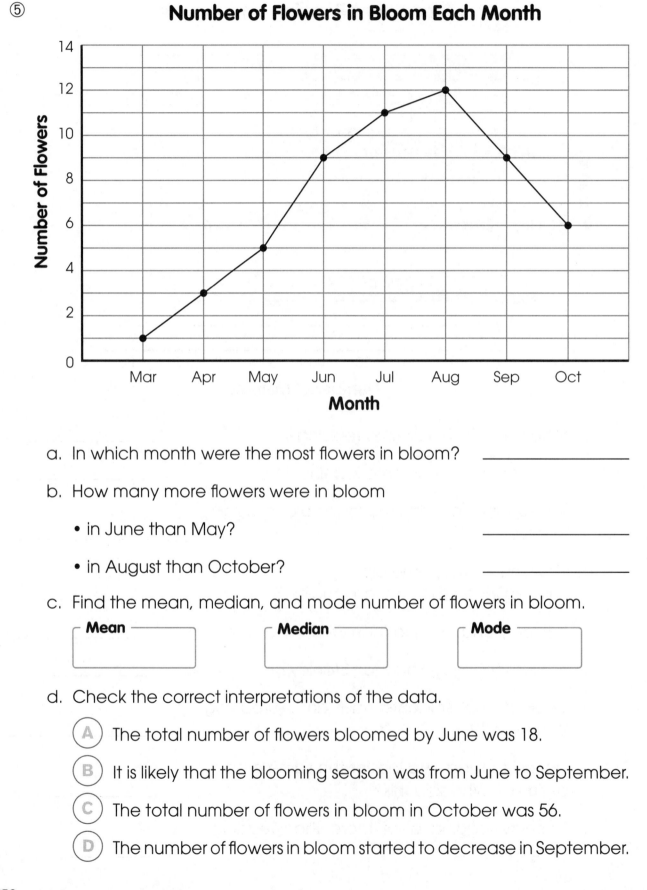

Number of Flowers in Bloom Each Month

a. In which month were the most flowers in bloom? _____

b. How many more flowers were in bloom

   • in June than May? _____

   • in August than October? _____

c. Find the mean, median, and mode number of flowers in bloom.

   ┌ **Mean** ─────┐   ┌ **Median** ─────┐   ┌ **Mode** ─────┐
   │   │   │   │   │   │
   └────────────────┘   └────────────────┘   └────────────────┘

d. Check the correct interpretations of the data.

   Ⓐ The total number of flowers bloomed by June was 18.

   Ⓑ It is likely that the blooming season was from June to September.

   Ⓒ The total number of flowers in bloom in October was 56.

   Ⓓ The number of flowers in bloom started to decrease in September.

Answer the questions about the line graph.

⑥

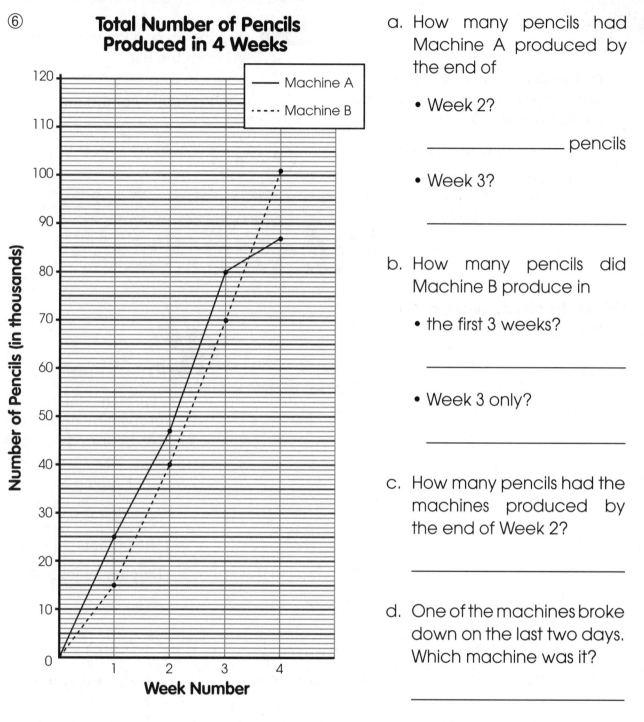

Total Number of Pencils Produced in 4 Weeks

Number of Pencils (in thousands)

Week Number

— Machine A
---- Machine B

a. How many pencils had Machine A produced by the end of

• Week 2?

_____ pencils

• Week 3?

_____

b. How many pencils did Machine B produce in

• the first 3 weeks?

_____

• Week 3 only?

_____

c. How many pencils had the machines produced by the end of Week 2?

_____

d. One of the machines broke down on the last two days. Which machine was it?

_____

e. Describe the change in the number of pencils produced by

• Machine A.

_____

• Machine B.

_____

18 Probability

• finding the probabilities of events occurring

Probability is a measure of how likely an event is to happen. It has a value between 0 and 1.

Probability of an Event

$$= \frac{\text{No. of Favourable Outcomes}}{\text{Total No. of Possible Outcomes}}$$

Example Find the probability of picking "A" from the bag.

Probability of picking "A"

$$= \frac{2}{3} \begin{array}{l} \leftarrow \text{2 "A" balls} \\ \leftarrow \text{3 balls in all} \end{array}$$

Try It

Probability of picking "B" = ☐

Probability of picking "C" = ☐

Colour the objects to match the probabilities.

Tips

P(A) represents the probability of event "A" occurring

e.g. Flipping a coin:

$$P(\text{heads}) = \frac{1}{2}$$

The probability of flipping heads is $\frac{1}{2}$.

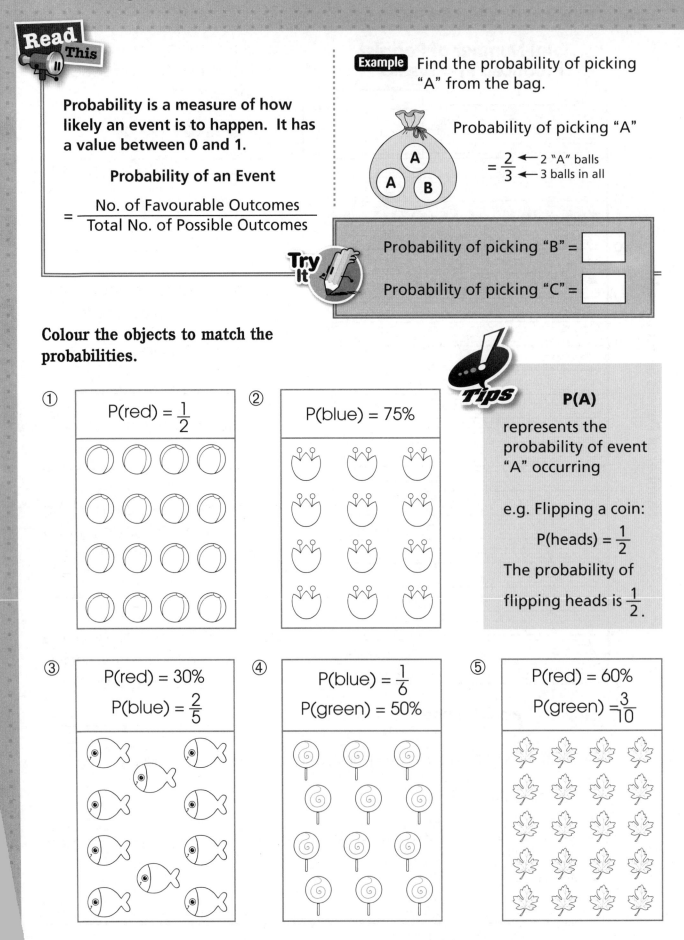

① $P(\text{red}) = \frac{1}{2}$

② $P(\text{blue}) = 75\%$

③ $P(\text{red}) = 30\%$
$P(\text{blue}) = \frac{2}{5}$

④ $P(\text{blue}) = \frac{1}{6}$
$P(\text{green}) = 50\%$

⑤ $P(\text{red}) = 60\%$
$P(\text{green}) = \frac{3}{10}$

Answer the questions.

⑥ 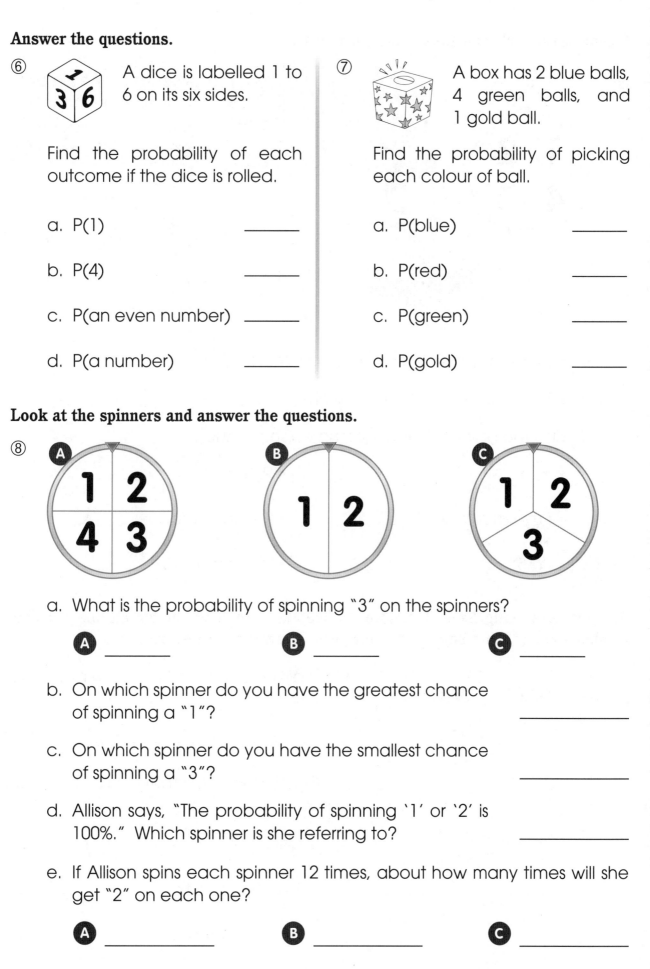 A dice is labelled 1 to 6 on its six sides.

Find the probability of each outcome if the dice is rolled.

a. P(1) _____

b. P(4) _____

c. P(an even number) _____

d. P(a number) _____

⑦ A box has 2 blue balls, 4 green balls, and 1 gold ball.

Find the probability of picking each colour of ball.

a. P(blue) _____

b. P(red) _____

c. P(green) _____

d. P(gold) _____

Look at the spinners and answer the questions.

⑧

A

B

C

a. What is the probability of spinning "3" on the spinners?

A _____   **B** _____   **C** _____

b. On which spinner do you have the greatest chance of spinning a "1"? _____

c. On which spinner do you have the smallest chance of spinning a "3"? _____

d. Allison says, "The probability of spinning '1' or '2' is 100%." Which spinner is she referring to? _____

e. If Allison spins each spinner 12 times, about how many times will she get "2" on each one?

A _____   **B** _____   **C** _____

Complete the table and answer the questions.

⑨

I spin the spinner twice and multiply the numbers on both spins.

a. Record all the possible outcomes in the table.

X	1	2	3	4
1				
2				
3				
4				

b. How many possible outcomes are there? _____

c. Which outcome is the most likely? _____

d. Find the probabilities of getting each product.

- P(3): _____
- P(16): _____

- P(greater than 10): _____
- P(odd number): _____

- P(15): _____
- P(less than 20): _____

Mr. and Mrs. Ling have 2 children. See the tree diagram for all the possible combinations ("B" for boy and "G" for girl). Answer the questions.

⑩

1st Child   2nd Child

B —< B
        G

G —< B
        G

a. List all the combinations. How many are there?

_____

b. What is the probability that the Lings have

- 2 girls? _____

- a boy and a girl? _____

- a boy and then a girl? _____

Check the tree diagram that correctly shows the possible outcomes of 2 coin flips. Then answer the questions.

⑪

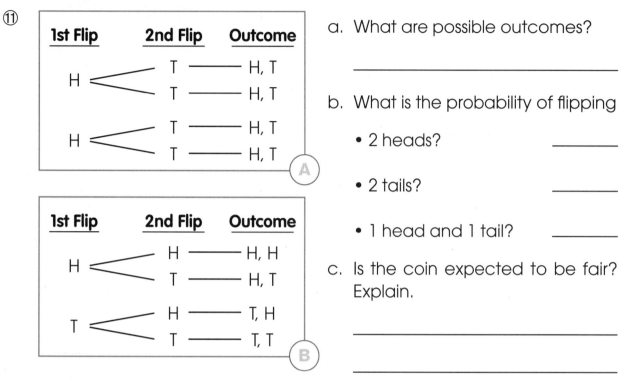

a. What are possible outcomes?

_____

b. What is the probability of flipping

• 2 heads? _____

• 2 tails? _____

• 1 head and 1 tail? _____

c. Is the coin expected to be fair? Explain.

_____

_____

Look at the menu. Choosing one item from each category, make a tree diagram to show all the possible combinations. Then answer the questions.

⑫

~ *Menu* ~

Main Course
  Burger
  Steak

Side Dish
  Salad
  Fries

Desserts
  Cake
  Jelly

Main Course	Side Dish	Dessert	Combination

a. How many combinations are there? _____

b. How many combinations include a burger and cake? _____

c. What is the probability of a customer choosing a meal with

• a burger, salad, and jelly? _____

• a burger, rice, and cake? _____

LEVEL 2 – FURTHER YOUR UNDERSTANDING

LEVEL 3
APPLICATIONS

1 Operations with Whole Numbers

• adding, subtracting, multiplying, and dividing whole numbers

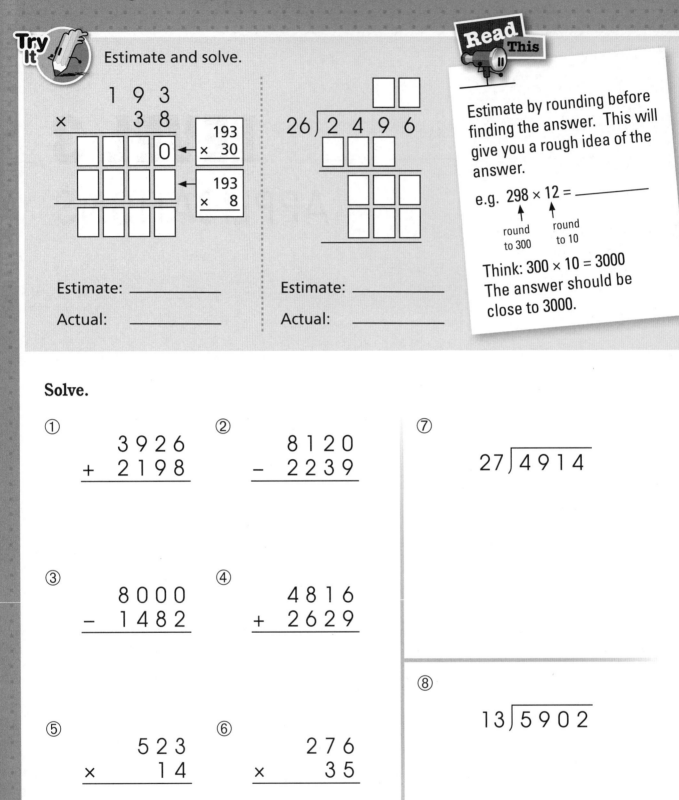

Try It

Estimate and solve.

$$\begin{array}{r} 1\ 9\ 3 \\ \times\quad 3\ 8 \\ \hline \end{array}$$

□□□□ ← $\begin{array}{r}193\\ \times\ 30\end{array}$
□□□□ ← $\begin{array}{r}193\\ \times\ 8\end{array}$
□□□□

Estimate: _____

Actual: _____

26)2 4 9 6

Estimate: _____

Actual: _____

Read This

Estimate by rounding before finding the answer. This will give you a rough idea of the answer.

e.g. 298 × 12 = _____
      ↑   ↑
   round   round
   to 300   to 10

Think: 300 × 10 = 3000
The answer should be close to 3000.

Solve.

① $\begin{array}{r} 3\ 9\ 2\ 6 \\ +\ 2\ 1\ 9\ 8 \\ \hline \end{array}$

② $\begin{array}{r} 8\ 1\ 2\ 0 \\ -\ 2\ 2\ 3\ 9 \\ \hline \end{array}$

③ $\begin{array}{r} 8\ 0\ 0\ 0 \\ -\ 1\ 4\ 8\ 2 \\ \hline \end{array}$

④ $\begin{array}{r} 4\ 8\ 1\ 6 \\ +\ 2\ 6\ 2\ 9 \\ \hline \end{array}$

⑤ $\begin{array}{r} 5\ 2\ 3 \\ \times\quad 1\ 4 \\ \hline \end{array}$

⑥ $\begin{array}{r} 2\ 7\ 6 \\ \times\quad 3\ 5 \\ \hline \end{array}$

⑦ 27)4 9 1 4

⑧ 13)5 9 0 2

⑨ 2398 + 1081 = _____

⑩ 12 345 – 1128 = _____

⑪ 398 × 52 = _____

⑫ 6864 ÷ 33 = _____

⑬ 5999 + 2198 = _____

⑭ 17 409 – 5280 = _____

⑮ 19 × 499 = _____

⑯ 5980 ÷ 52 = _____

⑰ 6848 + 3192 ÷ 21

=

⑱ 48 × (4329 + 2671)

=

⑲ (59 728 – 4173) × 12

=

⑳ 54 318 ÷ 22 + 11 682 ÷ 22

=

Solve the problems. Show your work.

㉑ Francis is helping out in the school library. The library has a collection of 2492 hardcover books, 4716 paperback books, and 378 DVDs.

a. How many books are there in the library?

_____

b. How many more paperback books than hardcover books are there?

_____

c. If a display shelf holds 16 hardcover books, how many display shelves does the library need to hold all the hardcover books?

_____

d. If a rack holds 48 DVDs, how many racks does the library need to hold all the DVDs?

_____

e. The library gets 17 new DVDs each month. How many more DVDs will the library have after 8 months?

_____

f. If there are 1296 paperback fiction books, how many paperback books are not fiction?

_____

㉒ Keith collects rocks as a hobby. He has collected 12 rocks a day for 365 days.

a. How many rocks has Keith collected?

_____

b. Keith puts all his rocks in 20 bags. How many rocks are in each bag?

_____

㉓ Mr. Neilson works in a factory that makes pencils and pens. The factory produces 10 320 pencils a day. 6144 pencils are put in packages of 64 and the rest in packages of 36.

a. How many pencils are put in packages of 36 each day?

_____

b. How many packages of 64 pencils are produced each day?

_____

c. How many packages of 36 pencils are produced each day?

_____

d. The factory produces 44 000 pens in 25 days. On average, how many pens are produced in one day?

_____

e. 2816 cartons of pens are delivered to Vancouver and 3844 are delivered to Montreal. How many cartons of pens are delivered in total?

_____

f. If the delivery cost for 32 cartons is $148, what is the delivery cost for the pens going to Vancouver?

_____

㉔ Michael has a small candy shop. He sells lots of candies every day.

a. He sold 31 small bags of candy and 27 big bags yesterday. Each small bag has 58 candies and each big bag has 96 candies. How many candies did he sell in all?

_____

b. A jar has 2858 candies and 1226 of them are red. If he evenly divides the candies that are not red into 32 boxes, how many candies will there be in each box?

_____

㉕ In Gary's school auditorium, there are 1252 seats in 35 rows. The average class size in Gary's school is 33 students.

a. The number of seats in each row is the same except the last one, which has 28 seats only. How many seats are there in each row?

_____

b. There are 35 classes in Gary's school. If 632 students are girls, how many students are not girls?

_____

c. If all the students are in the auditorium, how many seats will be left for the teachers?

_____

d. If the chairs are put in stacks of 12, how many stacks will there be? How many chairs will be left?

_____

2 Adding and Subtracting Decimals

- adding and subtracting decimals to thousandths

Try It

Doris mixes 0.375 L of strawberry juice, 0.428 L of pineapple juice, and 0.24 L of orange juice in a blender. If the blender has a capacity of 1.5 L, how much more juice can Doris add?

Amount of juice: 0.375 + 0.428 + 0.24 = ☐

Remaining capacity: 1.5 − ☐ = ☐

Doris can add ☐ L more juice.

Read This

Read the questions carefully and circle the keywords. Then break each question down into several steps and solve them one by one. You may draw diagrams or pictures to help visualize the questions.

Solve the problems. Show your work.

① Frank and Mindy were shopping for groceries. They bought some vegetables and fruits.

a. Mindy bought 2 bags of apples. 1 bag weighed 1.465 kg and the other 1.389 kg. What was the total weight of the apples?

_____

b. The prices of the 2 bags of apples were $1.45 and $1.38. What was the total cost of the apples?

_____

c. Frank bought some grapes. The total weight of 2 bags of grapes was 2.15 kg. If one bag weighed 1.309 kg, what was the weight of the other bag?

_____

d. Mindy bought a bag of red onions for $3.27 and a bag of white onions for $4.69. How much did Mindy spend on onions in all?

_____

e. The total cost of Mindy's purchases was $18.27. How much change did she receive for a $20 bill?

_____

f. The total cost of Frank's purchases was $23.19. If he had $4.58 left after paying, how much did he have at the start?

_____

② Frank lives 2.544 km from the grocery store and Mindy lives 3.068 km from the grocery store, but in the opposite direction.

a. How far apart do Frank and Mindy live?

_____

b. How much farther from the grocery store is Mindy than Frank?

_____

c. Mindy wanted to buy milk. How far would Mindy have to walk in all to get the milk and return home?

_____

d. Frank decided to walk to Mindy's house and go to the grocery store with her before returning home. How far did he have to walk?

_____

e. Mindy's mother gave Frank $5 to buy the milk that was on sale for $2.29. How much change did she get back?

_____

f. If Mindy's mother told Frank that he could buy a 79-cent candy bar for helping out, how much change would she get?

_____

g. If Frank bought a $0.56 pop instead, how much change would Mindy's mother get?

_____

h. It takes Frank 15.5 min to run to the grocery store from his house and 11.27 min to bike. How much time can he save if he bike there and back instead of running?

_____

i. The post office is between Frank's house and the grocery store. It is 1.865 km from Frank's house. How far is it from Mindy's house?

_____

③ Janet buys some stamps for $6.99 and a postcard for $3.45. She pays with $20. What is her change?

_____

④ A carton holds 1.5 L of iced tea. Cameron fills three glasses of iced tea, each with 0.345 L. How much iced tea is left in the carton?

_____

⑤ The height of the tide at the harbour was 16.243 cm. In the afternoon it dropped by 4.109 cm and at night it rose by 3.782 cm. What was the height of the tide by the end of the night?

_____

⑥ Wendy packed 2 bags for a trip: one is 21.349 kg and the other is 25.096 kg. The weight limit for each bag is 23 kg. If Wendy can move items from one bag to the other, will there still be an overweight bag? If so, by how much?

_____

⑦ A transit system consists of buses, trains, and subways. Every day approximately 0.407 million people ride the bus, 0.837 million ride the train, and 1.625 million ride the subway. How many people ride the transit system daily?

_____

⑧ Lisa has a puppy. It weighed 3.568 kg a year ago. Six months ago it had gained 2.708 kg. The puppy now weighs 9.058 kg. How much weight did Lisa's puppy gain in the last six months?

_____

⑨ A totem pole is 10.538 m tall and is divided into three sections. The first section is 5.037 m tall and the third section is 2.339 m tall. How tall is the second section?

_____

⑩ The length of a pool is 23.241 m. Casey wanted to swim three lengths of the pool, but on her last length she swam 11.976 m less. How far did Casey swim in total?

_____

⑪ Carl paddled a canoe 6.396 km up a river and then took a break. Meanwhile, the river carried the canoe 2.734 km downriver. Carl then finished his journey by paddling another 5.453 km. How far up the river did Carl travel in total?

_____

⑫ Stanley is training for long jump in track and field. On his first try, he jumped 2.351 m. On his second try, he jumped 0.455 m farther. His personal best was 0.312 m farther than his second try.

a. What was Stanley's personal best jump?

_____

b. At today's competition, Stanley jumped 0.937 m less than his personal best. How much shorter was Stanley's jump today than his first jump?

_____

3 Multiplying and Dividing Decimals

• solving problems by multiplying and dividing decimals

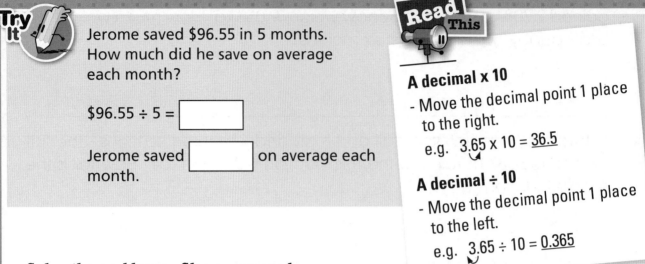

Try It

Jerome saved $96.55 in 5 months. How much did he save on average each month?

$96.55 ÷ 5 = ☐

Jerome saved ☐ on average each month.

Read This

A decimal x 10
- Move the decimal point 1 place to the right.
  e.g. 3.65 x 10 = 36.5

A decimal ÷ 10
- Move the decimal point 1 place to the left.
  e.g. 3.65 ÷ 10 = 0.365

Solve the problems. Show your work.

① Jim went on a road trip with his family. They drove 321.75 km on the first day, 297.54 km on the second day, and 306.9 km on the third day.

a. They travelled a total of 926.19 km in those 3 days. What was the mean distance they travelled?

_____

b. They drove for 3 hours on the first day. What was their average speed?

_____

c. They also drove for 3 hours on the second day. What was their average speed?

_____

d. They averaged 90 km/h on the third day. How many hours did they drive for?

_____

e. If their car consumed 1 L of gas for every 12 km driven, how much gas did they use on the second day?

_____

f. On the fourth day, they were still 210.72 km from their destination. How much more gas did they need to reach it?

_____

g. If it took 4 hours to reach their destination on the fourth day, what was their average speed?

_____

h. They used 94.7 L of gas for the trip. If 10 L of gas cost $9, how much did they spend on gas?

_____

② Theresa went shopping with her friends at Sweetie Candy Store. The sales tax was included in each purchase.

a. The average weight of 3 bags of candy was 1.19 kg. What was the total weight?

_____

b. If Theresa bought 1.45 kg of jelly beans at the special price of $9 per kilogram, how much did she pay?

_____

c. Elaine bought 9 packs of chewing gum for $7.74. How much did 1 pack of chewing gum cost?

_____

d. A box of 9 lollipops cost $35.37. How much did 1 lollipop cost?

_____

e. Fruit gums were $7.90 per kilogram. If David bought 4 kg, how much did he pay?

_____

f. Chocolate almonds were $23.71 per kilogram. If Theresa bought 5 kg, how much did she pay?

_____

g. A box of 6 chocolate bars cost $25.56. A bag of 8 chocolate bars cost $32.16. Which was a better buy?

_____

③ Kirby went camping with his family for 5 days. Kirby's parents prepared everything for the trip.

a. They bought 2 identical tents for $375.06. How much did 1 tent cost?

_____

b. They hiked 8.25 km each day. How far did they travel in all?

_____

c. Kirby hiked 8.2 km in 4 h. What was his average speed?

_____

d. The food cost $32.80 per day. How much was spent on food in all?

_____

e. There were 5 people on the trip. What was the food cost per person per day?

_____

f. They drank 8.25 L of water per day. How much water did they drink in all?

_____

g. The family brought 13.5 L of water in 9 bottles. How much water was in each bottle?

_____

h. Kirby's backpack was 4 times the weight of his sister's, which weighed 1.45 kg. How heavy was Kirby's backpack?

_____

i. Kirby's father's backpack was twice as heavy as Kirby's. How heavy was his father's backpack?

_____

j. The tent's base is 2.8 m long and 2 m wide. What is its area?

_____

k. The 2 tents are the same size. What is the total area of both tents?

_____

l. The rectangular campsite has an area of 36.5 m². If its width is 5 m, what is its length?

_____

④ Ms. Prem's class and Mr. Holly's class were in a basketball rivalry.

a. A basketball game is about 1.35 h long. How long are 4 basketball games?

_____

b. Mr. Holly's team practised for 1.45 h each day to get ready for the big game, which was 8 days away. How many hours of practice did his team get?

_____

c. Ms. Prem's team ran a total of 26 km in the 8 days before the big game. How many kilometres did they run on average each day?

_____

d. In the first 4 games of the season, Ms. Prem's team scored 277 points. How many points per game were scored by her team on average?

_____

e. In the first 4 games of the season, Mr. Holly's team scored an average of 68.25 points per game. How many points did his team get in all?

_____

f. In their final game, Mr. Holly's team scored an average of 18.25 points in each quarter of a game, while Ms. Prem's team scored an average of 9.75 points every 10 min. There are 80 minutes in a game. Which team won?

_____

4 Mixed Operations with Decimals

- adding, subtracting, multiplying, and dividing with decimals

Mrs. Brown has two carpets. The larger carpet is 4 m long and 3.25 m wide. The smaller carpet has an area of 5.2 m². What is the total area of the carpets?

$4 \times 3.25 + 5.2 = \boxed{}$

The carpets have a total area of $\boxed{}$ m².

Read This

Remember to follow the order of operations: multiplication and division first, and then addition and subtraction.

e.g. $1.5 - 0.2 \times 6$

$= 1.5 - 1.2$ Multiply first.

$= \underline{0.3}$

Solve the problems. Show your work.

① Lori just moved into a new apartment. She is measuring the dimensions of her living room, dining room, and hallway.

a. The area of her living room is 38.85 m². If the length of the room is 7 m, what is the width?

_____

b. The dining room is 5 m wide and 8.14 m long and has a plaster border around the top of the walls. What is the length of the border?

_____

c. What is the area of the dining room?

_____

d. The hallway is covered with 8 large tiles. Each tile has an area of 0.95 m². What is the area of the hallway?

_____

e. The width of the hallway is 2 m. What is the length of the hallway?

_____

② Paul and Petula went on a trip with their parents. They drove 259.79 km on the first day, 302.57 km on the second day, and an average of 225.67 km per day for the next 2 days.

a. How far did they drive for the trip?

_____

b. If the average speed was 75 km/h, how many hours did they drive for the trip?

_____

c. They filled up their car's gas 3 times: 46.37 L before the trip, 49.45 L on the second day, and 42.69 L on the fourth day. How many litres of gas did they buy altogether?

_____

d. If the average fill-up cost was $47.76, what was the total fill-up cost for the trip?

_____

e. They spent $58.27 on food on the first day, $63.39 on the second day, and $123.86 over the next 2 days. How much did they spend on food in all?

_____

f. How much did they spend on food per day?

_____

g. Paul's mother said, "The cost of food exceeded our budget by $25.52." What was their budget for food?

_____

h. Paul's mother bought 3 kg of ham at $2.29/kg, 6 kg of turkey at $3.40/kg, 4 kg of potatoes at $0.60/kg, and 8 kg of beans at $1.40/kg. How much more did she spend on meat than on vegetables?

_____

i. The lodging cost $26.69 per night per person. If they spent 3 nights there, what was their total lodging bill?

_____

③ Tony is the chairman of the Stamp Club. The club has 24 members, and each member pays $4.29 for his or her annual membership fee. Tony is also given $197.04 to go toward running the club this school year.

a. How much will Tony collect from the club's members this year?

_____

b. How much money is available for the club each month this school year, excluding the 2-month summer break?

_____

c. Tony wants to spend a quarter of the money on a newsletter to be published twice a year. How much money will there be for each issue?

_____

d. After budgeting for the newsletter, how much money will be left for other activities?

_____

e. Everybody in the club gets a stamp album that costs $9.95. Can the club afford to give each member, including Tony, an album?

_____

f. Last year, the membership fee was $3.99 and there were 20 members. How much more will the club collect from its members this year?

_____

④ Jane buys 5 chocolate bars at $1.25 each. She pays with a $10 bill. How much change does she get?

_____

⑤ Brenda wants to sew two quilts together. One quilt measures 4 m by 4.2 m and the other measures 4.1 m by 6 m. What is the area of the sewn quilt?

_____

⑥ Mrs. Smith buys the following groceries: 5 kg of bananas at $1.39/kg, 3 kg of apples at $2.69/kg, and 10 kg of potatoes at $1.29/kg. How much does she pay in all?

_____

⑦ Mr. Brown bought 3 magazines for $2.25 each and 2 books for $5.99 each. If he paid with a $20 bill, how much change did he get?

_____

⑧ Jerry runs 0.65 km in 5 min and Lillian runs 0.48 km in 2 min. How much faster does Lillian run than Jerry each minute?

_____

5 Fractions, Decimals, and Percents

- solving problems with fractions, decimals, and percents

Frank coloured 25 hundredths of his 100-square paper. What fraction or percent of his paper is coloured?

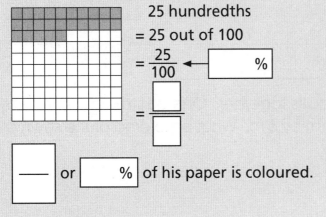

25 hundredths
= 25 out of 100

$= \dfrac{25}{100}$ ← ☐ %

$= \dfrac{☐}{☐}$

☐ or ☐ % of his paper is coloured.

Read This

When converting percents or decimals into fractions, remember to write the fractions in simplest form.

e.g.

$50\% = \dfrac{50}{100}$

$= \dfrac{1}{2}$ ← in simplest form

Solve the problems. Show your work.

① Henry and Molly were going shopping at the F & G Department Store.

a. Henry saw a big sign that read "$\dfrac{1}{2}$ off all shoes". What percent discount was offered?

A _____ discount was offered.

b. All suits were on sale at a 20% discount. What fraction of the original price was discounted?

_____

c. Molly paid $\dfrac{4}{5}$ of the price for a dress that she liked. What percent of the price of the dress did Molly pay?

_____

d. The store manager said that 45 out of 50 items were on sale. What percent of the items were on sale?

_____

e. The cashier said that 50 out of 200 pairs of shoes were sold. What percent of the shoes were sold?

_____

f. 0.15 of the socks on display were on sale. What fraction of the socks were on sale?

_____

② Ron and Judy were trying to increase their fitness levels. They wanted to improve a bit each day.

a. Ron was lifting weights. $\frac{3}{5}$ of the weights were over 10 kg. What percent of the weights were over 10 kg?

_____

b. 3 out of 10 weights were wrapped in vinyl. What percent of the weights were wrapped in vinyl?

_____

c. What percent of the weights were not wrapped in vinyl?

_____

d. Judy did aerobics for 0.6 hours. What fraction of an hour did she do aerobics for?

_____

e. 85% of the people in the aerobics class were girls. What fraction of those in the class were girls?

_____

f. Ron ran $\frac{7}{10}$ of a running track and walked the remaining distance. What percent of the track did Ron run?

_____

g. What percent of the track did Ron walk?

_____

h. Judy enjoyed skipping rope. She skipped 100 times the first day and wanted to increase this by $\frac{1}{10}$ each day. How many times would she have to skip on the second day?

_____

Look at Emily's stickers. Solve the problems. Show your work.

③ What percent of Emily's stickers are ♡ ?

_____

④ What percent of her stickers are 🌷 ?

_____

⑤ What percent of her stickers are ☀ ?

_____

⑥ What percent of her stickers are ☆ ?

_____

⑦ If Emily uses 20 stickers, what percent of her stickers will be left?

_____

⑧ If Emily uses 16 stickers, what percent of her stickers will be left?

_____

⑨ If Emily gives 0.35 of her stickers to her sister, what percent of her stickers will be left?

_____

⑩ If Emily uses $\frac{3}{4}$ of her stickers, what percent of her stickers will be left?

_____

⑪ If Emily uses 10 ♡ stickers, what percent of her ♡ stickers will be left?

_____

⑫ If Emily has 12 ☀ stickers left, what percent of her ☀ stickers did she use?

_____

⑬ If Emily uses 60% of her stickers, how many stickers will be left?

_____

Solve the problems. Show your work.

⑭ 5 out of 20 doughnuts in a box are chocolate flavoured. What percent of the doughnuts are chocolate flavoured?

_____

⑮ 42% of the drinks are cherry flavoured. Write a decimal for the drinks that are cherry flavoured.

_____

⑯ In a park, 18 out of the 30 squirrels are brown.

a. What fraction of the squirrels are brown?

_____

b. What percent of the squirrels are brown?

_____

⑰ Amy and Michael have the same number of cookies. $\frac{9}{22}$ of Amy's cookies and 0.45 of Michael's cookies have chocolate chips. Who has more cookies with chocolate chips?

_____

⑱ A sign says, "KICKBOXING IS TOUGH!" Which word in the sign has between 0.3 and 50% of its letters that are vowels?

_____

6 Ratios and Rates

- solving problems with ratios and rates

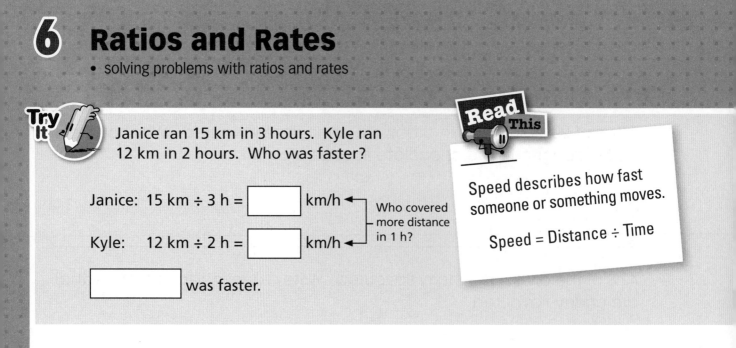

Try It

Janice ran 15 km in 3 hours. Kyle ran 12 km in 2 hours. Who was faster?

Janice: 15 km ÷ 3 h = [ ] km/h

Kyle: 12 km ÷ 2 h = [ ] km/h

Who covered more distance in 1 h?

[ ] was faster.

Read This

Speed describes how fast someone or something moves.

Speed = Distance ÷ Time

Solve the problems. Show your work. Write your answers in simplest form.

① What is the ratio of

a. history books to geography books?

The ratio is _____ .

b. geography books to history books?

_____

There is a total of 200 books in the classroom.

Classroom Books
- 25 history books
- 35 geography books
- others

c. history books to all books?

_____

d. geography books to all books?

_____

② There are 100 fiction books in the classroom. What is the ratio of

a. history books to fiction books?

b. fiction books to all books?

_____

③ If 50 history books are added to the classroom, what is the ratio of

a. new books to old books?

b. history books to all books?

_____

④ In Molly's collection of 20 dolls, 5 dolls have porcelain faces, 4 wear lace dresses, 2 have leather boots, and 12 are taller than 20 cm.

   a. What is the ratio of dolls with porcelain faces to dolls with faces made of other materials?

_____

   b. What is the ratio of dolls in lace dresses to dolls without lace dresses?

_____

   c. What is the ratio of dolls that are taller than 20 cm to the total number of dolls?

_____

   d. The dolls in leather boots are more valuable than the other dolls. What is the ratio of more valuable dolls to less valuable dolls?

_____

   e. Daisy, Molly's friend, has 16 dolls. 6 of her dolls have leather boots. What is the ratio of Daisy's dolls in leather boots to those without leather boots?

_____

   f. What is the ratio of Daisy's dolls to Molly's dolls?

_____

   g. If Daisy gives 4 of her dolls to Molly, what will the ratio of Daisy's dolls to Molly's dolls be?

_____

   h. If Molly gives 4 of her dolls to Daisy, what will the ratio of Daisy's dolls to Molly's dolls be?

_____

Wanda went shopping with her friends. Help her solve the problems.

⑤ 5 kg of apples cost $6.45.

    a. Find the unit price in kilograms.

    _____

    b. If Wanda wanted to buy 3 kg of apples, how much did she need to pay?

    _____

⑥ 4 kg of peaches cost $6.76.

    a. Find the unit price in kilograms.

    _____

    b. If Louis wanted to buy 3 kg of peaches, how much did he need to pay?

    _____

⑦ Catherine paid $1.96 to buy 4 kg of bananas.

    a. Find the unit price in kilograms.

    _____

    b. If Catherine bought 7 kg of bananas, how much did she need to pay?

    _____

⑧ A 3-kg basket of cherries cost $14.97. A 5-kg basket of cherries cost $25.80. Which was a better buy?

    _____

⑨ A 2-kg basket of plums cost $5.58. A 3-kg basket of plums cost $8.07.

    a. Which was a better buy?

    _____

    b. If Wanda bought two 3-kg baskets of plums, how much did she pay?

    _____

    c. If Wanda paid $80.70 to buy some 3-kg baskets of plums, how many baskets of plums did she buy?

    _____

⑩ The shopkeeper wanted to pack 350 apples in bags of 5 or 7. A bag of 5 apples would then be sold for $1.35 and a bag of 7 apples for $1.75.

> Which way should I pack the apples to make more money? How much more will I make?

_____

Solve the problems. Show your work. Round the answers to the nearest hundredth if needed.

⑪ Edwin travels 3 km in 20 minutes. What is his speed in km/h?

_____

⑫ William can read 27 pages in 1.5 hours. What is his reading rate in pages per minute?

_____

⑬ Donny earned $130 in 8 hours. How much did Donny earn each hour?

_____

⑭ Lily reads 108 words in 10 min while Henry reads 147 words in 15 min. Who reads faster? Explain.

_____

⑮ Bright Lite bulbs are sold in packs of 4 for $1.48 while Supergood bulbs are sold in packs of 12 for $4.92.

   a. Which is a better buy?

_____

   b. If Supergood bulbs last twice as long as Bright Lite bulbs, which brand offers a better value? Explain.

_____

⑯ Fred drives 96 km in 2 hours and Ivan drives 120 km in 3 hours.

   a. Find Fred's and Ivan's speeds.

_____

   b. Find the ratio of Fred's speed to Ivan's speed.

_____

7 Money

- solving problems involving money

Try It

Billy bought 2 boxes of chocolates for $12.70 each. The cashier charged him an additional $3.81 in taxes. What was his change from a $50 bill?

Read This

Remember to follow the order of operations to solve problems when the problems involve more than one operation.

Total cost: $12.7 × 2 + $3.81 = [ ]

Change: $50 − [ ] = [ ]

His change was [ ] .

Milly went shopping at the mall. All purchases were tax-free that day. Help her solve the problems. Show your work.

① Milly was looking for a blouse. Store A had a blouse for sale for $35.95. Store B had the same blouse for sale for $41.52 but offered her a $5.25 discount.

   a. Which store had the lower price?

   _____

   b. Milly bought the cheaper blouse with a $50 bill and the cashier gave the change in the fewest coins and bills. What was her change and which coins and bills did she receive?

   _____

② Milly wanted to buy some candy. She saw her favourite candy on sale for $1.45 per 100 g.

   a. How much would 0.7 kg of her favourite candy cost?

   _____

   b. If the cashier gave the change in the fewest coins, what was her change from a $10 bill and a toonie? What were the coins?

   _____

Solve the problems. Show your work.

③ Jeffrey wanted to buy some shoe polish for his old boots. Store C had a 125-g tube on sale for $3.95 and Store D had a 100-g jar for $2.99. Which store offered a better buy?

_____

④ Alan wanted to trade a $10 bill for quarters. How many quarters would he get?

_____

⑤ In a food court, hamburgers were sold for $2.49 each, orders of fries for $1.39 each, and soft drinks for $1.27 each.

   a. If Donald bought 2 hamburgers and 1 soft drink and paid with the fewest coins, what coins did he pay with?

   _____

   b. Milly used one eighth of her money to buy 1 hamburger, 1 order of fries, and 1 soft drink. How much money did Milly have before the purchase?

   _____

⑥ Ellen bought 4 boxes of chocolates for $11.16. She opened 1 box and found that the chocolates did not taste good, so she returned the unopened boxes. How much money did Ellen get back?

_____

⑦ A combo has 2 bags of popcorn and 1 soft drink. The average cost of each item in the combo is $4.32. Each bag of popcorn costs $4.59.

   a. How much does a soft drink cost?

   _____

   b. Joseph has 4 quarters, 24 dimes, and 16 nickels. Does he have enough money to buy a soft drink?

   _____

⑧ Jerry got a part-time job at Alco Parking Lot. He wanted to save some money for a summer trip.

   a. If he was paid $14.05 per hour and worked 18 hours a week, how much could he earn per week?

_____

   b. Jerry worked 6 days a week and took a bus to and from work. If the bus fare was $2.85 per trip, how much did he earn each week after paying for transit?

_____

   c. $5.38 of Jerry's weekly earnings was deducted for income tax. How much did he earn each week after paying for transit and tax?

_____

   d. Jerry wanted to save up $600 for the trip. Would he have enough money saved for the trip if he worked for 3 weeks?

_____

   e. At the parking lot, the parking fee is $1.75 for the first half hour and $3 for every extra half hour. What is the parking fee for 2 hours and 30 minutes?

_____

   f. Mr. Keller parked his car for 2 hours. Jerry gave him $1.25 in change. How much did Mr. Keller give Jerry for parking?

_____

   g. Jerry had to prepare some coins for change. If he traded a $5 bill for nickels, how many nickels would he get?

_____

⑨ Mrs. Kim bought 129 boxes of chocolates at a price of $16 for every 3 boxes. How much did she pay in all?

_____

⑩ Michael has 329 quarters, 215 dimes, and 279 nickels. How much money does Michael have in all?

_____

⑪ There are 12 girls and 15 boys in Ms. Link's class. If each student raises an average of $20.75 for charity, how much money will they raise altogether?

_____

⑫ A bag of raisins costs $0.50 and a bag of sunflower seeds costs $0.65. If Betsy sells 35 bags of raisins and 60 bags of sunflower seeds, how much money will she make?

_____

⑬ Elaine sold 108 glasses of orange juice for $1.25 each, 88 glasses of apple juice for $1.75 each, and 104 glasses of peach juice for $1.45 each. How much money did she make?

_____

⑭ If Kelly paid for the mirror with two $50 bills, what would her change be in the fewest bills and coins?

$57.65

_____

8 Perimeter and Area

• solving problems involving perimeter and area

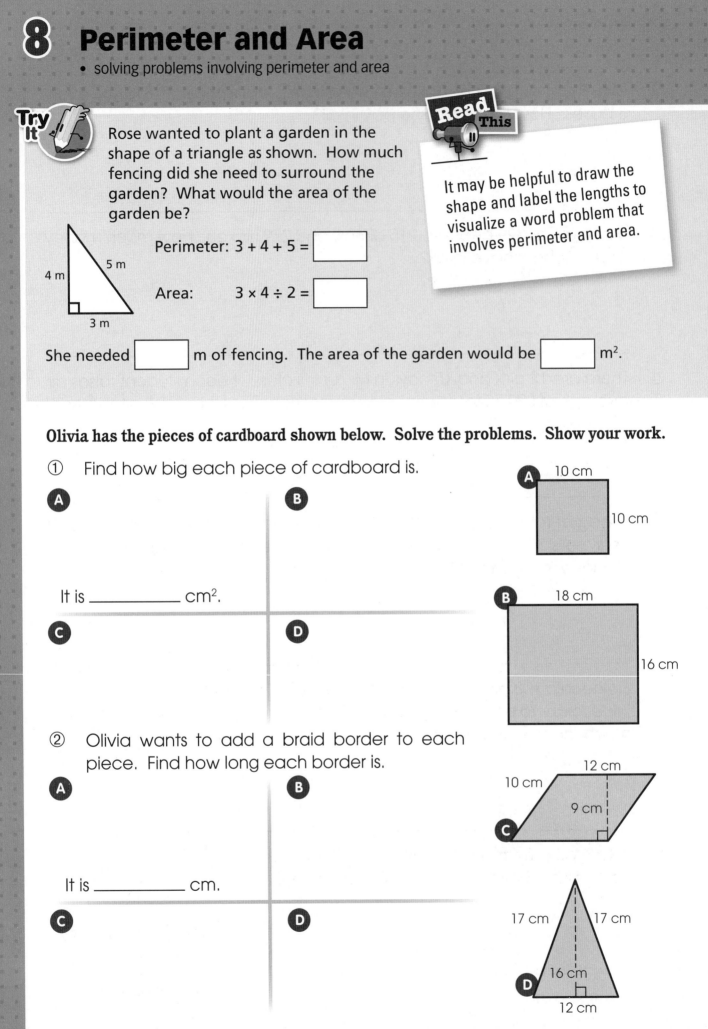

Rose wanted to plant a garden in the shape of a triangle as shown. How much fencing did she need to surround the garden? What would the area of the garden be?

Read This

It may be helpful to draw the shape and label the lengths to visualize a word problem that involves perimeter and area.

5 m
4 m
3 m

Perimeter: 3 + 4 + 5 = ☐

Area: 3 × 4 ÷ 2 = ☐

She needed ☐ m of fencing. The area of the garden would be ☐ m².

Olivia has the pieces of cardboard shown below. Solve the problems. Show your work.

① Find how big each piece of cardboard is.

A

B

It is _____ cm².

C

D

A 10 cm
10 cm

B 18 cm
16 cm

② Olivia wants to add a braid border to each piece. Find how long each border is.

A

B

It is _____ cm.

C

D

12 cm
10 cm
9 cm
C

17 cm 17 cm
16 cm
D
12 cm

③ Olivia cut out a parallelogram from the middle of Cardboard C as shown.

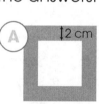

8 cm
6 cm
7 cm
cut-out

a. What is the area of the cardboard frame?

_____

b. What is the perimeter of the cut-out?

_____

④ Olivia cut a triangle out of Cardboard D with a base of 10 cm and a height of 13 cm as shown. What is the area of the cardboard frame?

cut-out

_____

⑤ Check the diagram each problem describes. Then find the answers.

a. Olivia cut out a square from the middle of Cardboard A, leaving 2 cm on each side. What is the area of the cardboard frame?

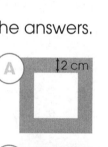

A   2 cm

B

2 cm

_____

b. Olivia cut out a rectangle from the middle of Cardboard B, leaving 2 cm on each side. What is the area of Cardboard B after removing the rectangle?

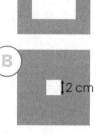

A   cut-out

2 cm

B

2 cm

_____

Lori did a home design project for school. Solve the problems. Show your work.

⑥ Lori designed a rectangular living room that has 180 m² of space.

     a. The living room is 15 m long. What is its width?

_____

     b. The ceiling is 3 m high. How much wallpaper is needed to cover all the walls of the living room? (Ignore the windows and doors.)

_____

⑦ Lori wanted to carpet the living room, leaving a 1-m border of hardwood floor around the room. How much carpet did she need?

carpet

_____

⑧ Lori's kitchen is in the shape of a triangle as shown.

     a. What is the perimeter of her kitchen?

Lori's Kitchen

5 m   13 m   12 m

_____

     b. How many square metres of tile did Lori need to cover the kitchen floor?

_____

     c. Lori's kitchen has a 3-m high ceiling. She wanted to paint the walls of the kitchen. If 1 can of paint covers 18 m², how many cans of paint did she need? (Ignore the windows and doors.)

_____

⑨ The bedroom is in the shape of a parallelogram with a base of 18 m and a height of 16 m. How much carpet did Lori need to cover the floor?

_____

Help the children draw the shapes they describe on the grid. Then answer the questions.

⑩

My square has a perimeter of 12 cm and an area of 9 cm².

1 cm
1 cm

a.   What is the side length?

_____

b.   Do you need to know both the perimeter and area to draw the square? Explain.

_____

_____

⑪

My parallelogram has an area of 15 cm².

a.   base: _____   height: _____

b.   Does the parallelogram have the same area if the base and height are swapped? Explain.

_____

_____

⑫

My triangle has an area of 6 cm².

a.   base: _____   height: _____

b.   If she draws one more triangle with the same area but makes its height the same as the base of the first one, what is the base of the second triangle? Explain.

_____

_____

9 Volume and Surface Area

• solving problems involving volume and surface area

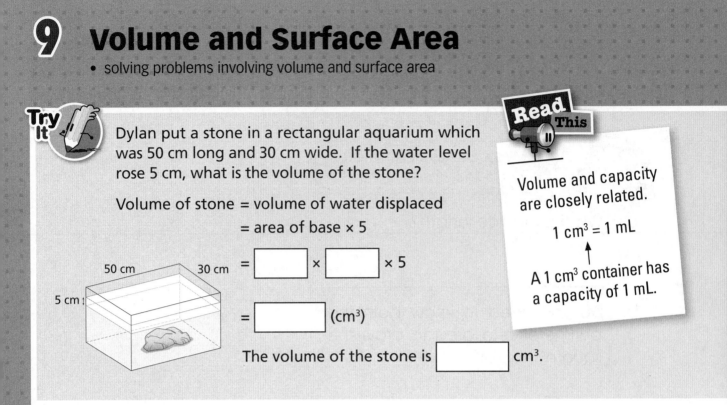

Dylan put a stone in a rectangular aquarium which was 50 cm long and 30 cm wide. If the water level rose 5 cm, what is the volume of the stone?

Volume of stone = volume of water displaced
= area of base × 5

50 cm   30 cm

5 cm

= ☐ × ☐ × 5

= ☐ (cm³)

The volume of the stone is ☐ cm³.

Read This

Volume and capacity are closely related.

1 cm³ = 1 mL

A 1 cm³ container has a capacity of 1 mL.

Solve the problems. Show your work.

① Gary wants to find the volume of each brick*. He puts each of them in a container with 200 mL of water.

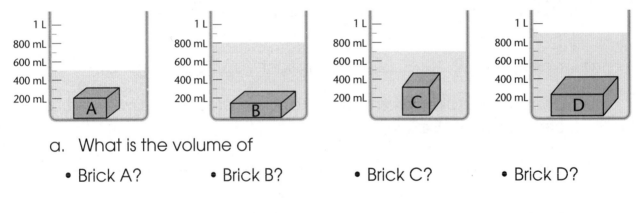

a. What is the volume of

• Brick A?   • Brick B?   • Brick C?   • Brick D?

_____   _____   _____   _____

b. List the bricks in order from greatest to least volume.

_____

c. Brick A has a height of 5 cm. What is the area of its base?

_____

d. If Brick A is 6 cm wide, what is its length?

_____

*Note: The sizes of the bricks shown are not true to scale.

See the bars of soap that Andy made. Solve the problems. Show your work.

4 cm 4 cm 4 cm **Soap A**	4 cm 5 cm 8 cm **Soap B**	3.5 cm 4 cm 4 cm 4 cm 9 cm **Soap C**

② Find the volume of the bars of soap.

    a. Soap A   b. Soap B   c. Soap C

_____   _____   _____

③ Andy wants to wrap them. Find how much wrapping paper Andy needs for each bar of soap.

    a. Soap A   b. Soap B   c. Soap C

_____   _____   _____

④ If Andy cuts Soap B in half as shown,

    a. what is the volume of each half?

_____

    b. how much wrapping paper is needed to wrap each half?

_____

⑤ If Andy cuts Soap C in half as shown,

    a. what is the volume of each half?

_____

    b. how much wrapping paper is needed to wrap each half?

_____

Dolores has a plastic box in the shape of a rectangular prism. Solve the problems. Show your work.

⑥ The length of the box is 15 cm. What is its width?

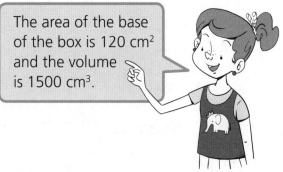

The area of the base of the box is 120 cm² and the volume is 1500 cm³.

_____

⑦ What is the height of the box?

_____

⑧ What is the capacity of the box in litres?

_____

⑨ Dolores is using her box to fill two containers with sand. Container A is a rectangular prism 0.5 m long, 0.45 m wide, and 0.2 m high.

   a. What is the volume of Container A?

_____

   b. How many boxes of sand fill up Container A?

_____

   c. 40 boxes of sand fill up Container B. What is the volume of Container B?

_____

   d. If the height of Container B is 60 cm, what is its base area?

_____

   e. If Dolores empties the sand in Container A into Container B, how high will the sand reach?

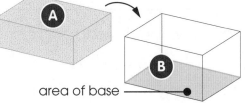

area of base

_____

Solve the problems. Show your work.

⑩ A swimming pool is 30 m long, 21 m wide, and 1.8 m deep.

a. What is the volume of the swimming pool?

_____

b. How many litres of water can the swimming pool hold?

Tips

$1 \text{ m}^3 = 1000 \text{ L}$

_____

c. If the swimming pool is filled to a depth of 1.6 m, how many litres of water will there be?

_____

d. How much water should be pumped into the swimming pool to raise the water level from 1.6 m to 1.7 m?

_____

e. If 300 000 L of water is pumped into the swimming pool each hour, how long will it take to fill up the entire swimming pool?

_____

f. If 126 000 L of water is pumped into the swimming pool, how much will the water level rise?

_____

⑪ Linda combines two blocks to create a structure as shown.

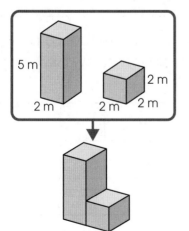

5 m
2 m
2 m
2 m
2 m

a. What is the volume of the structure?

_____

b. Linda wants to paint the combined structure except the bottom. If 1 L of paint covers 1 m², how much paint does she need?

_____

10 Patterning

- solving problems involving patterning

Try It

Darren is trying to increase the number of pages he reads each day. He reads 2 pages on Monday, 4 pages on Tuesday, and 6 pages on Wednesday. How many pages will he read on Saturday?

Read This

To solve problems, use a table to organize the information and then look for patterns.

Day	Mon	Tue	Wed	Thu	Fri	Sat
No. of Pages	2	4	6			

Darren will read ☐ pages on Saturday.

Complete the tables and solve the problems.

① Jimmy is making mixed nuts with peanuts, almonds, hazelnuts, and cashews.

a. If for every 1 almond he adds 5 peanuts, how many peanuts will he have when he has added 10 almonds?

No. of Almonds	1	2	3	4	5	6	7	8	9	10
No. of Peanuts	5									

He will have _____ peanuts.

b. If for every 3 peanuts he adds 2 hazelnuts, how many hazelnuts will he have when there are 27 peanuts?

_____

c. If for the first 3 almonds he adds 2 cashews, for the second 3 he adds 3, for the third 3 he adds 4, and so on, how many cashews will he add when he adds 3 almonds for the ninth time?

_____

Look at the table. Solve the problems. Show your work.

② Gary kept track of the growth of his favourite vine in his greenhouse.

Month	Sep	Oct	Nov	Dec	Jan	Feb	Mar	Apr
Length of Vine (cm)	10	20	30	40	50	60	70	80

a. What was the growth pattern of Gary's vine between September and April?

_____

b. If the growth pattern stays the same, when will the vine be 110 cm long?

_____

c. If the growth pattern stays the same, how long will the vine be in the coming September?

_____

d. Gary noticed that the number of leaves on his vine was increasing. For every 5 cm the vine grew, the number of leaves increased by 4. How many leaves had grown by April?

_____

e. Gary decides to cut off 2.5 cm for every 10 cm the vine grows from April. If the growth pattern of his vine stays the same, how long will it be in the coming August?

_____

Help Bill solve the problems. Show your work.

③ Bill won $5000 in a lottery. He decided to put the money in a new bank account and only use it to pay his monthly rent of $750.

    a. Make a table to show the pattern.

    b. What will the balance of the bank account in the third month be?

    _____

    c. For how many months can he pay his rent from this account?

    _____

    d. Describe the pattern of the balance of his account.

    _____

    e. If the bank gives him $8.80 interest in the second month, $7.70 in the third month, $6.60 in the fourth month, and so on, how much will he receive in the sixth month?

    _____

    f. Describe the pattern of Bill's interest.

    _____

    g. How much interest will Bill receive in total over 6 months?

    _____

    h. What will the balance of his account be after 5 months of paying rent and receiving interest?

    _____

Help Erin solve the problems. Show your work.

Make tables here if needed.

④ In the first month, Erin received $12 as a gift and spent $8 on books. In the second month, she received $14 as a gift and spent $10.50. In the third month, she received $16 and spent $13.

a. Describe the pattern of the money that Erin received.

_____

b. If this pattern continued, how much did she receive in the sixth month?

_____

c. Describe the pattern of the money that Erin spent.

_____

d. If this pattern continued, how much did she spend in the sixth month?

_____

e. How much money did she save over the first 6 months?

_____

f. When would the amount Erin received be the same as the amount she spent?

_____

g. How much more would Erin spend than receive in the 12th month?

_____

11 Equations

- solving problems using equations

Try It

Jody is thinking of a number. This number multiplied by 3 is 15. What is the number?

Check the equation that represents the problem. Then solve it.

(A) $n \times 3 = 15$

(B) $n \times 15 = 3$

The number is ☐.

Read This

Read the question carefully to determine the missing number, then choose a letter to represent it.

Represent the unknown of each problem with n. Check or write the correct equation. Then solve for n.

① A number divided by 2 is 5.

    (A) $n \div 2 = 5$

    (B) $5 \div n = 2$

    $n =$

② 4 multiplied by this number is 36.

    (A) $36 \times n = 4$

    (B) $4 \times n = 36$

③ 5 more than a number is 7.

    (A) $5 \times n = 7$

    (B) $n + 5 = 7$

④ A number minus 6 is 10.

    (A) $n - 6 = 10$

    (B) $6 - n = 10$

⑤ 16 divided by a number is 4.

    (A) $n \div 16 = 4$

    (B) $16 \div n = 4$

⑥ Half of a number is 12.

    $n \div 2 = 12$

    $n =$ _____

⑦ A number tripled is 21.

⑧ 28 divided by a number is 4.

⑨ Adding 6 to a number is 18.

⑩ This number multiplied by 3 is 27.

Match the equations with the problems. Write the letters. Then find the missing ages using the given information.

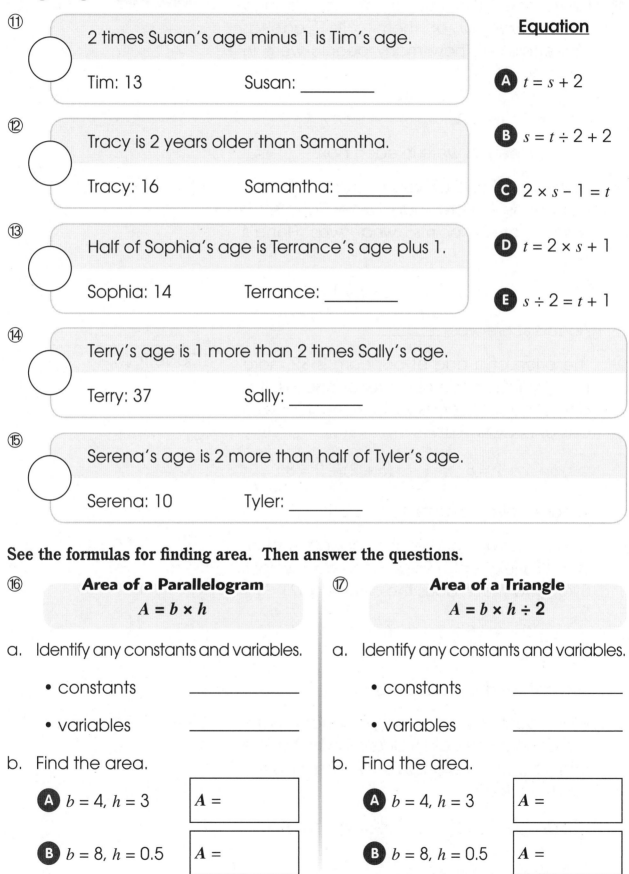

⑪
2 times Susan's age minus 1 is Tim's age.

Tim: 13   Susan: _____

Equation

Ⓐ $t = s + 2$

⑫
Tracy is 2 years older than Samantha.

Tracy: 16   Samantha: _____

Ⓑ $s = t \div 2 + 2$

Ⓒ $2 \times s - 1 = t$

⑬
Half of Sophia's age is Terrance's age plus 1.

Sophia: 14   Terrance: _____

Ⓓ $t = 2 \times s + 1$

Ⓔ $s \div 2 = t + 1$

⑭
Terry's age is 1 more than 2 times Sally's age.

Terry: 37   Sally: _____

⑮
Serena's age is 2 more than half of Tyler's age.

Serena: 10   Tyler: _____

See the formulas for finding area. Then answer the questions.

⑯   **Area of a Parallelogram**
$A = b \times h$

a. Identify any constants and variables.

• constants   _____

• variables   _____

b. Find the area.

Ⓐ $b = 4, h = 3$ $A =$

Ⓑ $b = 8, h = 0.5$ $A =$

⑰   **Area of a Triangle**
$A = b \times h \div 2$

a. Identify any constants and variables.

• constants   _____

• variables   _____

b. Find the area.

Ⓐ $b = 4, h = 3$ $A =$

Ⓑ $b = 8, h = 0.5$ $A =$

Check the equation that represents each problem. Then solve it.

⑱ Ryan opened 3 boxes of pencils and gave away 10 of them. If Ryan has 38 pencils left, how many pencils were in each box?

(A) $p \times 3 - 10 = 38$ (B) $10 \times 3 - p = 38$

_____ pencils were in each box.

Solve for p.

⑲ Elaine and Fiona played a game. Elaine's score was 1 more than twice Fiona's. If Elaine got 31 points, what was Fiona's score?

(A) $f \div 2 + 1 = 31$ (B) $2 \times f + 1 = 31$

Fiona's score was _____.

Solve for f.

⑳ The price of a bag of popcorn is $2 more than half the price of a box of biscuits. If a bag of popcorn costs $8, how much does a box of biscuits cost?

(A) $b \div 2 + 2 = 8$ (B) $(b + 2) \div 2 = 8$

A box of biscuits costs $_____ .

Solve for b.

㉑ Three times a dog's weight is equal to half of a cat's weight plus 9 kg. If the dog weighs 5 kg, how much does the cat weigh?

(A) $c \div 2 + 9 = 5 \times 3$ (B) $(c + 9) \div 2 = 5 \times 3$

The cat weighs _____ kg.

Solve for c.

㉒ Alan bought a burger using a coupon. With the coupon, he paid $3 less than half of the original price. If Alan paid $5, what was the original price?

(A) $(b - 3) \div 2 = 5$ (B) $(b \div 2) - 3 = 5$

The original price was $_____ .

Solve for b.

Solve each problem by formulating an equation first.

㉓ Harry and Anna went shopping at Super Discount Store.

a. A handbag cost $15 more than a wallet. If the wallet cost $12, how much was the handbag?

$h -$ ☐ $=$ ☐

$h =$ ☐   The handbag was $_____ .

b. The price difference between Skirt A and Skirt B was $7. Skirt A was less expensive than Skirt B. If Skirt A cost $35, how much did Skirt B cost?

_____

c. A sweater cost $25 less than a jacket. If the jacket cost $145, how much did the sweater cost?

_____

㉔ The store was having a promotion. Read the signs about this promotion.

a. The total cost of 3 T-shirts and a pair of shorts was $54 before discount. If one T-shirt cost $12, how much did the pair of shorts cost?

_____

b. Anna bought a pair of earrings which cost $12 before discount. If she got $3 change, how much did she give to the cashier?

_____

c. Harry bought a coat which cost $56 before discount. If he got $12 change, how much did he give to the cashier?

_____

$5 off
purchases of $20
and under

$8 off
purchases of
over $20

LEVEL 3 – APPLICATIONS

• reading and making graphs

Try
It

Barney kept track of the number of fiction and non-fiction books borrowed each week from his school library. Complete the graph.

Read
This

Always remember to add a descriptive title, appropriate labels, and any legend if needed to a graph.

Week No.	1	2	3	4	5	6
Fiction	70	75	65	50	40	70
Non-fiction	55	90	60	50	15	45

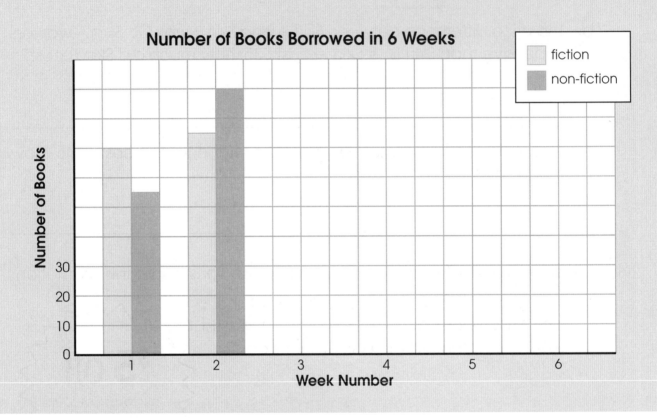

Number of Books Borrowed in 6 Weeks

Answer the questions about the double bar graph above.

① How many books were borrowed in Week 3?

_____

② In which week were the most books borrowed in total?

_____

③ In which week were the fewest non-fiction books borrowed?

_____

④ In how many weeks were fewer than 60 fiction books borrowed?

_____

⑤ How many more fiction books than non-fiction books were borrowed in the first week?

_____

⑥ In which week was the number of fiction books borrowed the same as the number of non-fiction books borrowed?

_____

⑦ In which week was the number of non-fiction books borrowed more than the number of fiction books borrowed?

_____

⑧ There were only 3 school days in one of the 6 weeks. Which week was it? Explain.

_____

⑨ When Barney checked over the math books, he found that $\frac{1}{4}$ of them were textbooks, $\frac{1}{4}$ activity books, and the rest workbooks.

a. Check the correct circle graph.

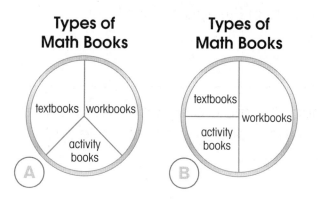

Types of Math Books

A

Types of Math Books

B

b. If there were 120 math books, how many were

• activity books?

_____

• workbooks?

_____

Brenda and Tammy recorded their spending on groceries each month in a table. Use a double line graph to show the data. Then answer the questions.

⑩

Month	Jan	Feb	Mar	Apr	May	Jun
Brenda's Spending	$275	$300	$250	$350	$175	$225
Tammy's Spending	$325	$200	$75	$200	$225	$300

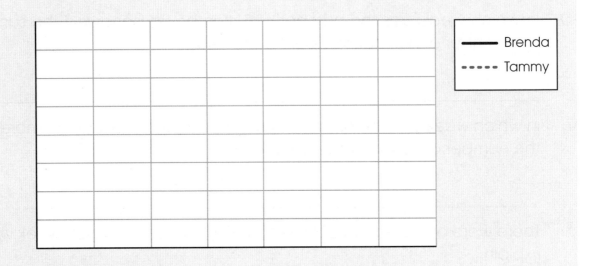

——— Brenda

----- Tammy

a. How much more did Brenda spend than Tammy in April?

_____

b. How much more did Tammy spend than Brenda in June?

_____

c. In which month did Brenda spend the most on groceries? How much more did she spend compared to the month she spent the least?

_____

⑪ In which month was the difference between Brenda's and Tammy's spending the greatest?

_____

⑫ Who spent more money in the six months? How much more?

_____

⑬ Below is the breakdown of Brenda's and Tammy's spending in February.

Brenda

- $\frac{1}{3}$ on meat
- $\frac{1}{6}$ on fruits
- the rest on vegetables

Tammy

- $\frac{1}{4}$ on meat
- $\frac{1}{8}$ on fruits
- the rest on vegetables

a. Label the circle graphs with the correct names.

_____'s
spending in February

_____'s
spending in February

b. In February, how much did Brenda spend on
   • meat?   • fruits?

   _____   _____

c. In February, how much did Tammy spend on
   • meat?   • vegetables?

   _____   _____

d. Who spent more on fruits in February? By how much?

   _____

13 Graphs (2)

- choosing the best graph to represent data

Check the graph that is more appropriate for the same set of data. Explain your choice.

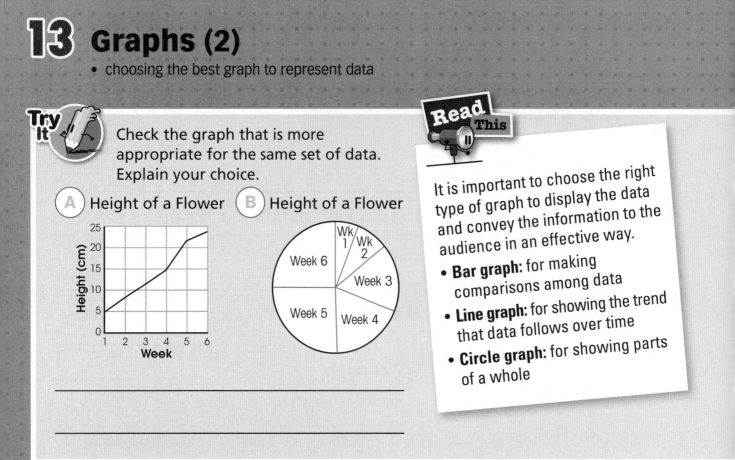

(A) Height of a Flower   (B) Height of a Flower

_____

_____

Read This

It is important to choose the right type of graph to display the data and convey the information to the audience in an effective way.

- **Bar graph:** for making comparisons among data
- **Line graph:** for showing the trend that data follows over time
- **Circle graph:** for showing parts of a whole

Choose the type of graph that best represents each set of data. Write "B" for bar graph, "L" for line graph, or "C" for circle graph.

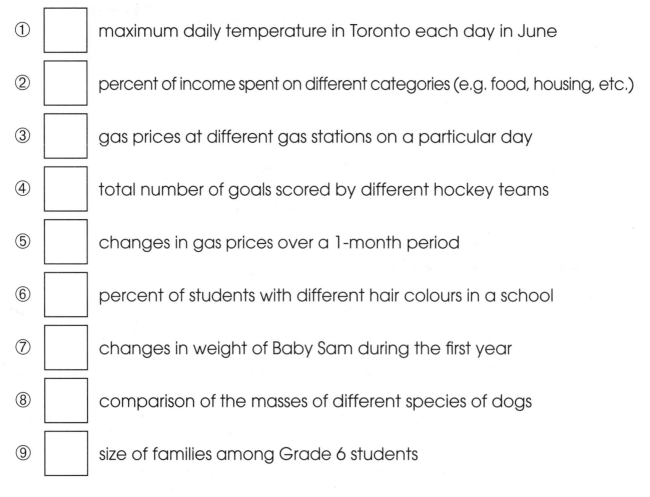

① ☐ maximum daily temperature in Toronto each day in June

② ☐ percent of income spent on different categories (e.g. food, housing, etc.)

③ ☐ gas prices at different gas stations on a particular day

④ ☐ total number of goals scored by different hockey teams

⑤ ☐ changes in gas prices over a 1-month period

⑥ ☐ percent of students with different hair colours in a school

⑦ ☐ changes in weight of Baby Sam during the first year

⑧ ☐ comparison of the masses of different species of dogs

⑨ ☐ size of families among Grade 6 students

A teacher measured the heights of her students. Complete the table and the circle graph using the data. Then answer the questions.

⑩

Heights of Students (cm)

| 152 | 158 | 167 | 182 | 156 | 150 | 156 | 165 | 173 | 189 |
| 168 | 171 | 170 | 153 | 164 | 185 | 159 | 168 | 174 | 155 |

Height (cm)	Tally	No. of Students	Fraction of the Whole
150 – 159			
160 – 169			
170 – 179			
180 – 189			

Heights of Students (cm)

a. What is the range of heights among the students? _____

b. Which height range is

• the most common? _____

• the least common? _____

c. Answer the question if the answer can be found by reading the above circle graph; otherwise, put a cross on the line.

• What is the mean height of the students? _____

• Which height range takes up about 50% of the graph? _____

• What percent of the graph does the 150 – 159 cm range take up? _____

• What is the median height of the students? _____

• How many students' heights were measured? _____

Use the information from the bar graph to complete the circle graph. Then answer the questions and check which graph(s) is/are appropriate for answering each question.

⑪

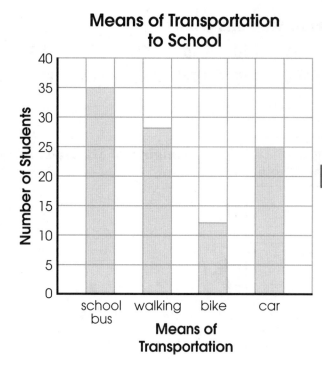

Means of Transportation to School

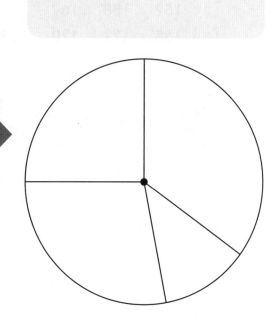

	bar graph	circle graph	both	answer
a.	Which is the most popular means of transportation to school?	○	○	○	_____
b.	How many more students walk than bike to school?	○	○	○	_____
c.	25% of the students take which means of transportation to school?	○	○	○	_____
d.	How many students were surveyed?	○	○	○	_____
e.	How many students bike to school?	○	○	○	_____
f.	What fraction of the students bike to school?	○	○	○	_____
g.	How many students ride a vehicle to school?	○	○	○	_____

Jonah recorded the heights of two plants over 6 weeks. Check the most appropriate graph to display the data. Then make the graph and answer the questions.

⑫

Heights of Plants

Week	1	2	3	4	5	6
Plant A (cm)	8	11	13	20	25	28
Plant B (cm)	5	7	15	18	24	26

Most Appropriate Graph

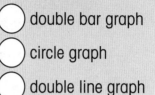

⚪ double bar graph
⚪ circle graph
⚪ double line graph

a. How much taller is Plant A than Plant B in Week 2?

_____

b. Jonah added fertilizer to the plants. In which week did he add fertilizer to

• Plant A?

_____

• Plant B?

_____

14 Probability

- solving problems involving probability

Try It

Paula has a bag with a red marble and a green marble. She picks a marble from the bag and flips a coin. Complete the tree diagram and list all the possible outcomes.

Read This

Tree diagrams help you visualize all the possible outcomes when there is more than one event.

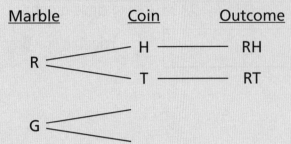

Marble	Coin	Outcome
R	H	RH
	T	RT
G		

Possible Outcomes:

_____

Look at the tree diagram above and answer the questions.

① What is the probability that Paula will get

   a. a red marble and a tail?

   _____

   b. a green marble and a head?

   _____

   c. 2 heads?

   _____

   d. a marble?

   _____

② Paula adds a blue marble to the bag. Draw a tree diagram to show all the possible outcomes.

Marble	Coin	Outcome

   a. How many possible outcomes are there?

   _____

   b. What is the probability that Paula will get a green marble and a head?

   _____

Read about the scenarios. Then answer the questions.

③

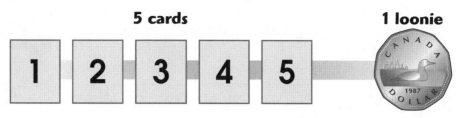

5 cards

| 1 | 2 | 3 | 4 | 5 |

1 loonie

Sally turns the cards face down and shuffles them. She then picks a card and flips the loonie.

a. Draw a tree diagram to show all the possible outcomes.

b. How many possible outcomes are there?

_____

c. What is the probability that she will get

- a "3" and a head?

_____

- a "5" and a tail?

_____

- an even number and a head?

_____

Sally decides to play this game with Linda. After each turn, the card is shuffled back into the deck. The person who gets "1" and a head first wins.

d. Sally did not win on her turn. What is the probability that

- Linda will win?   _____

- Linda will not win?   _____

e. Linda says, "I did not win in the last round, so I have a greater chance of winning this round." Is she correct? Explain.

_____

_____

Marley is making a probability game. Solve the problems. Show your work.

④ A box contains 10 balls: 2 red, 2 yellow, 2 green, 2 blue, and 2 white.

> I will draw a ball from this box at random.

Marley

a. How many possible outcomes are there?

_____

b. What is the probability that Marley will draw a

• red ball?   • white ball?

_____   _____

c. One ball of each colour is taken out of the box. Is the probability of drawing a ball of each colour still the same? Explain.

_____

_____

d. To make it a game, Marley will draw one of the five balls and spin the wheel below. Draw a tree diagram to show all the possible outcomes.

Grade 6
QR Code

QR Code – a quick way to access our fun-filled videos

Our QR code provides you with a quick and easy link to our fun-filled videos, which can help enrich your learning experience while you are working on the workbook. Below is a summary of the topics that the QR code brings you to. You may scan the QR code in each unit to learn about the topic or the QR code on the right to review all the topics you have learned in this book.

Scan this QR code or visit our Download Centre at *www.popularbook.ca.*

The topics introduced with the QR code:

1  **What are prime numbers?** (p. 11)
Learn what makes a number a prime number.

2  **How to Multiply a Decimal Number by a Whole Number** (p. 27)
See how multiplication with a decimal number is done.

3  **How to Divide a Decimal Number by a Whole Number** (p. 31)
See how division with a decimal number is done.

4  **Converting between Improper Fractions and Mixed Numbers** (p. 35)
Learn about how improper fractions and mixed numbers are related.

5  **Metric Prefixes** (p. 55)
Investigate the meaning of "kilo", "centi", and "milli".

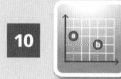

Level 1

1 Whole Numbers

Try It

T					
H	T	O	H	T	O
3	4	0	5	2	9
7	3	6	2	3	0

1.

T					
H	T	O	H	T	O
4	2	0	8	6	1

800 ; 60 ; 1

eight hundred sixty-one

2.

T					
H	T	O	H	T	O
3	0	8	0	9	5

300 000 + 8000 + 90 + 5

three hundred eight thousand ninety-five

3.

T					
H	T	O	H	T	O
5	2	0	1	7	0

500 000 + 20 000 + 100 + 70

five hundred twenty thousand one hundred seventy

4.

T					
H	T	O	H	T	O
	9	2	9	0	0

90 000 + 2000 + 900

ninety-two thousand nine hundred

5.

T					
H	T	O	H	T	O
2	5	6	8	0	3

200 000 + 50 000 + 6000 + 800 + 3

two hundred fifty-six thousand eight hundred three

6a. four hundred thirty-nine thousand two hundred twenty-five

b. five hundred sixty-eight thousand three hundred eight

c. seven hundred two thousand eight hundred forty-four

7a. 501 487   b. 28 715   c. 310 441

8a. 600 000 + 50 000 + 2000 + 90 + 3

b. 200 000 + 80 000 + 8000 + 500 + 60

c. 30 000 + 5000 + 700 + 10 + 3

9a. 50 000   b. 5000   c. 800

d. 400   e. 10   f. 6

g. 300 000   h. 7000

10a. hundred thousand

b. 10 000 times

11a. ten thousand   b. 200 times

12. B ; D   13. B ; D

14. C ; D   15. A ; B

16. B ; C

17. <

    186 470   208 944

180 000 190 000 200 000 210 000

18. <

    742 669   835 478

700 000 750 000 800 000 850 000

19. <   20. <   21. >

22. <   23. >   24. <

25. >

26. 46 328 < 47 985 < 48 864

27. 177 001 > 104 379 > 92 834

28. 209 501 ; 215 185 ; 216 920 ; 251 439

29. 397 973 ; 397 397 ; 379 739 ; 377 937

30. 502 397 ; 503 297 ; 520 793 ; 520 973

2 Prime and Composite Numbers

Try It

4 ; composite

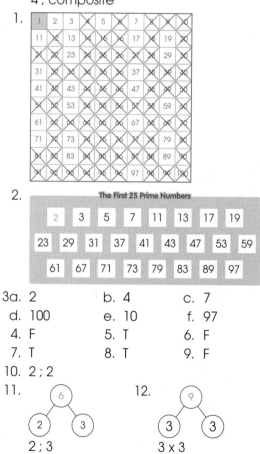

1.

2.

The First 25 Prime Numbers

2	3	5	7	11	13	17	19
23	29	31	37	41	43	47	53	59
61	67	71	73	79	83	89	97

3a. 2   b. 4   c. 7

d. 100   e. 10   f. 97

4. F   5. T   6. F

7. T   8. T   9. F

10. 2 ; 2

11.   12.

2 ; 3   3 x 3

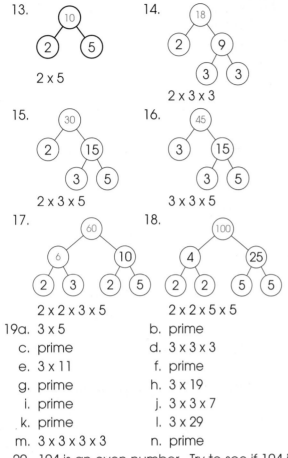

13. 2 x 5

14. 2 x 3 x 3

15. 2 x 3 x 5

16. 3 x 3 x 5

17. 2 x 2 x 3 x 5

18. 2 x 2 x 5 x 5

19a. 3 x 5
 b. prime
 c. prime
 d. 3 x 3 x 3
 e. 3 x 11
 f. prime
 g. prime
 h. 3 x 19
 i. prime
 j. 3 x 3 x 7
 k. prime
 l. 3 x 29
 m. 3 x 3 x 3 x 3
 n. prime

20. 104 is an even number. Try to see if 104 is a multiple of 2. If it is a multiple, then it is a composite number.

21. No, she is not correct. 121 is a composite number; 121 is divisible by 11.

22. No, she is not correct. 169 has 3 factors: 1, 13, and 169. It is a composite number.

3 Decimals

Try It

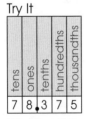

tens	ones	tenths	hundredths	thousandths
7	8	3	7	5

70 + 8 + 0.3 + 0.07 + 0.005

seventy-eight and three hundred seventy-five thousandths

1.

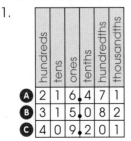

	hundreds	tens	ones	tenths	hundredths	thousandths
A	2	1	6	4	7	1
B	3	1	5	0	8	2
C	4	0	9	2	0	1

A: 200 + 10 + 6 + 0.4 + 0.07 + 0.001
two hundred sixteen and four hundred seventy-one thousandths

B: 300 + 10 + 5 + 0.08 + 0.002
three hundred fifteen and eighty-two thousandths

C: 400 + 9 + 0.2 + 0.001
four hundred nine and two hundred one thousandths

2. 0.4   3. 0.008
4. 0.05   5. 0.1
6. 90   7. 0.07
8. 0.002   9. 60
10. 0.2
11a. 1.568   b. 7.075
 c. 8.279   d. 1.659
12a. 5.111   b. 6.913
 c. 7.503   d. 0.593
13a. 59.01 ; 59.05 ; 59.1 ; 59.15
 b. 15.224 < 15.238 < 15.304 < 15.322
 c. 31.075 < 35.17 < 35.701 < 37.105
14a. 24.2 ; 22.04 ; 20.42 ; 20.24
 b. 37.423 > 37.342 > 37.243 > 37.234
 c. 79.38 > 78.93 > 78.309 > 78.093
15. A: 0.004   B: 0.008
 C: 0.021   D: 0.029
 E: 0.045
16. A: 8.32   B: 8.39
 C: 8.54   D: 8.64
 E: 8.74

17.

| 0.05 | 0.18 | 0.29 | 0.35 | 0.4 | 0.42 |

18.

| 5.007 | 5.019 | 5.025 | 5.028 | 5.036 | 5.042 |

19.

| 12.39 | 12.47 | 12.6 | 12.66 | 12.78 | 12.8 |

20. 0.42 ; 5.042 ; 12.8
21. 16 ; 15.5 ; 15.51   22. 42 ; 41.7 ; 41.70
23. 18 ; 18.1 ; 18.09   24. 25 ; 25.5 ; 25.50
25. 37 ; 36.5 ; 36.50
26. <   27. =
28. >   29. >
30. =   31. <
32. =   33. >
34. <   35. =
36. A ; D   37. B ; D
38. A ; D   39. C ; D

4 Adding Decimals

Try It
65.601
1. 8.988
2. 6.429
3. 25.093
4. 9.457
5. 9.797
6. 40.401
7. 13.407
8. 20.000
9. 14.271
10. 59.504
11. 40.841
12. 55.915
13. 11.607
14. 9.43
15. 4.931
16. 16.533
17. 29.815
18. 58.996
19. 75.216
20. 50.655
21. 44.369
22. 95.657
23. 32.313
24. 202.849
25. 389.308
26. 288.717
27. 345.993

28.

Sum	Estimate
79.132	80
+ 19.196	+ 19
98.328	99

29.

Sum	Estimate
47.748	48
+ 62.517	+ 63
110.265	111

30.

Sum	Estimate
194.057	194
+ 88.708	+ 89
282.765	283

31.

Sum	Estimate
70.831	71
+185.098	+ 185
255.929	256

32. ✔
33. ✘ ; 100.746
34. ✘ ; 98.308
35. ✔
36. ✘ ; 99.523
37. ✘ ; 78.415
38. 68.018
39. 233.869
40. 380.314
41. 274.391
42. 505.707
43. 787.409
44. 649.289
45a. 2.287 kg
b. 5.995 kg
c. 7.925 kg
d. 3.07 kg
46. The total weight is 16.608 kg, so it will not exceed the weight limit.

5 Subtracting Decimals

Try It
25.059
1. 2.235
2. 1.194
3. 5.865
4. 5.752
5. 3.375
6. 4.817
7. 9.163
8. 9.291
9. 10.789
10. 17.585
11. 5.656
12. 14.187
13. 1.576
14. 5.071
15. 8.938
16. 3.394
17. 4.097
18. 3.332
19. 2.838
20. 71.464
21. 4.452
22. 2.523
23. 4.981
24. 34.069
25. 60.744
26. 89.383
27. 29.409
28. 82.512
29. 64.101
30. 89.918
31. 154.607

32.

Difference	Estimate
16.479	16
− 10.640	− 11
5.839	5

33.

Difference	Estimate
25.170	25
− 19.525	− 20
5.645	5

34a. 18.773 ; 19
b. 48.351 ; 48
c. 7.372 ; 7
d. 70.488 ; 70

35.

39.457
− 11.509
27.948

36.

67.100
− 29.477
37.623

37.

167.040
− 0.256
166.784

38.

80.000
− 75.649
4.351

39.

24.130
− 13.488
10.642

40.

25.289
− 11.300
13.989

41.

40.100
− 28.324
11.776

42.

27.811
− 16.360
11.451

43a. 3.275 km
b. 6.9 km
c. 4.95 km
d. 2.797 km
e. 5.219 km
44. 0.478 km
45. 2.153 km
46. 4.103 km
47. 1.642 km
48a. 1.747 km
b. 1.896 km
c. 7.209 km
49. She travelled 9.745 km in all.

6 Multiplying Decimals

Try It
7.02
1. 9.2
2. 25.2
3. 32.4
4. 74.7
5. 51.55
6. 52.56
7. 73.98
8. 30.16
9. 66.25
10. 86.22
11. 57.52
12. 63.21
13. 61.80
14. 67.44
15. 15.24
16. 68.52
17. 42.4
18. 12.66
19. 12.84
20. 15.03
21. 17
22. 23.7
23. 18.6
24. 9.6
25. 11.31
26. 10.38
27. 31.4
28. 53.97
29. 20.3
30. 24.12
31a. 1 ; 23.1
b. 1 ; 45
c. 2 ; 399
d. 2 ; 1360
e. 2 ; 1415
f. 3 ; 4560

g. 3 ; 8090   h. 3 ; 11 280
i. 4 ; 54 300   j. 4 ; 164 800
32. 4.5 ; 1   33. 0.03 ; 2
34. 0.315 ; 3   35. 5.1 ; 2
36. 0.9 ; 2   37. 0.002 ; 3
38. 0.17 ; 2   39. 9 ; 13.5 ; 45
40. 37.8 ; 44.1 ; 630   41. 12 ; 33.6 ; 0.8
42. 14.4 ; 30.6 ; 0.06   43. 4.56 ; 5.7 ; 114
44. 10.8 ; 7.2 ; 0.4
45a. $2.60   b. $2.76
c. $4.32   d. $2.24
e. $5.20   f. $7.20
g. $4.60   h. $28
46a. 3.72 L   b. 2.64 L
c. 3.3 L   d. 6.2 L
e. 33 L   f. 56 L
g. 620 L   h. 7300 L
47a. 2.25 kg   b. 4.5 kg
c. 3.05 kg   d. 61 kg
e. 3.1 kg   f. 620 kg
g. 5.1 kg   h. 10 200 kg

7 Dividing Decimals

Try It
2.3
3)6.9
6
9
9

1. 2.4 / 2)4.8 / 4 / 8 / 8
2. 1.9 / 4)7.6 / 4 / 3 6 / 3 6
3. 3.7 / 5)18.5 / 15 / 3 5 / 3 5
4. 4.2 / 6)25.2 / 24 / 1 2 / 1 2
5. 2.25 / 3)6.75 / 6 / 7 / 6 / 15 / 15
6. 3.1 / 5)15.5 / 15 / 5 / 5
7. 0.38 / 4)1.52 / 1 2 / 32 / 32
8. 7.33 / 8)58.64 / 56 / 2 6 / 2 4 / 24 / 24

9. 4.21 / 7)29.47 / 28 / 1 4 / 1 4 / 7 / 7
10. 3.04 / 4)12.16 / 12 / 16 / 16
11. 7.09 / 2)14.18 / 14 / 18 / 18
12. 6.13 / 3)18.39 / 18 / 3 / 3 / 9 / 9

13. 2.3   14. 3.3   15. 1.6
16. 2.92   17. 7.11   18. 3.65
19. 9.95   20. 8.2   21. 3.9
22. 2.13   23. 2.74   24. 2.45
25. 2.9 ; 0.29   26. 4.5 ; 0.45
27. 350. ; 3.5   28. 24.3 ; 0.243
29. 1409. ; 1.409   30. 6. ; 0.6
31. 7.5 ; 0.075   32. 13.9 ; 0.0139
33. 10   34. 100   35. 100
36. 1000   37. 1   38. 10
39. 1000   40. 10   41. 100
42. 100   43. 100   44. 100
45. 12.8 ; 9.6 ; 3.84 ; 0.384
46. 10.6 ; 5.3 ; 0.212 ; 0.0212
47. 49.2 ; 19.68 ; 9.84 ; 0.984
48. 7.5 ; 4.5 ; 0.225 ; 0.0225
49. 49.56 ; 21.24 ; 14.868 ; 0.14868
50. 84.28 ; 36.12 ; 2.5284 ; 0.25284
51a. 0.2 kg   b. 0.18 kg   c. 0.15 kg
52a. 0.3 L   b. 0.225 L   c. 0.18 L
53a. 56.88 g   b. 50.56 g   c. 45.504 g
54a. 101.808 g ; 84.24 g
b. 84.84 g of cereal, 70.2 g of popcorn
c. 63.63 g of cereal, 52.65 g of popcorn
d. 50.904 g of cereal, 42.12 g of popcorn

8 Equivalent Fractions

Try It
(10/20) (5/10) 3/9
1. 2   2. 4   3. 8
4. 4   5. 2   6. 2
7. 3   8. 1   9. 4
10. 1   11. 4   12. 15
13. (Suggested answers)
a. 10/12 15/18 20/24   b. 6/16 9/24 12/32

c. $\dfrac{3}{5}$ $\dfrac{12}{20}$ $\dfrac{18}{30}$ d. $\dfrac{1}{4}$ $\dfrac{4}{16}$ $\dfrac{6}{24}$

e. $\dfrac{2}{3}$ $\dfrac{20}{30}$ $\dfrac{30}{45}$ f. $\dfrac{2}{3}$ $\dfrac{4}{6}$ $\dfrac{32}{48}$

14-25. (Suggested equivalent fractions)

14. = ; $\dfrac{2}{8}$ 15. not equivalent

16. = ; $\dfrac{2}{3}$ 17. not equivalent

18. = ; $\dfrac{2}{5}$ 19. = ; $\dfrac{6}{4}$

20. = ; $\dfrac{21}{15}$ 21. not equivalent

22. = ; $\dfrac{8}{6}$ 23. = ; $\dfrac{10}{4}$

24. not equivalent   25. = ; $\dfrac{12}{27}$

26. $\dfrac{6}{9}$ $\dfrac{12}{18}$ $\cancel{\dfrac{9}{12}}$ $\dfrac{2}{3}$ 27. $\dfrac{1}{3}$ $\dfrac{4}{12}$ $\cancel{\dfrac{3}{4}}$ $\dfrac{2}{6}$

28. $\dfrac{3}{5}$ $\cancel{\dfrac{5}{8}}$ $\dfrac{6}{10}$ $\dfrac{12}{20}$ 29. $\dfrac{10}{8}$ $\dfrac{15}{12}$ $\dfrac{5}{4}$ $\cancel{\dfrac{4}{5}}$

30. $\dfrac{9}{10}$ 31. $\dfrac{5}{6}$

32. $\dfrac{3}{4}$ 33. $\dfrac{2}{3}$

34. $\dfrac{1}{4}$ 35. $\dfrac{1}{2}$

36. $\dfrac{9}{10}$ 37. $\dfrac{5}{11}$

38. $\dfrac{7}{8}$ 39. $\dfrac{19}{20}$

40. $\dfrac{7}{9}$ 41. $\dfrac{9}{10}$

42. $\dfrac{5}{3}$; $1\dfrac{2}{3}$ 43. $\dfrac{6}{5}$; $1\dfrac{1}{5}$

44. $\dfrac{5}{3}$; $1\dfrac{2}{3}$ 45. $\dfrac{5}{2}$; $2\dfrac{1}{2}$

46. $\dfrac{9}{8}$; $1\dfrac{1}{8}$ 47. $\dfrac{3}{2}$; $1\dfrac{1}{2}$

48. $\dfrac{4}{3}$; $1\dfrac{1}{3}$ 49. $\dfrac{7}{5}$; $1\dfrac{2}{5}$

50. $4\dfrac{2}{7}$ 51. $2\dfrac{2}{5}$

52. $3\dfrac{1}{12}$ 53. $3\dfrac{1}{8}$

54. 4   55. $1\dfrac{1}{2}$

56. $1\dfrac{1}{5}$ 57. $10\dfrac{5}{9}$

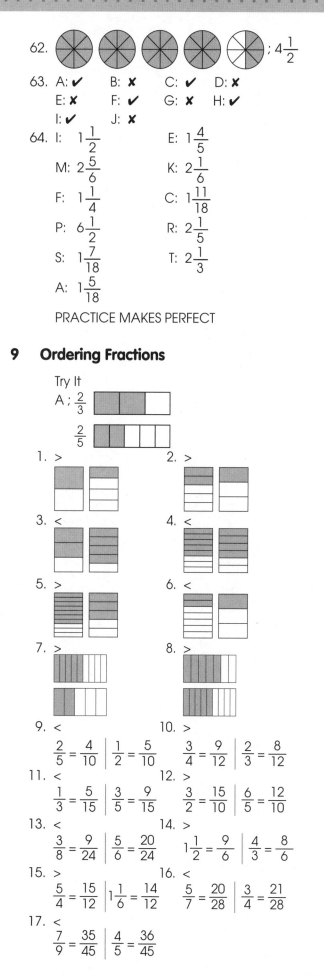

58. ; $1\dfrac{3}{4}$

59. ; $1\dfrac{2}{3}$

60. ; $1\dfrac{1}{4}$

61. ; $1\dfrac{3}{5}$

62. ; $4\dfrac{1}{2}$

63. A: ✔   B: ✘   C: ✔   D: ✘
     E: ✘   F: ✔   G: ✘   H: ✔
     I: ✔   J: ✘

64. I: $1\dfrac{1}{2}$ E: $1\dfrac{4}{5}$
     M: $2\dfrac{5}{6}$ K: $2\dfrac{1}{6}$
     F: $1\dfrac{1}{4}$ C: $1\dfrac{11}{18}$
     P: $6\dfrac{1}{2}$ R: $2\dfrac{1}{5}$
     S: $1\dfrac{7}{18}$ T: $2\dfrac{1}{3}$
     A: $1\dfrac{5}{18}$

PRACTICE MAKES PERFECT

9 Ordering Fractions

Try It

A ; $\dfrac{2}{3}$

$\dfrac{2}{5}$

1. >   2. >

3. <   4. <

5. >   6. <

7. >   8. >

9. <   10. >
    $\dfrac{2}{5} = \dfrac{4}{10}$ | $\dfrac{1}{2} = \dfrac{5}{10}$ $\dfrac{3}{4} = \dfrac{9}{12}$ | $\dfrac{2}{3} = \dfrac{8}{12}$

11. <   12. >
    $\dfrac{1}{3} = \dfrac{5}{15}$ | $\dfrac{3}{5} = \dfrac{9}{15}$ $\dfrac{3}{2} = \dfrac{15}{10}$ | $\dfrac{6}{5} = \dfrac{12}{10}$

13. <   14. >
    $\dfrac{3}{8} = \dfrac{9}{24}$ | $\dfrac{5}{6} = \dfrac{20}{24}$ $1\dfrac{1}{2} = \dfrac{9}{6}$ | $\dfrac{4}{3} = \dfrac{8}{6}$

15. >   16. <
    $\dfrac{5}{4} = \dfrac{15}{12}$ | $1\dfrac{1}{6} = \dfrac{14}{12}$ $\dfrac{5}{7} = \dfrac{20}{28}$ | $\dfrac{3}{4} = \dfrac{21}{28}$

17. <
    $\dfrac{7}{9} = \dfrac{35}{45}$ | $\dfrac{4}{5} = \dfrac{36}{45}$

18. <   19. <   20. <   21. >

22. >   23. <   24. <   25. >

26. <   27. >   28. >   29. >

30. $\frac{4}{8}$; $\frac{5}{8}$; $\frac{7}{5}$

31. $2\frac{3}{5} < 2\frac{4}{5} < 3\frac{1}{5}$

32. $\frac{6}{15} < \frac{7}{10} < \frac{4}{5}$

33. $\frac{1}{4} < \frac{7}{12} < \frac{2}{3}$

34. $\frac{5}{12} < \frac{1}{2} < \frac{2}{3} < \frac{5}{6}$

35. $1\frac{1}{3} < \frac{7}{5} < \frac{5}{3} < 1\frac{11}{15}$

36. $\frac{24}{10} < 2\frac{1}{2} < \frac{13}{5} < 2\frac{7}{10}$

37. $\frac{18}{20} < \frac{30}{20} < 1\frac{3}{4} < 2\frac{1}{5}$

38a. $\boxed{\frac{5}{6}}$ $\frac{5}{8}$ b. $\boxed{\frac{9}{11}}$ $\frac{9}{13}$

39a. $\boxed{\frac{9}{10}}$ $\frac{9}{8}$ b. $\frac{10}{7}$ $\boxed{\frac{10}{9}}$

40. $\frac{6}{7}$ $\boxed{\frac{6}{5}}$ $\frac{6}{15}$ $\frac{6}{10}$

41. $\frac{9}{12}$ $\frac{9}{11}$ $\frac{9}{10}$ $\boxed{\frac{9}{14}}$

42. >
$\frac{2}{5} = \frac{6}{15}$ $\frac{3}{13} = \frac{6}{26}$

43. >
$\frac{2}{7} = \frac{2}{7}$ $\frac{1}{12} = \frac{2}{24}$

44. <
$\frac{3}{8} = \frac{6}{16}$ $\frac{6}{13} = \frac{6}{13}$

45. >
$\frac{5}{9} = \frac{10}{18}$ $\frac{10}{21} = \frac{10}{21}$

46. >
$\frac{2}{5} = \frac{10}{25}$ $\frac{5}{17} = \frac{10}{34}$

47. >
$\frac{3}{47} = \frac{3}{47}$ $\frac{1}{19} = \frac{3}{57}$

48. >
$\frac{4}{13} = \frac{12}{39}$ $\frac{3}{12} = \frac{12}{48}$

49. $\frac{10}{13} < \frac{5}{6} < \frac{10}{11} < \frac{7}{6}$

50. $\frac{3}{11} < \frac{2}{7} < \frac{6}{19} < \frac{8}{19}$

51. $\frac{3}{5} < \frac{11}{17} < \frac{12}{17} < \frac{4}{5}$

52. $\frac{3}{10} < \frac{7}{9} < \frac{4}{5} < \frac{8}{9}$

53. $\frac{17}{8} < 2\frac{1}{6} < \frac{17}{6} < \frac{11}{3}$

54. $\frac{9}{5} < \frac{17}{4} < \frac{9}{2} < 4\frac{5}{8}$

10 Percents

Try It
C ; D

1. 63   2. 42%   3. 18%

4. 45%   5. 82%   6. 35%

7.   8.

9.

10. A: ✔   B: ✗ ; 4%   C: ✗ ; 42%
    D: ✗ ; 14%   E: ✔   F: ✔

11. A: 44%   B: 32%   C: 52%
    D: 24%   E: 45%

12.

13.

14. 100

Room	No. of ☐	Percent
kitchen	22	22%
living room	30	30%
hallway	18	18%
bathroom	12	12%
bedroom	18	18%

15a. 30%   b. 52%

16. living room and bathroom

17. Total no. of shapes: 100
    STARS: 30 ; 30 ; 30
    FLOWERS: 55 ; 55 ; 55
    HEARTS: 15 ; 15 ; 15

18. 100
    a. 32   b. 45%   c. 23%

19. 100
    a. 22%   b. 50%   c. 28%   d. 72%

11 Ratios

Try It
2 ; 3 ; 2 ; 3 ; $\frac{2}{3}$

1a. 3   b. 3:4   c. 4:7   d. 3:7

2a. 5:4   b. 4:5   c. 4:9   d. 5:9

3a. 3:7   b. 7:2   c. 2:3
    d. 2:7   e. 3:12   f. 12:2

4. 2 to 3 ; $\frac{2}{3}$ 5. 15:4 ; $\frac{15}{4}$

6. 6:13 ; $\frac{6}{13}$ 7. 3:8 ; 3 to 8

8. 3 to 10 ; $\frac{3}{10}$ 9. 5 to 8 ; $\frac{5}{8}$

10. 7:9 ; $\frac{7}{9}$ 11. 11:12 ; 11 to 12

12-20. (Suggested answers)
12. 6:8 ; 9:12   13. 2:1 ; 8:4

14. 1:3 ; 4:12   15. 4:5 ; 16:20
16. 2:3 ; 12:18   17. 14:8 ; 21:12
18. 4:2 ; 6:3   19. 2:5 ; 12:30
20. 10:6 ; 15:9   21. 2:3
22. 7:8   23. 3:4
24. 4:5   25. 2:5   26. 49:2
27. 19:2 28. 13:9 29. 1:12
30. 2:3   31. B ; A ; C

32.   33.

34.   35.

36.

37.   38.
    1:6   1:2

39.   40.
    3:4 ; 4:1   8:5 ; 3:5

12   Rates

Try It
5

1. 6   2. 5   3. 20
4. 80   5. 57   6. 150
7. 84 km/h   8. 2 cartons/week
9. 40 doughnuts/h   10. 13 km/h
11. 125 m/min   12. 5 apples/day
13. 1   14. 2   15. 3
16. 1.20   17. 1.40   18. 1.25
19. 1.25   20. 1.23   21. 5.50
22. 6.35   23. $3/box
24. $1.5/can   25. $11.50/T-shirt
26. $4.55/taco   27. $3.21/L
28a. $9/kg   b. $5.49/kg
   c. $1.91/L   d. $1.98/L
   e. $0.43/roll   f. $0.25/slice
   g. $0.54/muffin h. $0.18/Popsicle
   i. $4.13/light bulb   j. $1.06/battery
29. $3.18
30. 1.23
    a. $2.46   b. $3.69
31. $0.53/cookie
    a. $2.65   b. $3.18
32. $0.82/can
    a. $3.28   b. $4.92
33. $2.99/plant
    a. $8.97   b. $14.95
34. $1.65/bar
    a. $11.55   b. $14.85
35. $4.32/puck
    a. $25.92   b. $43.20
36. $8.26/bow
    a. $24.78   b. $49.56
37. $6.78/burger
    a. $13.56   b. $27.12
38. $3.05/drink
    a. $12.20   b. $15.25
39a. 200   b. 160 m/min

13   Unit Conversion

Try It
B ; B

1. A   2. B   3. A   4. B
5. A   6. B   7. A   8. A
9. 120   10. 600   11. 4000
12. 200   13. 3500   14. 50
15. 101   16. 217   17. 826
18. 4520   19. 5   20. 1209
21a. 3000   b. 2   c. 1600
   d. 3600   e. 4000   f. 4
22. 3000   23. 9000   24. 15 000
25. 10 000   26. 1500   27. 2100
28. 250   29. 1.31   30. 1.224
31. 0.108   32. 10.09   33. 7.31
34. 0.001   35. 2600   36. 3950
37. 1958   38. 1   39. 4
40. 2.2   41. 6000   42. 4000
43. 12 000   44. 20 000   45. 1300
46. 3200   47. 0.18   48. 0.86
49. 0.096   50. 0.47   51. 2.05
52. 1.45   53. 2250   54. 1340
55. 2219   56. 1.675   57. 2.175
58. 4.29

59.

Length			Weight		Capacity	
km	m	cm	kg	g	L	mL
3	3000	300 000	2	2000	5	5000
0.5	500	50 000	1.5	1500	0.3	300
0.09	90	9000	5	5000	4	4000
1.5	1500	150 000	10	10 000	2.5	2500
0.7	700	70 000	0.123	123	1.05	1050

60. 16:35 **61.** 06:12
62. 11:25:46 **63.** 22:42:11
64. 18:27:53
65. 5:35:10 p.m. **66.** 5:32:02 a.m.

67. 12:05:33 p.m. **68.** 9:16:45 p.m.

69a. 8:30 a.m. **b.** 1:25:40 p.m.
  c. 11:11:20 a.m. **d.** 1:06:17 p.m.
70a. 07:39 **b.** 07:12:37
  c. 10:24:01 **d.** 01:00:07
71. 2 h 10 min **72.** 8 h 45 min

14 Length and Perimeter

Try It
2 ; 8 ; 8 cm

1. 3 ; 1 ; 8 2. 5 ; 20
3. 4 ; 12 4. 4 ; 3 ; 14
5. 2 x 5 + 2 x 2 6. 4 x 7
  = 14 (cm)   = 28 (cm)
7. 5 x 2.3 8. 4 x 4.5
  = 11.5 (cm)   = 18 (cm)

9. rectangles

Length (cm)	Width (cm)	Perimeter(cm)
8	5	26
13.5	2	31
1.8	7	17.6
4	3.5	15
2.6	10.4	26

10. squares

Length (cm)	Perimeter (cm)
12	48
10.1	40.4
2.5	10
0.3	1.2
1.15	4.6

11. 36 ; 13.5 cm ; 24 cm ; 15 cm ; 15 cm

12.

3

Length (cm)	Width (cm)
5	1
4	2
3	3

13. 9 cm by 1 cm, 8 cm by 2 cm, 7 cm by 3 cm, 6 cm by 4 cm, or 5 cm by 5 cm (Individual drawing)

14. 4 cm

15.

	Place/Object	Length	Width	Perimeter
F	phone	130 mm	70 mm	400 mm
C	tablet	23 cm	16 cm	78 cm
E	town	12 km	12 km	48 km
A	mug coaster	7 cm	7 cm	28 cm
D	desk	2 m	1 m	6 m
B	tennis court	24 m	8 m	64 m

16. 2 **17.** 3 cm
18. 3 m **19.** 50 cm/0.5 m
20. 2 cm/20 mm **21.** 0.25 m
22. 0.25 m **23.** 220 m/0.22 km

15 Area

Try It
3 ; 3 ; 9 ; 9 cm²

1. 6 ; 6 ; 36 2. 9 x 3 ; 27 (km²)
3. 5 x 3 ; 15 (m²) 4. 6 x 5 ; 30 (km²)
5. 4 x 4 ; 16 (mm²) 6. 8 x 2 ; 16 (mm²)
7. B ; C ; A ; D
8. 10 ; 8 ; 80 9. 7 x 13 ; 91 (cm²)
10. 12 x 10 ; 120 (mm²)
11. 22 x 17 ; 374 (cm²)
12. 15 x 12 ; 180 (m²)
13. 12 cm² 14. 30 m²

15. 45 km² 16. 252 mm²

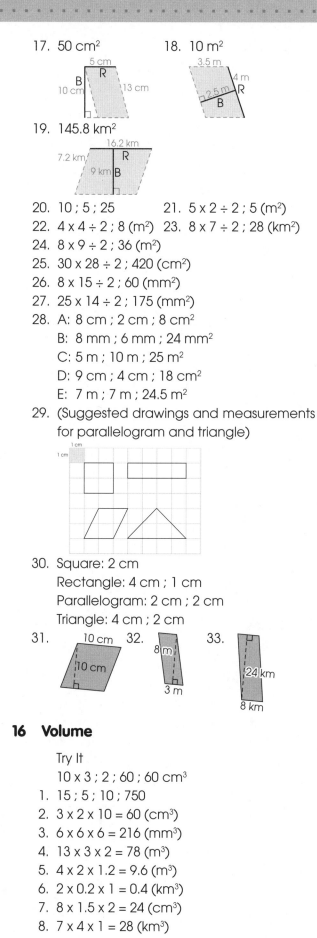

17. 50 cm²   18. 10 m²

19. 145.8 km²

20. 10 ; 5 ; 25   21. 5 x 2 ÷ 2 ; 5 (m²)
22. 4 x 4 ÷ 2 ; 8 (m²)   23. 8 x 7 ÷ 2 ; 28 (km²)
24. 8 x 9 ÷ 2 ; 36 (m²)
25. 30 x 28 ÷ 2 ; 420 (cm²)
26. 8 x 15 ÷ 2 ; 60 (mm²)
27. 25 x 14 ÷ 2 ; 175 (mm²)
28. A: 8 cm ; 2 cm ; 8 cm²
    B: 8 mm ; 6 mm ; 24 mm²
    C: 5 m ; 10 m ; 25 m²
    D: 9 cm ; 4 cm ; 18 cm²
    E: 7 m ; 7 m ; 24.5 m²
29. (Suggested drawings and measurements
    for parallelogram and triangle)

30. Square: 2 cm
    Rectangle: 4 cm ; 1 cm
    Parallelogram: 2 cm ; 2 cm
    Triangle: 4 cm ; 2 cm
31.   10 cm   32.   33.

16   Volume

Try It
10 x 3 ; 2 ; 60 ; 60 cm³

1. 15 ; 5 ; 10 ; 750
2. 3 x 2 x 10 = 60 (cm³)
3. 6 x 6 x 6 = 216 (mm³)
4. 13 x 3 x 2 = 78 (m³)
5. 4 x 2 x 1.2 = 9.6 (m³)
6. 2 x 0.2 x 1 = 0.4 (km³)
7. 8 x 1.5 x 2 = 24 (cm³)
8. 7 x 4 x 1 = 28 (km³)

9. corn flakes: 19 x 5 x 25 = 2375 (cm³)
   coffee: 12 x 12 x 12 = 1728 (cm³)
   chocolates: 22 x 10 x 3 = 660 (cm³)
   juice: 6 x 4 x 10 = 240 (cm³)
   crackers: 18 x 11 x 7 = 1386 (cm³)
   butter: 12 x 6 x 6 = 432 (cm³)
10. A: 18 x (7 + 7) x 11 = 2772 (cm³)
    B: (18 + 18) x 7 x 11 = 2772 (cm³)
    yes
11a. 150 cm²   b. 300 cm³   c. 6000 cm³
12. 6 ; 3 ; 2 ; 18
13. 4 x 7 ÷ 2 x 2 = 28 (m³)
14. 9 x 3 ÷ 2 x 1 = 13.5 (cm³)
15. 8 x 6 ÷ 2 x 0.5 = 12 (mm³)
16. 5 x 5 ÷ 2 x 6 = 75 (cm³)
17. 10 x 3 ÷ 2 x 2.5 = 37.5 (km³)
18.

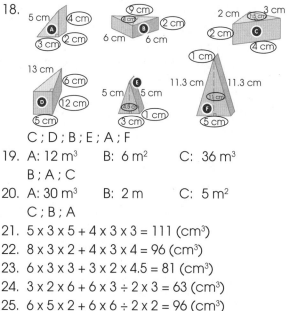

C ; D ; B ; E ; A ; F
19. A: 12 m³   B: 6 m²   C: 36 m³
    B ; A ; C
20. A: 30 m³   B: 2 m   C: 5 m²
    C ; B ; A
21. 5 x 3 x 5 + 4 x 3 x 3 = 111 (cm³)
22. 8 x 3 x 2 + 4 x 3 x 4 = 96 (cm³)
23. 6 x 3 x 3 + 3 x 2 x 4.5 = 81 (cm³)
24. 3 x 2 x 6 + 6 x 3 ÷ 2 x 3 = 63 (cm³)
25. 6 x 5 x 2 + 6 x 6 ÷ 2 x 2 = 96 (cm³)
26. 5 x 3 x 2 + 5 x 4 ÷ 2 x 3 = 60 (cm³)

17   Surface Area

Try It
1 x 1 x 6 = 6
6 m²

1. 5 ; 5 ; 150   2. 2 x 2 x 6 ; 24 (km²)
3. 3 x 3 x 6 ; 54 (m²) 4. 6 x 6 x 6 ; 216 (mm²)
5. A   6. B   7. A
8. A ; 150   9. B ; 62 cm²
10. 16 x 5 x 2 + 16 x 1 x 2 + 5 x 1 x 2 = 202 (cm²)
11. 12 x 5 x 2 + 12 x 3 x 2 + 5 x 3 x 2 = 222 (mm²)
12. 5 x 4 x 2 + 5 x 3 x 2 + 4 x 3 x 2 = 94 (cm²)
13. 9 x 4 x 2 + 9 x 4 x 2 + 4 x 4 x 2 = 176 (m²)
14. 15 x 8 x 2 + 15 x 6 x 2 + 8 x 6 x 2 = 516 (mm²)
15. 10 x 10 x 2 + 10 x 2 x 2 + 10 x 2 x 2 = 280 (mm²)

16. $11 \times 9 \times 2 + 11 \times 4 \times 2 + 9 \times 4 \times 2 = 358 \ (\text{cm}^2)$
17. $16 \times 3 \times 2 + 16 \times 2 \times 2 + 3 \times 2 \times 2 = 172 \ (\text{m}^2)$
18. A ; 96   19. B ; 41 cm²
20. $(3 \times 4 \div 2) \times 2 + 3 \times 2 + 4 \times 2 + 5 \times 2 = 36 \ (\text{cm}^2)$
21. $(10 \times 4 \div 2) \times 2 + 10 \times 3 + 8 \times 3 + 5 \times 3 = 109 \ (\text{m}^2)$
22. $(7 \times 6 \div 2) \times 2 + 7 \times 10 + 7 \times 10 + 7 \times 10 = 252 \ (\text{m}^2)$
23. $(11 \times 8 \div 2) \times 2 + 11 \times 5 + 11 \times 5 + 9 \times 5 = 243 \ (\text{mm}^2)$
24. $(4 \times 12 \div 2) \times 2 + 15 \times 3 + 13 \times 3 + 4 \times 3 = 144 \ (\text{cm}^2)$
25. $(9 \times 4 \div 2) \times 2 + 9 \times 1 + 6 \times 1 + 6 \times 1 = 57 \ (\text{m}^2)$
26. A: $9 \times 6 \times 2 + 9 \times 3 \times 2 + 6 \times 3 \times 2 = 198 \ (\text{mm}^2)$
    B: $(7 \times 5.8 \div 2) \times 2 + 8 \times 2 + 7 \times 2 + 6 \times 2 = 82.6 \ (\text{m}^2)$
    C: $10 \times 10 \times 2 + 10 \times 35 \times 2 + 10 \times 35 \times 2 = 1600 \ (\text{cm}^2)$
    D: $(10 \times 6 \div 2) \times 2 + 10 \times 12 + 8 \times 12 + 8 \times 12 = 372 \ (\text{m}^2)$
27. A: 106 cm²   B: 150 cm²
    C: 144 cm²   D: 120 cm²
a. 44 cm² ; 24 cm²   b. Boxes A, C, and D

18 Shapes

Try It

1. (Colour shapes a, b, d, e, g, and h.)
   a. trapezoid   b. kite
   c.   d. parallelogram
   e. rectangle   f.
   g. rhombus   h. square

2.

3. 4 ; 2 ; 4   4. 0 ; 1 ; 0   5. 4 ; 2 ; 0
6.

	pairs of equal sides	pairs of parallel sides	right angles
kite	2	0	0
parallelogram	2	2	0
rectangle	2	2	4

7. no parallel sides: A, F
   no equal sides: B, F
   no right angles: D, E
   1 pair of parallel sides: B, E

8. (Suggested drawings)

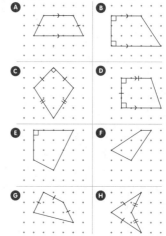

9.

	rectangle	rhombus	parallelogram	square
opposite sides parallel	✔	✔	✔	✔
all sides equal		✔		✔
2 pairs of opposite sides equal	✔	✔	✔	✔
all angles 90°	✔			✔
2 pairs of opposite angles equal	✔	✔	✔	✔

10a.
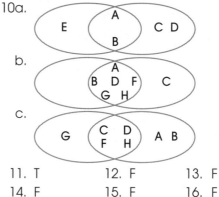
b.
c.

11. T   12. F   13. F
14. F   15. F   16. F

19 Solids

Try It

1. top ; side ; front   2. top ; front ; side
3. front ; side ; top   4. top ; front ; side
5. side ; top ; front   6. front ; side ; top
7.   8.
9.   10.
11.
12.

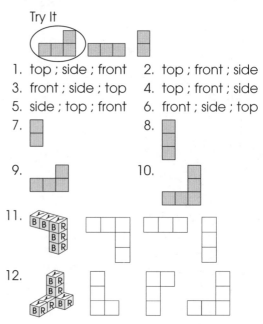

13.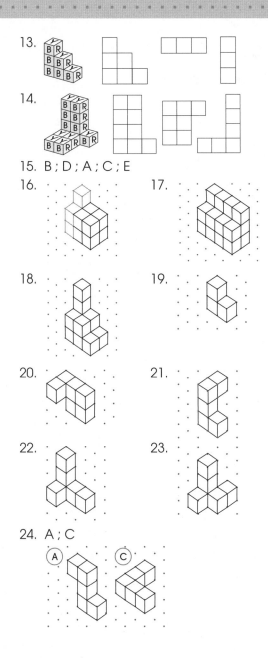

14.

15. B ; D ; A ; C ; E

16.   17.

18.   19.

20.   21.

22.   23.

24. A ; C

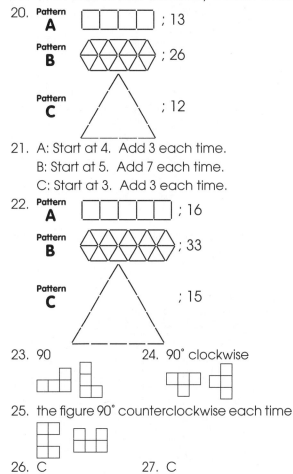

17. 54 ; 110 ; Start at 5. Multiply by 2 and add 2 each time.
18. 42 ; 123 ; Start at 3. Multiply by 3 and subtract 3 each time.
19. 9 ; 3 ; Start at 243. Divide by 3 each time.
20. Pattern A ▭▭▭▭ ; 13
    Pattern B ⬡⬡⬡ ; 26
    Pattern C △ ; 12
21. A: Start at 4. Add 3 each time.
    B: Start at 5. Add 7 each time.
    C: Start at 3. Add 3 each time.
22. Pattern A ▭▭▭▭▭ ; 16
    Pattern B ⬡⬡⬡⬡ ; 33
    Pattern C △ ; 15
23. 90   24. 90° clockwise

25. the figure 90° counterclockwise each time

26. C   27. C

21   Mean, Median, and Mode

Try It
2, 5, 5, 5, 5, 6, 7
5 ; 5 ; 5

1. 4, 4, 5, 8, 9
   6 ; 5 ; 4
2. 12, 13, 15, 16, 17, 17
   15 ; 15.5 ; 17
3. 2, 7, 9, 14, 14, 20, 25
   13 ; 14 ; 14
4. 6, 8, 10, 13, 16, 16, 24, 31
   15.5 ; 14.5 ; 16
5. 2, 9, 9, 13, 13, 16, 25, 26, 31
   16 ; 13 ; 9, 13

20   Patterning

Try It
Start at 1. Multiply by 3 and subtract 1 each time.

1. growing ; B   2. shrinking ; C
3. growing ; A   4. shrinking ; D
5. 4, 6, 8, 10   6. 7, 15, 31, 63
7. 66, 21, 6, 1
8. 12 ; B   9. 35 ; B
10. 94 ; A   11. 17 ; B
12. 487 ; B   13. 243 ; A
14. 16 ; 15 ; Start at 19. Subtract 1 each time.
15. 64 ; 32 ; Start at 512. Divide by 2 each time.
16. 115 ; 235 ; Start at 10. Multiply by 2 and add 5 each time.

6.

	Chris	Anna	Joseph	Eric	Sylvia	Olivia
mean	28	30	24	22	26	26
median	27	26	26	19	26.5	25
mode	28, 31	21	26	15, 30	27	25

a. Olivia said that. Her mode number of marbles is 25.
b. Eric said that. His median number of marbles is 19.
c. To find the total, we can multiply the mean by the number of bags of marbles. Since each child has 10 bags of marbles and Anna's mean number of marbles is the greatest, she has the most marbles.

7. Park A: 9 ; 9 ; 4
Park B: 9 ; 9 ; 9

8. C

9. Yes, because all three measures of central tendency are 9.

10a. Park B   b. Park A
c. Park B

11a.

Machine A		Machine B	
Day	No. of Bags	Day	No. of Bags
1	100	1	120
2	100	2	130
3	120	3	100
4	100	4	110
5	100	5	130
6	100	6	100
7	80	7	80

Machine A:
100 ; 100 ; 100

Machine B:
110 ; 110 ; 100, 130

b. Machine A ; Machine B

Level 2

1   Order of Operations

Try It
18 ; 3
2 ; 28

1. $20 - (4 \times 2)$
$20 - 8$
12

2. $(6 \times 5) - 9$
$30 - 9$
21

3. $(8 \div 2) + 7$
$4 + 7$
11

4. $5 + (18 \div 9)$
$5 + 2$
7

5. $11 - (15 \div 5)$
$11 - 3$
8

6. $10 + (4 \times 6)$
$10 + 24$
34

7. $(2 + 3) \times 5$
5×5
25

8. $8 \div (9 - 5)$
$8 \div 4$
2

9. $(15 - 7) \times 3$
8×3
24

10. $(13 + 7) \div 5$
$20 \div 5$
4

11. $7 \times (3 + 7)$
7×10
70

12. $45 \div (13 - 4)$
$45 \div 9$
5

13. $= 29 + 11 + 16$
$= 40 + 16$
$= 56$

14. $= 4 \times 25 \times 23$
$= 100 \times 23$
$= 2300$

15. $= 15 \times 4 \times 8$
$= 60 \times 8$
$= 480$

16. $= 8 + 22 + 59$
$= 30 + 59$
$= 89$

17. $= 5 \times 8 \times 17$
$= 40 \times 17$
$= 680$

18. $= 7 + 3 + 38$
$= 10 + 38$
$= 48$

19.

20. $= 8 \times 5 + 5 \times 5$
$= 40 + 25$
$= 65$

21. $= 4 \times 11 - 4 \times 7$
$= 44 - 28$
$= 16$

22. $= 17 \times 7 + 6 \times 7$
$= 119 + 42$
$= 161$

23. $= 6 \times 3 + 8 \times 3$
$= 18 + 24$
$= 42$

24. $= 12 \times 2 - 7 \times 2$
$= 24 - 14$
$= 10$

25. $= 6 \times 15 - 6 \times 6$
$= 90 - 36$
$= 54$

26. $= 5 \times 8 + 5 \times 11$
    $= 40 + 55$
    $= 95$

27. 36 ; 16
    20
    100

28. $= 8 \times (12 + 18)$
    $= 8 \times 30$
    $= 240$

29. $= 9 \times (31 - 16)$
    $= 9 \times 15$
    $= 135$

30. $= 7 \times (18 + 3)$
    $= 7 \times 21$
    $= 147$

31. $= 6 \times (23 - 5)$
    $= 6 \times 18$
    $= 108$

32. $= 6 \times (32 + 28)$
    $= 6 \times 60$
    $= 360$

33. $= 15 + 18 - 9$
    $= 33 - 9$
    $= 24$

34. $= 15 - 24 \div 8$
    $= 15 - 3$
    $= 12$

35. $= 150 \div 6 + 9$
    $= 25 + 9$
    $= 34$

36. $= 14 + 6 \times 20 - 12$
    $= 14 + 120 - 12$
    $= 134 - 12$
    $= 122$

37. $= 51 - 24 \div 4$
    $= 51 - 6$
    $= 45$

38. $= 37 \times 6 - 7 \times 6$
    $= 6 \times (37 - 7)$
    $= 6 \times 30$
    $= 180$

39. $= 18 \div 3 - 4 + 12 \times 9$
    $= 6 - 4 + 108$
    $= 2 + 108$
    $= 110$

40. $= 15 \times 7 - 7 \times 6$
    $= 7 \times (15 - 6)$
    $= 7 \times 9$
    $= 63$

41a. x ; +   b. + ; ÷   c. + ; +   d. – ; +

42a. $2 \times (4 + 5) \div 3 = 6$
  b. $4 \times (9 - 4) - 2 = 18$
  c. $(20 - 8 + 6) \div 2 = 9$
  d. $11 + 3 \times (6 - 2) = 23$

2   Adding and Subtracting Decimals

Try It
5.061 ; 7.258

1. 9.109	2. 15.951	3. 1.191
4. 88.145	5. 6.045	6. 4.002
7. 12.119	8. 1.757	9. 8.263
10. 0.791	11. 105.491	
12. 325.073	13. 24.417	
14. 6.21	15. 10.224	
16. 5.81	17. 18.997	
18. 21.831	19. 0.954	

20. 2.912   3.000   21.   6.470   6.470
    + 3.000   – 2.912   + 2.103   – 2.103
      5.912   0.088   8.573   4.367

22. 7.200   9.124   23. 10.948   25.010
    + 9.124   – 7.200   + 25.010 – 10.948
     16.324   1.924   35.958   14.062

24. 15.862   51.620   25.   8.100   8.100
   + 51.620   – 15.862   + 0.624   – 0.624
     67.482   35.758   8.724   7.476

26a.
    12.480   → 6.223   b.   13.000   → 12.791
    – 6.257   + 6.257   – 0.209   + 0.209
      6.223   12.480   12.791   13.000
      6.223   12.791

27a.
     9.200   → 9.671   b.   6.313   → 14.603
    + 0.471   – 0.471   + 8.290   – 8.290
      9.671   9.200   14.603   6.313
      9.671   14.603

28. A: ✔ ; 12.140   B: ✔ ; 18.732
    C: D: ✔ ; 10.867
    E: ✔ ; 18.280   F:

29a. 560.946 + 650 = 1210.946 ; 1210.946 g
  b. 409.177 + 907.185 = 1316.362 ; 1316.362 g
  c. 860.914 + 340.7 = 1201.614 ; 1201.614 g
  d. 409.177 + 650 + 860.914 = 1920.091 ;
     1920.091 g
  e. 560.946 + 860.914 = 1421.86 ; 1421.86 g
  f. 340.7 + 409.177 + 650 = 1399.877 ; 1399.877 g

30a. 409.177 + 409.177 + 907.185 = 1725.539
     Yes, the toys can be packed into a box.
  b. 560.946 + 340.7 + 860.914 = 1762.56
     Yes, the toys can be packed into a box.
  c. 650 + 860.914 = 1510.914
     2000 – 1510.914 = 489.086
     A doll or a stacking ring set can be packed.

3   Multiplying and Dividing Decimals

Try It
4.51 ; 0.54 ; 201

1. 2.5	2. 0.5	3. 0.19
9	34	0.34
17 000	0.71	0.0007
8300	0.04	0.028
610	0.006	0.0079
0.07	0.2011	0.0021
90.1	0.00161	0.0092
2080	0.02	0.001
1000	1.42	0.075
4. 11.95		5. 27.44
6. 23.04		7. 5.34

8.
```
      1.4 1
6 ) 8.4 6
    6
    2 4
    2 4
       6
       6
```

9.
```
       2.9 7
5 ) 1 4.8 5
    1 0
       4 8
       4 5
          3 5
          3 5
```

10.
```
      3.0 5
3 ) 9.1 5
    9
    1 5
    1 5
```

11. 6.65   12. 69.36   13. 2.36
14. 3.68   15. 1.68   16. 14.65
17. 24.91   18. 27.58   19. 2.97
20. 29.22   21. 24.72   22. 6.69
23. 113.04   24. 8.23   25. 2.07 ; 132.48
26. 37.89 ; 4.21
27. 60 ; 20 ; 3   28. 3 ; 90 ; 270
29. 4 ; 2 ; 8   30. 4 ; 2 ; 2
31. 16 ; 4 ; 4   32. 36 ; 6 ; 6
33. 12 ; 4 ; 3   34. 100 ; 25 ; 4
35. 144 ; 12 ; 12   36. 225 ; 9 ; 25
37. 6 ; 10 ; 60   38. 20 ; 3 ; 60
39. ✗   40. ✔   41. ✗
42. ✗   43. ✔   44. ✔
45. 0.528   46. 0.17   47. 2.4
48. 10.2   49. 6   50. 10
51. 2.9   52. 10   53. 0.32
54. 0.035   55. 10.15   56. 0.212
57. 2.5   58. 1.275   59. 9.13
60. 0.136   61. 5.94
62. not between 5 and 10
63. 5.34
64. not between 5 and 10
65. 5.76   66. 6.39
67.
```
      6.62
3 ) 1 9.86
    1 8
      1 8
      1 8
         6
         6
```
68. not between 5 and 10
69.
```
      6.89
8 ) 5 5.1 2
    4 8
      7 1
      6 4
         7 2
         7 2
```

4   Fractions

Try It

$\dfrac{3}{2}$; $\dfrac{15}{10}$; $\dfrac{12}{10}$

greater

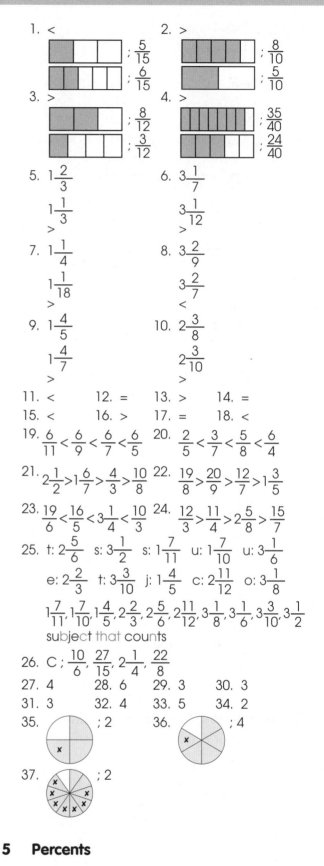

1. <   2. >

3. >   4. >

5. $1\dfrac{2}{3}$ 6. $3\dfrac{1}{7}$

$1\dfrac{1}{3}$ $3\dfrac{1}{12}$

>   >

7. $1\dfrac{1}{4}$ 8. $3\dfrac{2}{9}$

$1\dfrac{1}{18}$ $3\dfrac{2}{7}$

>   <

9. $1\dfrac{4}{5}$ 10. $2\dfrac{3}{8}$

$1\dfrac{4}{7}$ $2\dfrac{3}{10}$

>   >

11. <   12. =   13. >   14. =
15. <   16. >   17. =   18. <
19. $\dfrac{6}{11} < \dfrac{6}{9} < \dfrac{6}{7} < \dfrac{6}{5}$ 20. $\dfrac{2}{5} < \dfrac{3}{7} < \dfrac{5}{8} < \dfrac{6}{4}$
21. $2\dfrac{1}{2} > 1\dfrac{6}{7} > \dfrac{4}{3} > \dfrac{10}{8}$ 22. $\dfrac{19}{8} > \dfrac{20}{9} > \dfrac{12}{7} > 1\dfrac{3}{5}$
23. $\dfrac{19}{6} < \dfrac{16}{5} < 3\dfrac{1}{4} < \dfrac{10}{3}$ 24. $\dfrac{12}{3} > \dfrac{11}{4} > 2\dfrac{5}{8} > \dfrac{15}{7}$
25. t: $2\dfrac{5}{6}$ s: $3\dfrac{1}{2}$ s: $1\dfrac{7}{11}$ u: $1\dfrac{7}{10}$ u: $3\dfrac{1}{6}$

e: $2\dfrac{2}{3}$ t: $3\dfrac{3}{10}$ j: $1\dfrac{4}{5}$ c: $2\dfrac{11}{12}$ o: $3\dfrac{1}{8}$

$1\dfrac{7}{11}, 1\dfrac{7}{10}, 1\dfrac{4}{5}, 2\dfrac{2}{3}, 2\dfrac{5}{6}, 2\dfrac{11}{12}, 3\dfrac{1}{8}, 3\dfrac{1}{6}, 3\dfrac{3}{10}, 3\dfrac{1}{2}$

subject that counts

26. C ; $\dfrac{10}{6}, \dfrac{27}{15}, 2\dfrac{1}{4}, \dfrac{22}{8}$
27. 4   28. 6   29. 3   30. 3
31. 3   32. 4   33. 5   34. 2
35.   ; 2   36.   ; 4
37.   ; 2

5   Percents

Try It

C

1. 25   2. 50%   3. 75%
4. 10%   5. 100%   6. 25%

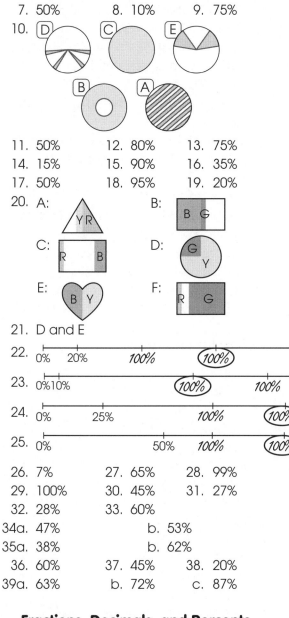

7. 50% 8. 10% 9. 75%

10.

11. 50% 12. 80% 13. 75%
14. 15% 15. 90% 16. 35%
17. 50% 18. 95% 19. 20%

20. A: B:
    C: D:
    E: F:

21. D and E

22.
23.
24.
25.

26. 7% 27. 65% 28. 99%
29. 100% 30. 45% 31. 27%
32. 28% 33. 60%
34a. 47% b. 53%
35a. 38% b. 62%
36. 60% 37. 45% 38. 20%
39a. 63% b. 72% c. 87%

6 Fractions, Decimals, and Percents

Try It
20 ; 20 ; =
1. $0.2 ; 0.75 ; \frac{1}{4} ; \frac{2}{5}$
2. 15% ; 20% ; 0.4 ; 0.65
3. $\frac{2}{5} ; \frac{1}{10} ; 60\% ; 70\%$
4. $\frac{3}{5} ; 0.6 ; 60\%$ 5. $\frac{7}{10} ; 0.7 ; 70\%$
6. $\frac{3}{4} ; 0.75 ; 75\%$ 7. $\frac{1}{2} ; 0.5 ; 50\%$
8a. 90% b. 24% c. 35%
d. 70% e. 80% f. 30%
g. 15% h. 5% i. 76%
9a. 0.19 b. 0.18 c. 0.12
d. 0.15 e. 0.32 f. 0.6
g. 0.7 h. 0.08 i. 0.02

10a. $\frac{11}{20}$ b. $\frac{7}{20}$ c. $\frac{3}{5}$
d. $\frac{7}{10}$ e. $\frac{7}{25}$ f. $\frac{2}{5}$
g. $\frac{17}{20}$ h. $\frac{3}{5}$ i. $\frac{1}{20}$

11. 0.28 ; 28% ; B
$\frac{4}{5}$; 80% ; A
$\frac{7}{10}$; 0.7 ; C
0.14 ; 14% ; D
$\frac{19}{20}$; 0.95 ; E

12. < 13. = 14. <
15. > 16. > 17. <
18. > 19. = 20. >
21. 0.1 ; 20% ; $\frac{1}{4}$ 22. $70\% < 0.73 < \frac{3}{4}$
23. $10\% < \frac{3}{25} < 0.15$ 24. $0.27 < \frac{19}{50} < 59\%$
25. $64\% < \frac{18}{25} < 0.93$ 26. $\frac{3}{5} < 61\% < 0.63$
27a. 0.55 b. 0.86 c. 0.8
d. 0.25 e. 0.08 f. 0.96
28a. 26% b. 78% c. 86%
d. 52% e. 11% f. 7%
29a. $\frac{3}{20}$ b. $\frac{23}{25}$ c. $\frac{18}{25}$
d. $\frac{1}{4}$ e. $\frac{7}{10}$ f. $\frac{4}{5}$
30. T 31. F 32. F

7 Ratios

Try It
B
1. 3 ; 4 ; 3 ; 4 2. 1 to 2 ; $\frac{1}{2}$
3. 3:5 ; $\frac{3}{5}$ 4. 6 to 5 ; $\frac{6}{5}$
5. 7 to 2 ; $\frac{7}{2}$ 6. 8:5 ; $\frac{8}{5}$
7. 10 ; 14 ; 15 ; 21 8. 8:18 ; 12:27
9. 2:3 ; 20:30 10. 3:5 ; 6:10
11. 3:2 ; 18:12 12. 5:4 ; 10:8
13. 2:3 14. 3:1 15. 1:4
16. 17:3 17. 7:18 18. 2:3
19a. 1:2 b. 2:3 c. 5:9
d. 5:12 e. 6:5 f. 5:6
g. 5:18 h. 12:5 i. 2:1
j. 1:9 k. 2:9 l. 2:5
20a. 4:11 b. 1:2 c. 11:10 d. 1:5
21a. 1:3 b. 3:5 c. 6:35 d. 3:7
22. D ; A ; C ; B

23. 4 ; 6 ; 8 ; 10 ; 12 ; 14 ; 16
   a. 2:1
   b. 6 cups ; 12 cups ; 16 cups
   c. 20 cups   d. 9 cups   e. 1:3
24a. 2:1 ; 1:3 ; 2:3 ; 1:6
   b. 3:4 ; 2:3 ; 1:2 ; 4:13
25a. 2:3 ; 6:5 ; 2:1 ; 1:3
   b. 3:5 ; 5:8 ; 1:1 ; 1:2

8   Rates

Try It
$6.55 ÷ 5 cookies = $1.31/cookie
does not

1. 1.74 ; 3 ; 0.58 ; 0.58
2.85 ; 5 ; 0.57 ; $0.57/notebook ; ✔
2. 2.4 ; 2 ; 1.2 ; $1.20/doughnut ; ✔
9.6 ; 4 ; 2.4 ; $2.40/doughnut
3. 6.3 ; 3 ; 2.1 ; $2.10/carton ; ✔
4.3 ; 2 ; 2.15 ; $2.15/carton
4. 27.95 ; 5 ; 5.59 ; $5.59/pen ; ✔
22.4 ; 4 ; 5.6 ; $5.60/pen
5. A: 2.59 ; ✔   B: $2.13/pot
    $2.62/carton $2.12/pot ; ✔
    C: $2.99/cup   D: $0.89/bar
    $2.75/cup ; ✔ $0.86/bar ; ✔
6. 6.60 ; $6.45/kg ; $6.85/kg
$1.19/bottle ; $1.25/bottle ; $1.42/bottle
$0.79/cup ; $0.68/cup ; $0.89/cup
7. B ; A ; B
8. 1.66 cm ; 2 month ; 0.83 cm/month
0.83 ; 5 ; 4.15
4.15
9. $62.50 ; 5 weeks ; $12.50/week
12.5 ; 3 ; 37.5
37.50
10. $3 ÷ 4 L = $0.75/L
0.75 x 5 = 3.75
It costs $3.75.
11. $4.26 ÷ 6 L = $0.71/L
0.71 x 10 = 7.1
It costs $7.10.
12. $187 ÷ 6 tickets = $31.17/ticket
31.17 x 4 = 124.68
They cost $124.68.
13a. $109.50 ÷ 5 h = $21.90/h
21.9 x 3 = 65.7
She charges $65.70.
   b. 21.9 x 6 = 131.4
She charges $131.40.

14. Allen's Boutique:
$29.55 ÷ 3 T-shirts = $9.85/T-shirt
Outfit Store: $38.56 ÷ 4 T-shirts = $9.64/T-shirt
Outfit Store has the better buy.
15. Sheila: 9 books ÷ 12 days = 0.75 books/day
Karen: 5 books ÷ 8 days = 0.625 books/day
Sheila reads faster.
16. Apples: $5.88 ÷ 6 apples = $0.98/apple
Oranges: $3.04 ÷ 4 oranges = $0.76/orange
Apples are more expensive.
17. 12 eggs: $4.44 ÷ 12 eggs = $0.37/egg
18 eggs: $6.84 ÷ 18 eggs = $0.38/egg
A carton of 12 eggs is the better buy.
18a. Susan: $71.25 ÷ 5 h = $14.25/h
Susan is better paid.
   b. Janet: $7/30 min x 2 = $14/h
Susan is paid best.

9   Perimeter and Area

Try It
10 ; 40
10 ; 10 ; 100

1. 2 x 4 + 2 x 2 = 12 (cm)
4 x 2 = 8 (cm²)
2. 4 x 2 = 8 (cm)
2 x 2 = 4 (cm²)
3. 2 x 12 + 2 x 9 = 42 (cm)
9 x 10 = 90 (cm²)
4. 12 + 11 + 8 = 31 (cm)
12 x 7 ÷ 2 = 42 (cm²)
5. 4 x 8 = 32 (cm)
8 x 8 = 64 (cm²)
6. 2 x 8.5 + 2 x 3 = 23 (cm)
3 x 7 = 21 (cm²)
7. 6.5 + 4.5 + 3 = 14 (cm)
3 x 4 ÷ 2 = 6 (cm²)
8. 2 x 2 + 2 x 0.5 = 5 (cm)
2 x 0.5 = 1 (cm²)
9. A: 54 km ; 180 km²
B: 24 km ; 36 km²
C: 32 m ; 50 m²   D: 31 cm ; 42 cm²
E: 31 m ; 55 m²   F: 43 km ; 54 km²
G: 280 mm ; 4900 mm²
H: 21 mm ; 10.5 mm²
I: 40 km ; 60 km²   J: 44.4 m ; 86 m²
K: 26 m ; 35 m²
10. ✔ ; Area: 16 cm²
11. ✔ ; Perimeter: 42 m

12. ✔ ; Perimeter: 18 km
    ✔ ; Area: 15.6 km²
13. (Suggested drawings)

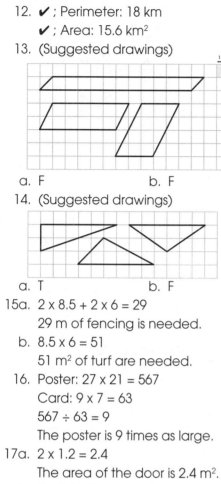

1 cm
1 cm

a. F   b. F
14. (Suggested drawings)

a. T   b. F
15a. 2 x 8.5 + 2 x 6 = 29
     29 m of fencing is needed.
  b. 8.5 x 6 = 51
     51 m² of turf are needed.
16. Poster: 27 x 21 = 567
    Card: 9 x 7 = 63
    567 ÷ 63 = 9
    The poster is 9 times as large.
17a. 2 x 1.2 = 2.4
     The area of the door is 2.4 m².
  b. 5 x 2.4 – 2.4 = 9.6
     The area is 9.6 m².
18a. 20 x 13 ÷ 2 = 130
     The area is 130 km².
  b. 24 + 20 + 13 = 57
     The route is 57 km long.

10 Volume and Surface Area

    Try It
    27 m³ ; 54 m²
  1. 8 x 5 x 3 ; 120 (mm³)
     8 x 5 x 2 + 8 x 3 x 2 + 5 x 3 x 2 ; 158 (mm²)
  2. 7 x 7 x 2 ; 98 (km³)
     7 x 7 x 2 + 7 x 2 x 2 + 7 x 2 x 2 ; 154 (km²)
  3. 10 x 6 x 5 ; 300 (m³)
     10 x 6 x 2 + 10 x 5 x 2 + 6 x 5 x 2 ; 280 (m²)
  4. 12 x 5 x 2 ; 120 (cm³)
     12 x 5 x 2 + 12 x 2 x 2 + 5 x 2 x 2 ; 188 (cm²)
  5. 9 x 1 x 1 ; 9 (m³)
     9 x 1 x 2 + 9 x 1 x 2 + 1 x 1 x 2 ; 38 (m²)
  6. 6 x 8 ÷ 2 x 4 ; 96 (m³)
     6 x 8 ÷ 2 x 2 + 10 x 4 + 8 x 4 + 6 x 4 ; 144 (m²)

  7. 10 x 5 ÷ 2 x 5 ; 125 (cm³)
     10 x 5 ÷ 2 x 2 + 10 x 5 + 7 x 5 + 7 x 5 ; 170 (cm²)
  8. 5 x 6.4 ÷ 2 x 3 ; 48 (m³)
     5 x 6.4 ÷ 2 x 2 + 13 x 3 + 9 x 3 + 5 x 3 ; 113 (m²)
  9. 2 x 1 ÷ 2 x 1 ; 1 (km³)
     2 x 1 ÷ 2 x 2 + 2 x 1 + 1.5 x 1 + 1.5 x 1 ; 7 (km²)
 10. 7 x 2.5 ÷ 2 x 1.5 ; 13.125 (m³)
     7 x 2.5 ÷ 2 x 2 + 7 x 1.5 + 6 x 1.5 + 3 x 1.5 ; 41.5 (m²)
 11. A: 240 m³ ; 236 m²
     B: 10.5 cm³ ; 38.6 cm²
     C: 18 m³ ; 48 m²
     D: 110 mm³ ; 174 mm²
     E: 36 mm³ ; 78 mm²

 12.
V: 6	V: 6	V: 3	V: 3
S.A.: 24	S.A.: 22	S.A.: 15	S.A.: 14

 13. T   14. T   15. F   16. F
 17. F   18. T   19. T
 20. 7 cm ; 242 cm²   21. 64 cm² ; 512 cm³
 22. 6 cm ; 8 cm   23. 2 cm ; 38 cm²
 24. A: V: 3 x 4 ÷ 2 x 3 + 3 x 3 x 3 = 45 (m³)
        S.A.: 3 x 4 ÷ 2 x 2 + 5 x 3 + 4 x 3 + 3 x 3 x 5
        = 84 (m²)
     B: V: 3 x 4 ÷ 2 x 3 + 4 x 3 x 1 = 30 (m³)
        S.A.: 3 x 4 ÷ 2 x 2 + 5 x 3 + 3 x 3 + 4 x 3 +
        4 x 1 x 2 + 3 x 1 x 2 = 62 (m²)
     C: V: 3 x 3 x 3 + 4 x 3 x 1 = 39 (m³)
        S.A.: 3 x 3 x 5 + 4 x 3 x 2 + 4 x 1 x 2 + 3 x 1 +
        (3 x 3 – 3 x 1) = 86 (m²)
 25. 8400 mL
 26a. yes   b. no
 27a. The volume will not change.
   b. S.A.: 3 x 3 x 5 + 4 x 3 + 4 x 1 x 2 + 3 x 1 x 2 +
        (4 x 3 – 3 x 3) = 74 (m²)
      Difference: 86 – 74 = 12
      The surface area will change. It will be
      12 m² smaller.

11 Angles

    Try It
    90° ; 115°
  1. acute angle ; 30°   2. obtuse angle ; 105°
  3. right angle ; 90°   4. straight angle ; 180°

5. A: B: C:

D: E: F:

G: H: I:

J: K: L:

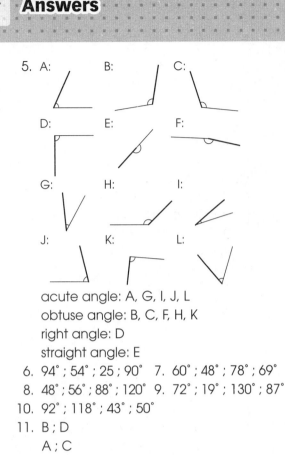

acute angle: A, G, I, J, L
obtuse angle: B, C, F, H, K
right angle: D
straight angle: E

6. 94° ; 54° ; 25 ; 90° 7. 60° ; 48° ; 78° ; 69°

8. 48° ; 56° ; 88° ; 120° 9. 72° ; 19° ; 130° ; 87°

10. 92° ; 118° ; 43° ; 50°

11. B ; D
    A ; C

12a. A, C   b. B, D   c. A, C, E   d. B, F

13. 60°
    40° ; 20° ; 60°
    20° ; 20° ; 20° ; 60°

14. The measure of Angle *a* is the sum of the measures of the smaller angles that Angle *a* is composed of.

12   Shapes

Try It
4 ; 2

1. 3   2. 6   3. 5   4. 1
5. 2   6. 2   7. 1   8. 4
9.   10.   11.

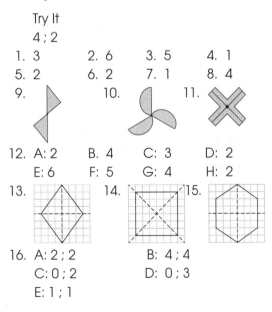

12. A: 2   B. 4   C: 3   D: 2
     E: 6   F: 5   G: 4   H: 2

13.   14.   15.

16. A: 2 ; 2   B: 4 ; 4
     C: 0 ; 2   D: 0 ; 3
     E: 1 ; 1

17.

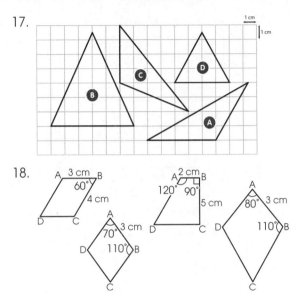

18.

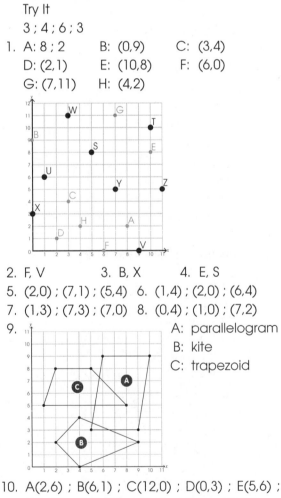

19. The sum of the angles in each quadrilateral is 360°.

13   Cartesian Coordinate Plane

Try It
3 ; 4 ; 6 ; 3

1. A: 8 ; 2   B: (0,9)   C: (3,4)
    D: (2,1)   E: (10,8)   F: (6,0)
    G: (7,11)   H: (4,2)

2. F, V   3. B, X   4. E, S

5. (2,0) ; (7,1) ; (5,4)   6. (1,4) ; (2,0) ; (6,4)

7. (1,3) ; (7,3) ; (7,0)   8. (0,4) ; (1,0) ; (7,2)

9.   A: parallelogram
                            B: kite
                            C: trapezoid

10. A(2,6) ; B(6,1) ; C(12,0) ; D(0,3) ; E(5,6) ;
     F(5,12) ; G(8,12) ; H(1,0) ; I(3,9) ; J(0,10)

11-15.
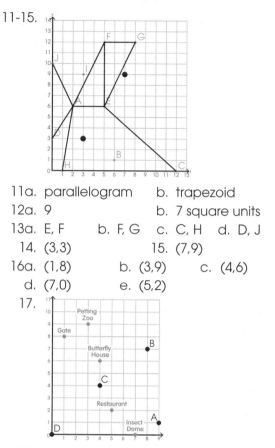

8.
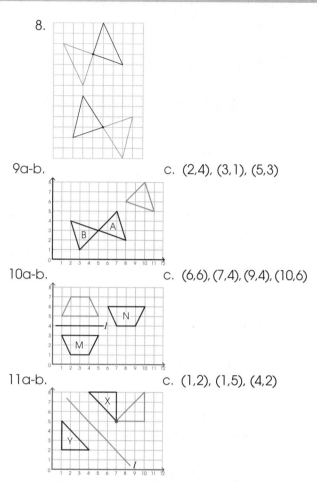

11a. parallelogram   b. trapezoid
12a. 9   b. 7 square units
13a. E, F   b. F, G   c. C, H   d. D, J
14. (3,3)   15. (7,9)
16a. (1,8)   b. (3,9)   c. (4,6)
  d. (7,0)   e. (5,2)
17.
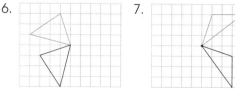

18. I would assign Rebecca to sit at (7,3) because it is closer to the front of the classroom where the blackboard is .
19. The other two could not sit at (1,2), (3,2), or (3,3).

9a-b.   c. (2,4), (3,1), (5,3)

10a-b.   c. (6,6), (7,4), (9,4), (10,6)

11a-b.   c. (1,2), (1,5), (4,2)
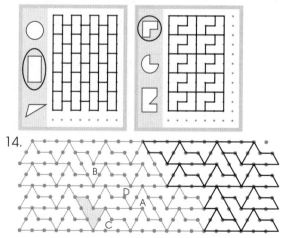

12. The image is congruent with the original figure.
13. (Suggested answers)

14.
a. rotation   b. translation
c. reflection
d. (Suggested answer)
  I will use rotation and reflection.

14 Transformations

Try It
90° turn counterclockwise
1. B, D
   A, F
   C, E
2. 180° turn   3. 90° turn clockwise
4. 90° turn counterclockwise
5. A: 180° turn
   B: 90° turn counterclockwise
   C: 90° turn counterclockwise
   D: 90° turn clockwise
   E: 90° turn clockwise
   F: 180° turn
6.   7.

15 Patterning

Try It
16 ; 19

1. 9 ; 10 ; A   2. 8 ; 10 ; B
3. 5 ; 6 ; A   4. 12 ; 15 ; B
5. A: Multiply the term number by 2 and add 1.
   B: Multiply the term number by 5 and add 2.
   C: Multiply the term number by 3 and subtract 3.
6a. Start at 4. Add 3 each time.
   22 ; 34 ; 46
   Multiply the term number by 3 and add 1.
   22 ; 34 ; 46
b. I would use the pattern rule in Way 2 because it is much faster to do the calculation based on the term number than to count forward until reaching the 100th term.
7. 8 ; 10
a. Multiply the term number by 2.
b. 14 ; 24 ; 50
c. 9th term ; 18th term ; 35th term
8. 16 ; 20
a. Multiply the term number by 4.
b. 32 ; 60 ; 120
c. 7th term ; 10th term ; 25th term
9. △△△
a.

Frame Number	Number of Triangles	Number of Sticks
1	1	3
2	2	5
3	3	7
4	4	9
5	5	11

b. Multiply the term number by 1.
   Multiply the term number by 2 and add 1.
c. There are 10 triangles and 21 sticks.
10. 9
   Multiply the term number by 2 and subtract 1.
   1 ; (2,3) ; (3,5) ; (4,7) ; (5,9)
11. 8
   Multiply the term number by 2 and subtract 2.
   (1,0) ; (2,2) ; (3,4) ; (4,6) ; (5,8)

12.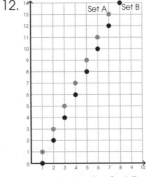

13. Set A: (6,11) (7,13)
    Set B: (6,10) (7,12)

14. It belongs to Set B.

16 Simple Equations

Try It
3, 18 ; x, y

1. $\triangle{p} + \boxed{3} = \triangle{q}$
   will

2. $(\triangle{x} + \triangle{y}) \times \boxed{2} = \triangle{a}$
   will

3. $\triangle{t} = \triangle{m} \times \triangle{n} \div \boxed{9}$
   will not

4. $\boxed{5} + \triangle{d} = \boxed{10} - \triangle{e}$
   will not

5. 14   6. 9   7. 7   8. 7
9. 115   10. 6   11. 50   12. 9
13. 15   14. 6   15. 7   16. 7
17-20. (Individual guesses)
17. 2   18. 3   19. 3   20. 6

21.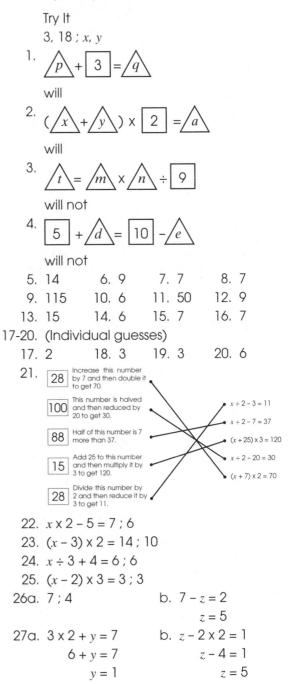

22. $x \times 2 - 5 = 7$; 6
23. $(x - 3) \times 2 = 14$; 10
24. $x \div 3 + 4 = 6$; 6
25. $(x - 2) \times 3 = 3$; 3
26a. 7 ; 4   b. $7 - z = 2$
                      $z = 5$
27a. $3 \times 2 + y = 7$ b. $z - 2 \times 2 = 1$
     $6 + y = 7$ $z - 4 = 1$
     $y = 1$ $z = 5$

28a. $(5 + y) \times 2 = 20$ b. $(z - 5) \div 2 = 3$
        $5 + y = 10$ $z - 5 = 6$
            $y = 5$ $z = 11$

29. 5

30. $x + 9 = 13$
          $x = 4$

31. $x \div 5 = 2$ 32. $x \div 8 = 2$
       $x = 10$ $x = 16$

33. $3 \times x = 12$ 34. $6 \times x = 18$
        $x = 4$ $x = 3$

35. $x \times 2 = 8$ 36. $9 - x = 2$
       $x = 4$ $x = 7$

37. $20 - x = 8$
       $x = 12$

17   Graphs

Try It
blue

1. Jenny: B ; Kenny: A
2. Friday ; Monday and Tuesday
3. Kenny
4a. Stanley   b. Erin   c. Erin
  d. 15 min ; 10 min ; 55 min
  e. Stanley   f. Tyler   g. Erin
5a. August   b. 4 flowers ; 6 flowers
  c. 7 flowers ; 7.5 flowers ; 9 flowers
  d. A ; B ; D
6a. 47 thousand ; 80 thousand pencils
  b. 70 thousand pencils ; 30 thousand pencils
  c. 87 thousand pencils
  d. Machine A
  e. Machine A: The total number of pencils produced increased steadily until Week 3. Machine B: The total number of pencils produced increased steadily starting in Week 1.

18   Probability

Try It
$\frac{1}{3}$; 0

1.   2.

3.

4.

5.

6a. $\frac{1}{6}$ b. $\frac{1}{6}$ c. $\frac{1}{2}$ d. 1

7a. $\frac{2}{7}$ b. 0   c. $\frac{4}{7}$ d. $\frac{1}{7}$

8a. A: $\frac{1}{4}$ B: 0   C: $\frac{1}{3}$
  b. Spinner B
  c. Spinner B
  d. Spinner B
  e. A: 3 times   B: 6 times   C: 4 times

9a.

X	1	2	3	4
1	1	2	3	4
2	2	4	6	8
3	3	6	9	12
4	4	8	12	16

  b. 16   c. 4
  d. $\frac{1}{8}$; $\frac{1}{16}$
    $\frac{3}{16}$; $\frac{1}{4}$
    0 ; 1

10a. BB, BG, GB, GG. There are 4 combinations.
  b. $\frac{1}{4}$; $\frac{1}{2}$; $\frac{1}{4}$

11. B
  a. HH, HT, TH, TT   b. $\frac{1}{4}$; $\frac{1}{4}$; $\frac{1}{2}$
  c. Yes, because the probability of flipping each side of the coin is the same, which is $\frac{1}{2}$.

12.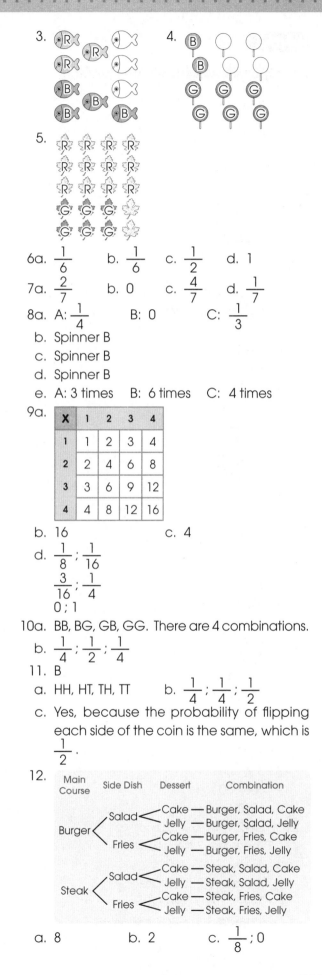

  a. 8   b. 2   c. $\frac{1}{8}$; 0

Level 3

1 Operations with Whole Numbers

Try It

```
      1 9 3
  ×     3 8
  ─────────
  5 7 9 0
  1 5 4 4
  ─────────
  7 3 3 4
```

```
            9 6
  26) 2 4 9 6
      2 3 4
      ─────
        1 5 6
        1 5 6
```

(Individual estimates)
Actual: 7334 ; 96

1. 6124
2. 5881
3. 6518
4. 7445

5.
```
      523
  ×    14
  ──────
     5230
     2092
  ──────
     7322
```

6.
```
      276
  ×    35
  ──────
     8280
     1380
  ──────
     9660
```

7.
```
        182
  27) 4914
      27
      ───
      221
      216
      ───
        54
        54
```

8.
```
        454
  13) 5902
      52
      ──
      70
      65
      ──
        52
        52
```

9. 3479
10. 11 217
11. 20 696
12. 208
13. 8197
14. 12 129
15. 9481
16. 115
17. 7000
18. 336 000
19. 666 660
20. 3000
21a. 2492 + 4716 = 7208
    There are 7208 books.
  b. 4716 – 2492 = 2224
    There are 2224 more.
  c. 2492 ÷ 16 = 155R12
    It needs 156 display shelves.

d. 378 ÷ 48 = 7R42
    It needs 8 racks.
  e. 17 × 8 = 136
    It will have 136 more DVDs.
  f. 4716 – 1296 = 3420
    3420 paperback books are not fiction.
22a. 12 × 365 = 4380
    He has collected 4380 rocks.
  b. 4380 ÷ 20 = 219
    219 rocks are in each bag.
23a. 10 320 – 6144 = 4176
    4176 pencils are put in packages of 36
    each day.
  b. 6144 ÷ 64 = 96
    96 packages of 64 pencils are produced
    each day.
  c. 4176 ÷ 36 = 116
    116 packages of 36 pencils are produced
    each day.
  d. 44 000 ÷ 25 = 1760
    1760 pens are produced in one day on
    average.
  e. 2816 + 3844 = 6660
    6660 cartons of pens are delivered in total.
  f. 2816 ÷ 32 × 148 = 13 024
    The delivery cost is $13 024.
24a. 58 × 31 + 96 × 27 = 4390
    He sold 4390 candies in all.
  b. (2858 – 1226) ÷ 32 = 51
    There will be 51 candies in each box.
25a. (1252 – 28) ÷ (35 – 1) = 36
    There are 36 seats in each row.
  b. 33 × 35 – 632 = 523
    523 students are not girls.
  c. 1252 – 33 × 35 = 97
    97 seats will be left for the teachers.
  d. 1252 ÷ 12 = 104R4
    There will be 104 stacks and 4 chairs will be
    left.

2 Adding and Subtracting Decimals

Try It
1.043 ; 1.043 ; 0.457 ; 0.457
1a. 1.465 + 1.389 = 2.854
    The total weight was 2.854 kg.
  b. $1.45 + $1.38 = $2.83
    The total cost was $2.83.
  c. 2.15 – 1.309 = 0.841
    The weight was 0.841 kg.

d. $3.27 + $4.69 = $7.96
   She spent $7.96.
e. $20 − $18.27 = $1.73
   She received $1.73.
f. $23.19 + $4.58 = $27.77
   He had $27.77.
2a. 2.544 + 3.068 = 5.612
   They live 5.612 km apart.
b. 3.068 − 2.544 = 0.524
   Mindy is 0.524 km farther than Frank.
c. 3.068 + 3.068 = 6.136
   She would have to walk 6.136 km.
d. 2.544 + 3.068 + 3.068 + 2.544 = 11.224
   He had to walk 11.224 km.
e. $5 − $2.29 = $2.71
   She got $2.71 back.
f. $2.71 − $0.79 = $1.92
   She would get $1.92.
g. $2.71 − $0.56 = $2.15
   She would get $2.15.
h. (15.5 − 11.27) + (15.5 − 11.27) = 8.46
   He can save 8.46 min.
i. 2.544 − 1.865 + 3.068 = 3.747
   It is 3.747 km from Mindy's house.
3. $20 − $6.99 − $3.45 = $9.56
   Her change is $9.56.
4. 1.5 − 0.345 − 0.345 − 0.345 = 0.465
   0.465 L of iced tea is left.
5. 16.243 − 4.109 + 3.782 = 15.916
   The height was 15.916 cm.
6. 25.096 − 23 + 21.349 = 23.445
   Yes, there will still be an overweight bag.
   23.445 − 23 = 0.445
   It is over the limit by 0.445 kg.
7. 0.407 + 0.837 + 1.625 = 2.869
   2.869 million people ride the transit system daily.
8. 9.058 − (3.568 + 2.708) = 2.782
   It gained 2.782 kg.
9. 10.538 − 5.037 − 2.339 = 3.162
   The second section is 3.162 m tall.
10. 23.241 + 23.241 + (23.241 − 11.976) = 57.747
   Casey swam 57.747 m in total.
11. 6.396 − 2.734 + 5.453 = 9.115
   He travelled 9.115 km up the river.
12a. 2.351 + 0.455 + 0.312 = 3.118
   His personal best jump was 3.118 m.
b. 2.351 − (3.118 − 0.937) = 0.17
   His jump was 0.17 m shorter.

3 Multiplying and Dividing Decimals

Try It
$19.31 ; $19.31
1a. 926.19 ÷ 3 = 308.73
   The mean distance travelled was 308.73 km.
b. 321.75 ÷ 3 = 107.25
   The average speed was 107.25 km/h.
c. 297.54 ÷ 3 = 99.18
   The average speed was 99.18 km/h.
d. 306.9 ÷ 90 = 3.41
   They drove for 3.41 h.
e. 297.54 ÷ 12 x 1 = 24.795
   They used 24.795 L of gas.
f. 210.72 ÷ 12 x 1 = 17.56
   They needed 17.56 L more.
g. 210.72 ÷ 4 = 52.68
   The average speed was 52.68 km/h.
h. 94.7 ÷ 10 x 9 = 85.23
   They spent $85.23 on gas.
2a. 1.19 x 3 = 3.57
   The total weight was 3.57 kg.
b. $9 x 1.45 = $13.05
   She paid $13.05.
c. $7.74 ÷ 9 = $0.86
   It cost $0.86.
d. $35.37 ÷ 9 = $3.93
   It cost $3.93.
e. $7.90 x 4 = $31.60
   He paid $31.60.
f. $23.71 x 5 = $118.55
   She paid $118.55.
g. 6 bars: $25.56 ÷ 6 = $4.26
   8 bars: $32.16 ÷ 8 = $4.02
   A bag of 8 chocolate bars was a better buy.
3a. $375.06 ÷ 2 = $187.53
   It cost $187.53.
b. 8.25 x 5 = 41.25
   They travelled 41.25 km in all.
c. 8.2 ÷ 4 = 2.05
   His average speed was 2.05 km/h.
d. $32.80 x 5 = $164
   $164 was spent on food.
e. $32.80 ÷ 5 = $6.56
   It was $6.56.
f. 8.25 x 5 = 41.25
   They drank 41.25 L of water in all.

g. $13.5 \div 9 = 1.5$
   1.5 L of water was in each bottle.
h. $1.45 \times 4 = 5.8$
   It was 5.8 kg.
i. $5.8 \times 2 = 11.6$
   It was 11.6 kg.
j. $2.8 \times 2 = 5.6$
   It is 5.6 m².
k. $5.6 \times 2 = 11.2$
   The total area is 11.2 m².
l. $36.5 \div 5 = 7.3$
   Its length is 7.3 m.
4a. $1.35 \times 4 = 5.4$
   4 basketball games are 5.4 h long.
b. $1.45 \times 8 = 11.6$
   His team had 11.6 h of practice.
c. $26 \div 8 = 3.25$
   They ran 3.25 km on average each day.
d. $277 \div 4 = 69.25$
   69.25 points were scored on average.
e. $68.25 \times 4 = 273$
   His team got 273 points in all.
f. Mr. Holly's team: $18.25 \times 4 = 73$
   Ms. Prem's team: $9.75 \times (80 \div 10) = 78$
   Ms. Prem's team won.

4   Mixed Operations with Decimals

Try It
18.2 ; 18.2
1a. $38.85 \div 7 = 5.55$
   The width is 5.55 m.
b. $8.14 \times 2 + 5 \times 2 = 26.28$
   The length of the border is 26.28 m.
c. $8.14 \times 5 = 40.7$
   The area of the dining room is 40.7 m².
d. $0.95 \times 8 = 7.6$
   The area of the hallway is 7.6 m².
e. $7.6 \div 2 = 3.8$
   The length of the hallway is 3.8 m.
2a. $259.79 + 302.57 + 225.67 \times 2 = 1013.7$
   They drove for 1013.7 km.
b. $1013.7 \div 75 = 13.516$
   They drove for 13.516 h.
c. $46.37 + 49.45 + 42.69 = 138.51$
   They bought 138.51 L of gas altogether.
d. $\$47.76 \times 3 = \$143.28$
   The total fill-up cost was $143.28.

e. $\$58.27 + \$63.39 + \$123.86 = \$245.52$
   They spent $245.52 on food.
f. $\$245.52 \div 4 = \$61.38$
   They spent $61.38 on food per day.
g. $\$245.52 - \$25.52 = \$220$
   Their budget for food was $220.
h. $(2.29 \times 3 + 3.4 \times 6) - (0.6 \times 4 + 1.4 \times 8) = 13.67$
   She spent $13.67 more on meat than on vegetables.
i. $\$26.69 \times 4 \times 3 = \$320.28$
   Their total lodging bill was $320.28.
3a. $\$4.29 \times 24 = \$102.96$
   He will collect $102.96 this year.
b. $(\$102.96 + \$197.04) \div 10 = \$30$
   $30 is available for the club each month.
c. $\$300 \div 4 \div 2 = \$37.50$
   There will be $37.50 for each issue.
d. $\$300 - \$37.50 \times 2 = \$225$
   $225 will be left for other activities.
e. $\$9.95 \times 25 = \$248.75$
   No, the club cannot afford it.
f. $\$102.96 - \$3.99 \times 20 = \$23.16$
   The club will collect $23.16 more this year.
4. $\$10 - \$1.25 \times 5 = \$3.75$
   She gets $3.75 in change.
5. $4 \times 4.2 + 4.1 \times 6 = 41.4$
   The area of the sewn quilt is 41.4 m².
6. $1.39 \times 5 + 2.69 \times 3 + 1.29 \times 10 = 27.92$
   She pays $27.92 in all.
7. $\$20 - (\$2.25 \times 3 + \$5.99 \times 2) = \$1.27$
   He got $1.27 in change.
8. $(0.48 \div 2) - (0.65 \div 5) = 0.11$
   Lillian runs 0.11 km faster than Jerry each minute.

5   Fractions, Decimals, and Percents

Try It
$25 ; \frac{1}{4} ; \frac{1}{4} ; 25\%$
1a. $\frac{1}{2} = \frac{50}{100} = 50\% ; 50\%$
b. $20\% = \frac{20}{100} = \frac{1}{5}$
   $\frac{1}{5}$ of the price was discounted.
c. $\frac{4}{5} = \frac{80}{100} = 80\%$
   Molly paid 80% of the price.

d. $\frac{45}{50} = \frac{90}{100} = 90\%$

   90% of the items were on sale.

e. $\frac{50}{200} = \frac{25}{100} = 25\%$

   25% of the shoes were sold.

f. $0.15 = \frac{15}{100} = \frac{3}{20}$

   $\frac{3}{20}$ of the socks were on sale.

2a. $\frac{3}{5} = \frac{60}{100} = 60\%$

   60% of the weights were over 10 kg.

b. $\frac{3}{10} = \frac{30}{100} = 30\%$

   30% of the weights were wrapped in vinyl.

c. $100\% - 30\% = 70\%$

   70% of the weights were not wrapped in vinyl.

d. $0.6 = \frac{6}{10} = \frac{3}{5}$

   She did aerobics for $\frac{3}{5}$ of an hour.

e. $85\% = \frac{85}{100} = \frac{17}{20}$

   $\frac{17}{20}$ in the class were girls.

f. $\frac{7}{10} = \frac{70}{100} = 70\%$

   Ron ran 70% of the track.

g. $100\% - 70\% = 30\%$

   Ron walked 30% of the track.

h. $\frac{1}{10} = \frac{10}{100}$

   She would have to skip 110 times on the second day.

3. $\frac{25}{100} = 25\%$

   25% of her stickers are ♡.

4. $\frac{10}{100} = 10\%$

   10% of her stickers are 🌷.

5. $\frac{20}{100} = 20\%$

   20% of her stickers are ⚙.

6. $\frac{45}{100} = 45\%$

   45% of her stickers are ☆.

7. $100 - 20 = 80$

   $\frac{80}{100} = 80\%$

   80% of her stickers will be left.

8. $100 - 16 = 84$

   $\frac{84}{100} = 84\%$

   84% of her stickers will be left.

9. $0.35 = 35\%$

   $100\% - 35\% = 65\%$

   65% of her stickers will be left.

10. $\frac{3}{4} = \frac{75}{100} = 75\%$

   $100\% - 75\% = 25\%$

   25% of her stickers will be left.

11. $25 - 10 = 15$

   $\frac{15}{25} = \frac{60}{100} = 60\%$

   60% of them will be left.

12. $20 - 12 = 8$

   $\frac{8}{20} = \frac{40}{100} = 40\%$

   She used 40% of them.

13. $100\% - 60\% = 40\%$

   $40\% = \frac{40}{100}$

   40 stickers will be left.

14. $\frac{5}{20} = \frac{25}{100} = 25\%$

   25% of the doughnuts are chocolate flavoured.

15. $42\% = 0.42$

   0.42 of the drinks are cherry flavoured.

16a. $\frac{18}{30} = \frac{3}{5}$

   $\frac{3}{5}$ of the squirrels are brown.

b. $\frac{3}{5} = \frac{60}{100} = 60\%$

   60% of the squirrels are brown.

17. $0.45 = \frac{45}{100} = \frac{9}{20} > \frac{9}{22}$

   Michael has more cookies with chocolate chips.

18. KICKB**O**XING: $\frac{3}{10} = \frac{30}{100} = 0.3$

   IS: $\frac{1}{2} = \frac{50}{100} = 50\%$

   TOU**GH**: $\frac{2}{5} = \frac{40}{100} = 40\%$

   The word is "TOUGH".

6   Ratios and Rates

Try It

5 ; 6 ; Kyle

1a. 25:35 = 5:7

   5:7

  b. 35:25 = 7:5

   The ratio is 7:5.

  c. 25:200 = 1:8

   The ratio is 1:8.

  d. 35:200 = 7:40

   The ratio is 7:40.

2a. 25:100 = 1:4

   The ratio is 1:4.

  b. 100:200 = 1:2

   The ratio is 1:2.

3a. 50:200 = 1:4

   The ratio is 1:4.

  b. 75:250 = 3:10

   The ratio is 3:10.

4a. 5:15 = 1:3

   The ratio is 1:3.

  b. 4:16 = 1:4

   The ratio is 1:4.

  c. 12:20 = 3:5

   The ratio is 3:5.

  d. 2:18 = 1:9

   The ratio is 1:9.

  e. 6:10 = 3:5

   The ratio is 3:5.

   f. 16:20 = 4:5

   The ratio is 4:5.

  g. 12:24 = 1:2

   The ratio will be 1:2.

  h. 20:16 = 5:4

   The ratio will be 5:4.

5a. $6.45 ÷ 5 kg = $1.29/kg

   The unit price is $1.29/kg.

  b. $1.29/kg x 3 kg = $3.87

   She needed to pay $3.87.

6a. $6.76 ÷ 4 kg = $1.69/kg

   The unit price is $1.69/kg.

  b. $1.69/kg x 3 kg = $5.07

   She needed to pay $5.07.

7a. $1.96 ÷ 4 kg = $0.49/kg

   The unit price is $0.49/kg.

  b. $0.49/kg x 7 kg = $3.43

   She needed to pay $3.43.

8. $14.97 ÷ 3 kg = $4.99/kg

   $25.80 ÷ 5 kg = $5.16/kg

   A 3-kg basket of cherries was a better buy.

9a. $5.58 ÷ 2 kg = $2.79/kg

   $8.07 ÷ 3 kg = $2.69/kg

   A 3-kg basket of plums was a better buy.

  b. $8.07 x 2 = $16.14

   She paid $16.14.

  c. $80.70 ÷ $8.07 = 10

   She bought 10 baskets.

10. Packs of 5: 350 ÷ 5 = 70

               $1.35 x 70 = $94.50

   Packs of 7: 350 ÷ 7 = 50

               $1.75 x 50 = $87.50

   Difference: $94.50 – $87.50 = $7

   He should pack the apples in bags of 5.

   He will make $7 more.

11. 3 km in 20 min = 9 km in 60 min = 9 km/h

   His speed is 9 km/h.

12. 1.5 h = 90 min

   27 pages ÷ 90 min = 0.3 pages/min

   His reading rate is 0.3 pages/min.

13. $130 ÷ 8 h = $16.25/h

   He earned $16.25/h.

14. Lily: 108 words ÷ 10 min = 10.8 words/min

   Henry: 147 words ÷ 15 min = 9.8 words/min

   Lily reads faster; she can read more words

   per minute.

15a. Bright Lite: $1.48 ÷ 4 bulbs = $0.37/bulb

   Supergood: $4.92 ÷ 12 bulbs = $0.41/bulb

   Bright Lite bulbs are a better buy.

  b. Supergood bulbs offer a better value

   because each bulb lasts twice as long but

   costs less than two Bright Lite bulbs.

16a. Fred: 96 km ÷ 2 h = 48 km/h

   Ivan: 120 km ÷ 3 h = 40 km/h

   Fred's speed is 48 km/h and Ivan's speed

   is 40 km/h.

  b. 48:40 = 6:5

   The ratio is 6:5.

7   Money

Try It

$29.21 ; $29.21 ; $20.79 ; $20.79

1a. Store B: $41.52 – $5.25 = $36.27

   Store A had the lower price.

b. $50 – $35.95 = $14.05
Her change was $14.05. She received one
$10 bill, two toonies, and one nickel.

2a. 0.7 kg = 700 g
$1.45 x 7 = $10.15
It would cost $10.15.

b. $12 – $10.15 = $1.85
Her change was $1.85. The coins were one
loonie, three quarters, and one dime.

3. Store C: $3.95 ÷ 125 g = $0.0316/g
Store D: $2.99 ÷ 100 g = $0.0299/g
Store D offered a better buy.

4. $1 = 4 quarters
$10 = 40 quarters
He would get 40 quarters.

5a. $2.49 x 2 + $1.27 = $6.25
He paid with three toonies and one
quarter.

b. ($2.49 + $1.39 + $1.27) x 8 = $41.20
She had $41.20.

6. $11.16 ÷ 4 x 3 = $8.37
She got back $8.37.

7a. $4.32 x 3 – $4.59 x 2 = $3.78
A soft drink costs $3.78.

b. $0.25 x 4 + $0.10 x 24 + $0.05 x 16 = $4.20
Yes, he has enough money.

8a. $14.05/h x 18 h = $252.90
He could earn $252.90 per week.

b. $252.90 – $2.85 x 2 x 6 = $218.70
He earned $218.70 each week after paying
for transit.

c. $218.70 – $5.38 = $213.32
He earned $213.32 after paying for transit
and tax.

d. $213.32 x 3 = $639.96
Yes, he would.

e. 2 hours and 30 minutes equal 5 half hours.
$1.75 + $3 x 4 = $13.75
The parking fee is $13.75.

f. 2 hours equal 4 half hours.
Parking fee: $1.75 + $3 x 3 = $10.75
Amount given: $10.75 + $1.25 = $12
He gave $12 for parking.

g. $1 = 20 nickels
$5 = 100 nickels
He would get 100 nickels.

9. 129 ÷ 3 x $16 = $688
She paid $688 in all.

10. $0.25 x 329 + $0.10 x 215 + $0.05 x 279 =
$117.70
He has $117.70 in all.

11. $20.75 x (12 + 15) = $560.25
They will raise $560.25 altogether.

12. $0.50 x 35 + $0.65 x 60 = $56.50
She will make $56.50.

13. $1.25 x 108 + $1.75 x 88 + $1.45 x 104 =
$439.80
She made $439.80.

14. $50 x 2 – $57.65 = $42.35
Her change would be two $20 bills,
one toonie, one quarter, and one dime.

8   Perimeter and Area

Try It
12 ; 6 ; 12 ; 6

1. A: 10 x 10 = 100   B: 18 x 16 = 288
   100   It is 288 cm².
   C: 12 x 9 = 108   D: 12 x 16 ÷ 2 = 96
   It is 108 cm².   It is 96 cm².

2. A: 10 x 4 = 40
   40
   B: 18 x 2 + 16 x 2 = 68
   It is 68 cm.
   C: 12 x 2 + 10 x 2 = 44
   It is 44 cm.
   D: 17 + 17 + 12 = 46
   It is 46 cm.

3a. 108 – 8 x 6 = 60
   The area is 60 cm².

b. 8 x 2 + 7 x 2 = 30
   The perimeter is 30 cm.

4. 96 – 10 x 13 ÷ 2 = 31
   The area is 31 cm².

5a. A
   Side length of cut-out: 10 – 2 – 2 = 6
   Area left: 100 – 6 x 6 = 64
   The area is 64 cm².

b. B
   Length of cut-out: 18 – 2 – 2 = 14
   Width of cut-out: 16 – 2 – 2 = 12
   Area left: 288 – 14 x 12 = 120
   The area is 120 cm².

6a. 180 ÷ 15 = 12
   Its width is 12 m.

b. 15 x 3 x 2 + 12 x 3 x 2 = 162
   162 m² of wallpaper is needed.

7. Length: 15 − 1 − 1 = 13
   Width: 12 − 1 − 1 = 10
   Area: 13 x 10 = 130
   She needed 130 m² of carpet.
8a. 13 + 12 + 5 = 30
    The perimeter is 30 m.
  b. 12 x 5 ÷ 2 = 30
    She needed 30 m² of tile.
  c. Area: 13 x 3 + 12 x 3 + 5 x 3 = 90
    No. of cans: 90 ÷ 18 = 5
    She needed 5 cans of paint.
9. 18 x 16 = 288
   She needed 288 m² of carpet.
10-12. (Suggested answers and drawings)

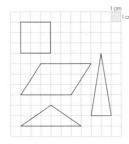

10a. 12 ÷ 4 = 3
    The side length is 3 cm.
  b. No, you only need to know the perimeter
    or area, because the side lengths of a
    square are all equal.
11a. 5 cm ; 3 cm
  b. Yes, they have the same area. This
    is because switching the order in a
    multiplication gives the same answer.
12a. 2 cm ; 6 cm
  b. Since the two triangles have the same
    area and the height of second triangle is
    the same as the base of the first one, the
    base of the second triangle should be the
    same as the height of the first triangle. The
    bases and heights of the two triangles are
    just swapped.

9   Volume and Surface Area

   Try It
   50 ; 30 ; 7500 ; 7500 cm³
1a. 500 − 200 = 300 ; It is 300 cm³.
    800 − 200 = 600 ; It is 600 cm³.
    700 − 200 = 500 ; It is 500 cm³.
    900 − 200 = 700 ; It is 700 cm³.
  b. Brick D, Brick B, Brick C, Brick A

c. 300 ÷ 5 = 60
   The area of its base is 60 cm².
d. 60 ÷ 6 = 10
   Its length is 10 cm.
2a. 4 x 4 x 4 = 64
    It is 64 cm³.
  b. 8 x 5 x 4 = 160
    It is 160 cm³.
  c. 4 x 3.5 ÷ 2 x 9 = 63
    It is 63 cm³.
3a. 4 x 4 x 6 = 96
    96 cm² of wrapping paper is needed.
  b. 8 x 5 x 2 + 8 x 4 x 2 + 5 x 4 x 2 = 184
    184 cm² of wrapping paper is needed.
  c. 4 x 3.5 ÷ 2 x 2 + 4 x 9 + 4 x 9 + 4 x 9 = 122
    122 cm² of wrapping paper is needed.
4a. 160 ÷ 2 = 80
    It is 80 cm³.
  b. New length: 8 ÷ 2 = 4
    4 x 5 x 2 + 4 x 4 x 2 + 5 x 4 x 2 = 112
    112 cm² of wrapping paper is needed.
5a. 63 ÷ 2 = 31.5
    It is 31.5 cm³.
  b. New base: 4 ÷ 2 = 2
    2 x 3.5 ÷ 2 x 2 + 4 x 9 + 3.5 x 9 + 2 x 9 = 92.5
    92.5 cm² of wrapping paper is needed.
6. 120 ÷ 15 = 8
   Its width is 8 cm.
7. 1500 ÷ 120 = 12.5
   The height is 12.5 cm.
8. 1500 cm³ = 1500 mL = 1.5 L
   The capacity of the box is 1.5 L.
9a. 50 x 45 x 20 = 45 000
    It is 45 000 cm³.
  b. 45 000 ÷ 1500 = 30
    30 boxes of sand fill it up.
  c. 1500 x 40 = 60 000
    It is 60 000 cm³.
  d. 60 000 ÷ 60 = 1000
    It is 1000 cm².
  e. 45 000 ÷ 1000 = 45
    The sand will reach 45 cm.
10a. 30 x 21 x 1.8 = 1134
    It is 1134 m³.
  b. 1134 m³ = 1 134 000 L
    It can hold 1 134 000 L.
  c. 30 x 21 x 1.6 = 1008
    1008 m³ = 1 008 000 L
    There will be 1 008 000 L of water.

d. $30 \times 21 \times (1.7 - 1.6) = 63$
   $63 \text{ m}^3 = 63\,000 \text{ L}$
   $63\,000$ L of water should be pumped.
e. $1\,134\,000 \div 300\,000 = 3.78$
   It will take 3.78 h.
f. $126\,000 \text{ L} = 126 \text{ m}^3$
   $126 \div 30 \div 21 = 0.2$
   The water level will rise by 0.2 m.

11a. $5 \times 2 \times 2 + 2 \times 2 \times 2 = 28$
    It is 28 m³.
 b. $5 \times 2 \times 4 - 2 \times 2 + 2 \times 2 \times 5 = 56$
    The area of the structure is 56 m², so she needs 56 L of paint.

10 Patterning

Try It
8 ; 10 ; 12 ; 12

1a. 10 ; 15 ; 20 ; 25 ; 30 ; 35 ; 40 ; 45 ; 50
    50

b.

No. of Peanuts	3	6	9	12	15	18	21	24	27
No. of Hazelnuts	2	4	6	8	10	12	14	16	18

He will have 18 hazelnuts.

c.

No. of Almonds	3	6	9	12	15	18	21	24	27
No. of Cashews	2	3	4	5	6	7	8	9	10

He will add 10 cashews.

2a. It grew 10 cm each month.

b.

Month	Apr	May	Jun	Jul
Length of Vine (cm)	80	90	100	110

It will be 110 cm long in July.

c.

Month	Apr	May	Jun	Jul	Aug	Sep
Length of Vine (cm)	80	90	100	110	120	130

It will be 130 cm long.

d.

Month	Sep	Oct	Nov	Dec	Jan	Feb	Mar	Apr
No. of Leaves	8	16	24	32	40	48	56	64

64 leaves had grown.

e.

Month	Apr	May	Jun	Jul	Aug
Length of Vine (cm)	80	87.5	95	102.5	110

It will be 110 cm long.

3a.

Month No.	0	1	2	3	4	5	6
Balance ($)	5000	4250	3500	2750	2000	1250	500

b. It will be $2750.
c. He can pay his rent for 6 months.
d. The balance decreases by $750 each month.
e. He will receive $4.40 in the sixth month.

f. The interest decreases by $1.10 each month.
g. $8.80 + $7.70 + $6.60 + $5.50 + $4.40 = $33
   He will receive $33.
h. $1250 + $8.80 + $7.70 + $6.60 + $5.50 = $1278.60
   It will be $1278.60.

4a. She received $2 more each month.
 b. She received $22 in the sixth month.
 c. She spent $2.50 more each month.
 d. She spent $20.50 in the sixth month.
 e. $(12 - 8) + (14 - 10.5) + (16 - 13) + (18 - 15.5) + (20 - 18) + (22 - 20.5) = 16.5$
    She saved $16.50.
 f. The amount received and spent are the same in the ninth month.
 g. She would spend $1.50 more than she received in the 12th month.

11 Equations

Try It
A ; 5

1. A ; 10
2. B ; $n = 9$
3. B ; $n = 2$
4. A ; $n = 16$
5. B ; $n = 4$
6. 24
7. $n \times 3 = 21$
   $n = 7$
8. $28 \div n = 4$
   $n = 7$
9. $n + 6 = 18$
   $n = 12$
10. $n \times 3 = 27$
    $n = 9$
11. C ; 7
12. A ; 14
13. E ; 6
14. D ; 18
15. B ; 16
16a. none ; A, b, h
  b. 12 ; 4
17a. 2 ; A, b, h
  b. 6 ; 2
18. A ; 16
    $p \times 3 - 10 = 38$
    $p \times 3 = 48$
    $p = 16$
19. B ; 15
    $2 \times f + 1 = 31$
    $2 \times f = 30$
    $f = 15$
20. A ; 12
    $b \div 2 + 2 = 8$
    $b \div 2 = 6$
    $b = 12$

21. A ; 12

   $c \div 2 + 9 = 5 \times 3$

   $c \div 2 + 9 = 15$

   $c \div 2 = 6$

   $c = 12$

22. B ; 16

   $(b \div 2) - 3 = 5$

   $b \div 2 = 8$

   $b = 16$

23a. 15 ; 12 ; 27 ; 27

   b. $b - 7 = 35$

   $b = 42$

   Skirt B cost $42.

   c. $s + 25 = 145$

   $s = 120$

   The sweater cost $120.

24a. $s + 12 \times 3 = 54$

   $s + 36 = 54$

   $s = 18$

   The pair of shorts cost $18.

   b. $c - 3 = 12 - 5$

   $c - 3 = 7$

   $c = 10$

   She gave $10 to the cashier.

   c. $c - 12 = 56 - 8$

   $c - 12 = 48$

   $c = 60$

   He gave $60 to the cashier.

12 Graphs (1)

Try It

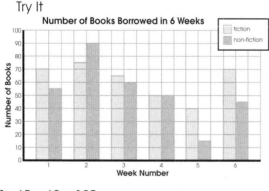

1. $65 + 60 = 125$

   125 books were borrowed.

2. Most books were borrowed in Week 2.

3. The fewest non-fiction books were borrowed in Week 5.

4. There were 2 weeks when fewer than 60 fiction books were borrowed.

5. $70 - 55 = 15$

   15 more fiction books were borrowed.

6. It was in Week 4.

7. It was in Week 2.

8. It was Week 5, because it had the fewest books borrowed.

9a. B

   b. $120 \div 4 = 30$

   30 were activity books.

   $120 \div 2 = 60$

   60 were workbooks.

10.

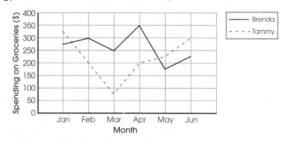

Brenda and Tammy's Grocery Spending in 6 Months

   a. $350 - 200 = 150$

   Brenda spent $150 more.

   b. $300 - 225 = 75$

   Tammy spent $75 more.

   c. $350 - 175 = 175$

   Brenda spent the most in April. She spent $175 more.

11. The greatest difference was in March.

12. Brenda: $275 + 300 + 250 + 350 + 175 + 225$
      $= 1575$

   Tammy: $325 + 200 + 75 + 200 + 225 + 300$
      $= 1325$

   Difference: $1575 - 1325 = 250$

   Brenda spent $250 more.

13a. Tammy ; Brenda

   b. $300 \div 3 = 100$

   She spent $100 on meat.

   $300 \div 6 = 50$

   She spent $50 on fruits.

   c. $200 \div 4 = 50$

   She spent $50 on meat.

   $200 - 50 - 200 \div 8 = 125$

   She spent $125 on vegetables.

d. Brenda: 50
Tammy: 200 ÷ 8 = 25
Difference: 50 – 25 = 25
Brenda spent more on fruits by $25.

13 Graphs (2)

Try It
A ; The height of a flower changes over time and is best-suited for a line graph.

1. L
2. C
3. B
4. B
5. L
6. C
7. L
8. B
9. B

10.

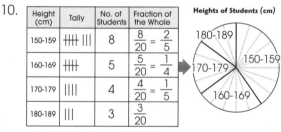

Height (cm)	Tally	No. of Students	Fraction of the Whole
150-159	⊪⊪ ‖‖‖	8	$\frac{8}{20} = \frac{2}{5}$
160-169	⊪⊪	5	$\frac{5}{20} = \frac{1}{4}$
170-179	‖‖‖‖	4	$\frac{4}{20} = \frac{1}{5}$
180-189	‖‖‖	3	$\frac{3}{20}$

a. 39 cm
b. 150 – 159 cm ; 180 – 189 cm
c. ✗ ; 150 – 159 cm ; 40% ; ✗ ; ✗

11.

Means of Transportation to School

a. both ; school bus
b. bar graph ; 16 students
c. circle graph ; car
d. bar graph ; 100 students
e. bar graph ; 12 students
f. circle graph ; $\frac{3}{25}$
g. bar graph ; 72 students

12. double line graph

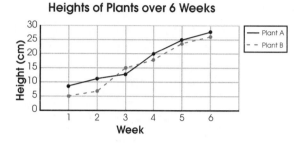

Heights of Plants over 6 Weeks

a. Plant A is 4 cm taller than Plant B in Week 2.
b. He added fertilizer to Plant A in Week 3. He added fertilizer to Plant B in Week 2.

14 Probability

Try It

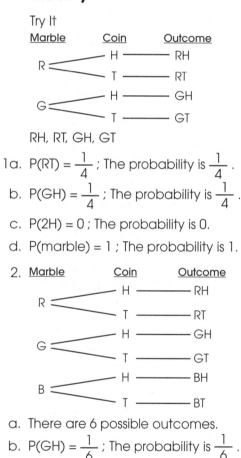

RH, RT, GH, GT

1a. $P(RT) = \frac{1}{4}$; The probability is $\frac{1}{4}$.
b. $P(GH) = \frac{1}{4}$; The probability is $\frac{1}{4}$.
c. $P(2H) = 0$; The probability is 0.
d. $P(marble) = 1$; The probability is 1.

2. Marble   Coin   Outcome

a. There are 6 possible outcomes.
b. $P(GH) = \frac{1}{6}$; The probability is $\frac{1}{6}$.

3a.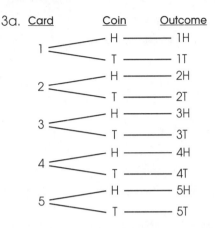

Card   Coin   Outcome

b. There are 10 possible outcomes.

c. $P(3H) = \frac{1}{10}$; The probability is $\frac{1}{10}$.

$P(5T) = \frac{1}{10}$; The probability is $\frac{1}{10}$.

$P(\text{even no. and }H) = \frac{1}{5}$; The probability is $\frac{1}{5}$.

d. $P(1H) = \frac{1}{10}$; The probability is $\frac{1}{10}$.

$P(\text{not }1H) = \frac{9}{10}$; The probability is $\frac{9}{10}$.

e. She is not correct. Since the card is put back after each turn, the probability of winning each round does not change.

4a. There are 5 possible outcomes.

b. $P(R) = \frac{1}{5}$; The probability is $\frac{1}{5}$.

$P(W) = \frac{1}{5}$; The probability is $\frac{1}{5}$.

c. Yes, the probability is still the same because there are still an equal number of balls in each colour.

d.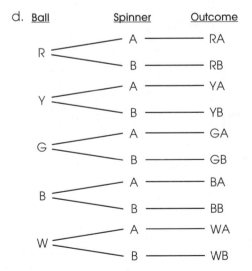

Ball   Spinner   Outcome

ASSESSMENT TESTS 1 AND 2

Test-taking Tips

Writing tests can be stressful for many students. The best way to prepare for a test is by practising! In addition to practising, the test-taking tips below will also help you prepare for tests.

Multiple-choice Questions

- Read the question twice before finding the answer.
- Skip the difficult questions and do the easy ones first.
- Come up with an answer before looking at the choices.
- Read all four choices before deciding which is the correct answer.
- Eliminate the choices that you know are incorrect.
- Read and follow the instructions carefully:
    - Use a pencil only.
    - Fill one circle only for each question.
    - Fill the circle completely.
    - Cleanly erase any answer you wish to change.
      e.g.

      ●   ⊗ ⊘ ◉ ◐
      correct   incorrect

Open-response Questions

- Read the question carefully.
- Highlight (i.e. underline/circle) important information in the question.
- Use drawings to help you better understand the question if needed.
- Find out what needs to be included in the solution.
- Estimate the answer.
- Organize your thoughts before writing the solution.
- Write in the space provided.
- Always write a concluding sentence for your solution.
- Check if your answer is reasonable.
- Never leave a question blank. Show your work or write down your reasoning. Even if you do not get the correct answer, you might get some marks for showing your work.

Multiple-choice Questions

① Which number has 5 in its ten thousands place?

    ○ 80 000 + 9000 + 500 + 60

    ○ one hundred five thousand four hundred forty-one

    ○ 564 251

    ○ 200 000 + 50 000 + 4000 + 200 + 50 + 1

② The height of the prism below is half of its length.

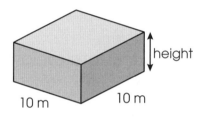

    10 m   10 m   height

What is its volume?

    ○ 250 m³

    ○ 400 m³

    ○ 500 m³

    ○ 2000 m³

③ Which decimal is between 8.932 and 9.041?

    ○ 8.795

    ○ 8.906

    ○ 9.028

    ○ 9.057

④ The missing digits in the vertical addition are the same. What are the missing digits?

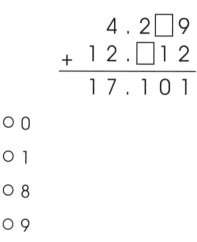

$$
\begin{array}{r}
4\,.\,2\,\square\,9 \\
+\ 12\,.\,\square\,1\,2 \\
\hline
17\,.\,1\,0\,1
\end{array}
$$

    ○ 0

    ○ 1

    ○ 8

    ○ 9

⑤ John splits 257 g of sugar into 7 equal portions. How much sugar is there in each portion?

○ under 36 g

○ from 36 g to 36.5 g

○ from 36.6 g to 37 g

○ over 37 g

⑥ Which of the following fractions is not equivalent to the others?

○ $1\frac{6}{15}$

○ $\frac{8}{5}$

○ $1\frac{2}{5}$

○ $\frac{14}{10}$

⑦ Which has a ratio of 5:9?

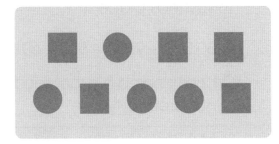

○ 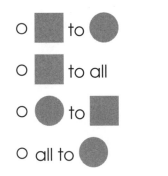 to ⬤

○ ◼ to all

○ ⬤ to ◼

○ all to ⬤

⑧ What is the total weight of the crackers?

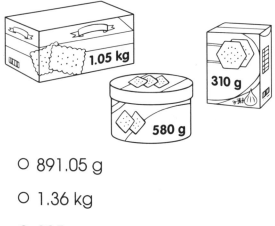

○ 891.05 g

○ 1.36 kg

○ 995 g

○ 1.94 kg

⑨ The perimeter of the kite below is 21 cm.

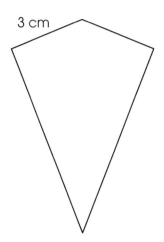

3 cm

What is the length of one of the long sides of the kite?

○ 7 cm

○ 7.5 cm

○ 9 cm

○ 15 cm

⑩ Which is the correct way to write 84 as a product of prime numbers?

○ 3 × 4 × 7

○ 1 × 2 × 3 × 7

○ 2 × 2 × 3 × 7

○ 2 × 6 × 7

⑪ Which quadrilateral has all of the following properties?

- at least one pair of parallel sides
- two pairs of equal sides
- no right angles

○ trapezoid

○ rectangle

○ rhombus

○ square

⑫ Which is the correct pattern rule for the following number pattern?

2, 3, 5, 9, 17

○ Start at 2. Add 1 and 2 alternately.

○ Start at 2. Multiply by 3 and subtract 3 each time.

○ Start at 2. Add 7 and divide by 3 each time.

○ Start at 2. Multiply by 2 and subtract 1 each time.

⑬ The figure below is rotated 90° counterclockwise each time to form a pattern. What is the third figure?

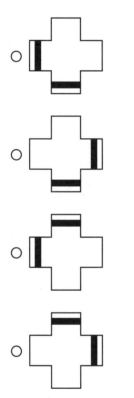

⑭ What is the mean of this set of data?

22	24	17
24	24	24
24	13	21
17	21	21

○ 13

○ 17

○ 21

○ 24

⑮ How many acute angles does this shape have?

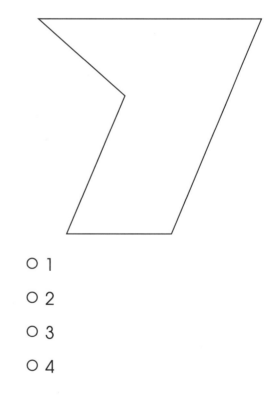

○ 1

○ 2

○ 3

○ 4

Open-response Questions

⑯ A lunch combo consists of a main, a drink, and a snack. Create a tree diagram to find all the possible outcomes.

Main	Drink	Snack
• sandwich • burger	• orange juice • milk	• chips • cookies • apple

What is the probability that a customer orders a lunch combo that includes milk and cookies?

⑰ **Days Spent Swimming and Running in Each Season**

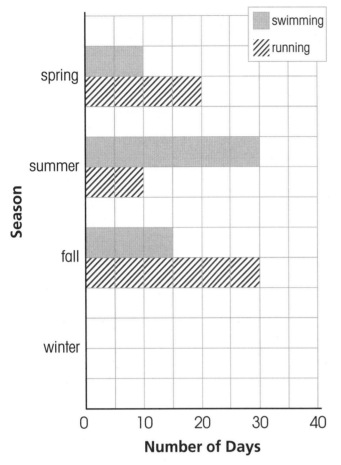

Cindy recorded the number of days she swam and ran in each season in the graph. Use the given information to fill out the days in winter.

- The mean number of days Cindy swam is 15.

- The median number of days Cindy ran is 15.

On how many days did Cindy swim or run in the year?

⑱ The score of a game, S, is determined by the equation: $S = 2 \times m + n$. The one with the highest score wins the game. Read what the children said to find their scores and the winner of the game.

Adam: "My m has a value of 5 and my n has a value of 2."

Betty: "My m is one less than double Adam's n. My n is three more than my m."

Cam: "My m and n are integers that have a sum of 10. My m is between Adam's m and Betty's m."

Multiple-choice Questions

① Which set of numbers is in the correct order?

   ○ 625 434 < 622 696 < 825 951

   ○ 324 278 > 359 216 > 397 240

   ○ 672 525 < 713 024 < 736 643

   ○ 791 441 > 618 171 > 717 902

② What is the order of rotational symmetry of this figure?

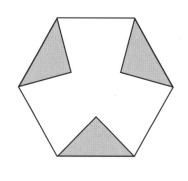

   ○ 0

   ○ 1

   ○ 3

   ○ 6

③ What is the difference of 0.468 and 10.2?

   ○ 9.468

   ○ 9.732

   ○ 9.842

   ○ 10.668

④ What is the surface area of the triangular prism?

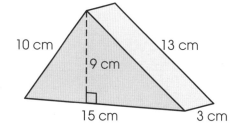

10 cm   13 cm   9 cm   15 cm   3 cm

   ○ 135 cm²

   ○ 181.5 cm²

   ○ 228 cm²

   ○ 249 cm²

⑤ Which fraction is less than $\frac{4}{7}$?

○ $\frac{2}{3}$

○ $\frac{5}{7}$

○ $\frac{8}{14}$

○ $\frac{10}{21}$

⑥ What percent of the diagram is shaded?

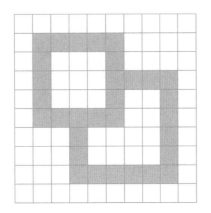

○ 25%

○ 31%

○ 36%

○ 69%

⑦ What is the unit rate?

○ $0.27/candle

○ $0.34/candle

○ $0.36/candle

○ $2.94/candle

⑧ The concert started at 10:24:29 and ended at 14:05:45. How long did it last?

○ 3 h 29 min 21 s

○ 3 h 41 min 16 s

○ 4 h 29 min 16 s

○ 4 h 41 min 21 s

⑨ What is the area of the triangle?

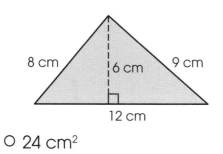

○ 24 cm²

○ 36 cm²

○ 54 cm²

○ 72 cm²

⑩ A juice box has a capacity of 0.37 L. What is the total capacity of 6 juice boxes?

○ 2.22 mL

○ 2220 mL

○ 3700 mL

○ 3.7 L

⑪ Which solid has the following views?

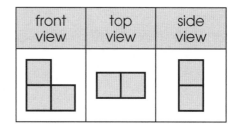

front view	top view	side view

○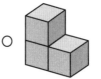

○

○

○

⑫ Which of the following is not a prime number?

○ 57

○ 67

○ 71

○ 83

Use this set of data for Questions 13 and 14.

58	55	50	59	53	54
56	47	48	59	57	50

⑬ What is the median?

○ 53.5

○ 54

○ 54.5

○ 55

⑭ What is the mode?

○ 50

○ 59

○ 50 and 59

○ none

⑮ A shape is shown on the grid.

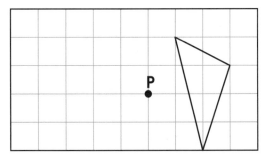

Which of the following shows the image of the shape after a 270° clockwise rotation about Point P?

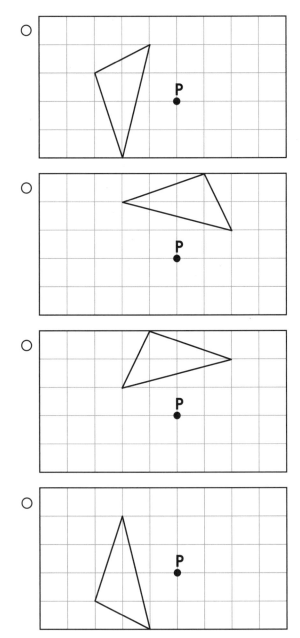

Open-response Questions

⑯ Amy and Ben plot points on the Cartesian coordinate plane to make shapes. Plot and draw the shapes.

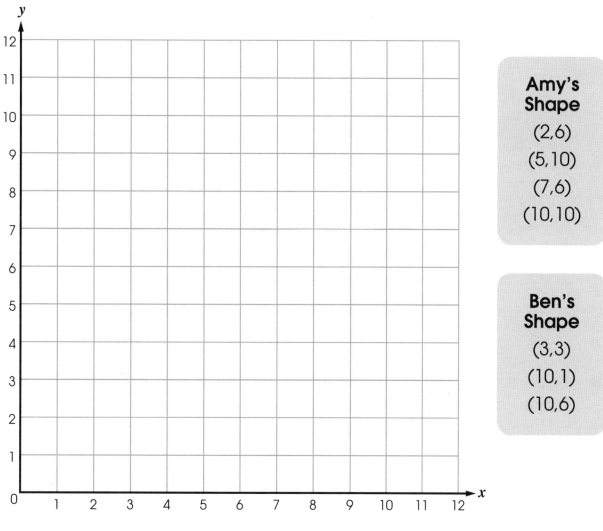

Amy's Shape

(2,6)

(5,10)

(7,6)

(10,10)

Ben's Shape

(3,3)

(10,1)

(10,6)

Whose shape has a greater area?

⑰ Leo paid for 2 potted plants with a $50 bill and got $8 change back. The cost of a dozen roses is $3 less than the cost of a potted plant. How much does Emily have to pay if she buys 3 potted plants and 4 roses? Use simple equations to find the answer.

⑱ Below is a pattern made with sticks. Terms 3, 4, and 5 are shown, but not Terms 1 and 2.

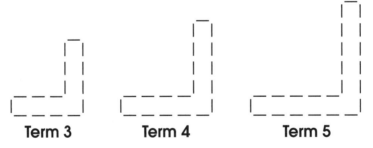

Term 3   Term 4   Term 5

Find the total number of sticks used in Term 1 and Term 2 of this pattern. Explain.

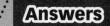

Assessment Test 1

1. 200 000 + 50 000 + 4000 + 200 + 50 + 1
2. 500 m³
3. 9.028
4. 8
5. from 36.6 g to 37 g
6. $\frac{8}{5}$
7. ■ to all
8. 1.94 kg
9. 7.5 cm
10. 2 x 2 x 3 x 7
11. rhombus
12. Start at 2. Multiply by 2 and subtract 1 each time.

13.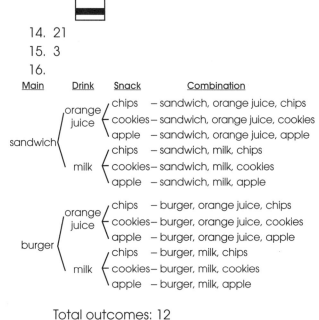

14. 21
15. 3
16.

Main	Drink	Snack	Combination
sandwich	orange juice	chips	– sandwich, orange juice, chips
		cookies	– sandwich, orange juice, cookies
		apple	– sandwich, orange juice, apple
	milk	chips	– sandwich, milk, chips
		cookies	– sandwich, milk, cookies
		apple	– sandwich, milk, apple
burger	orange juice	chips	– burger, orange juice, chips
		cookies	– burger, orange juice, cookies
		apple	– burger, orange juice, apple
	milk	chips	– burger, milk, chips
		cookies	– burger, milk, cookies
		apple	– burger, milk, apple

Total outcomes: 12
Milk and cookies: 2
Probability: $\frac{2}{12} = \frac{1}{6}$
The probability is $\frac{1}{6}$.

17. No. of days swam: 15 x 4 – 10 – 30 – 15 = 5
No. of days ran: 10 ? 20 30
$$(? + 20) \div 2 = 15$$
$$? = 10$$

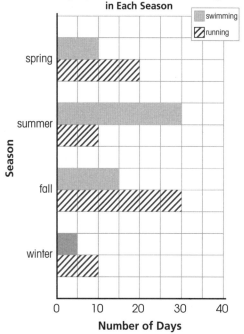

Days Spent Swimming and Running in Each Season

Cindy swam or ran on 130 days in the year.

18. Adam: $S = 2 \times 5 + 2 = 12$
Betty: $m = 2 \times 2 – 1 = 3$
$$n = 3 + 3 = 6$$
$$S = 2 \times 3 + 6 = 12$$
Cam: $m = 4$
$$n = 10 – 4 = 6$$
$$S = 2 \times 4 + 6 = 14$$
Adam and Betty have a score of 12. Cam has a score of 14. Cam is the winner of the game.

 **Answers**

Assessment Test 2

1. 672 525 < 713 024 < 736 643
2. 3
3. 9.732
4. 249 cm²
5. $\frac{10}{21}$
6. 31%
7. $0.34/candle
8. 3 h 41 min 16 s
9. 36 cm²
10. 2220 mL
11.

12. 57
13. 54.5
14. 50 and 59
15.

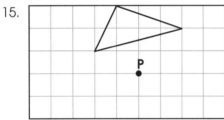

16.

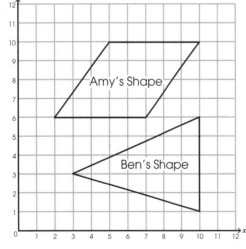

Amy's Shape: 5 x 4 = 20
Ben's Shape: 5 x 7 ÷ 2 = 17.5
Amy's shape has a greater area.

17. Let p be the cost of a potted plant and r be the cost of a rose.

$2p + 8 = 50$
$\quad 2p = 42$
$\quad\; p = 21$

$12r = p - 3$
$12r = 21 - 3$
$12r = 18$
$\quad r = 1.5$

$3p + 4r$
$= 3 \times 21 + 4 \times 1.5$
$= 69$
Emily has to pay $69.

18.

Term	1	2	3	4	5
No. of Sticks	8	12	16	20	24

-4   -4   -4   -4

Each term uses 4 more sticks. Term 1 uses 8 sticks and Term 2 uses 12 sticks. The total number of sticks used in Term 1 and Term 2 is 20.